Our Amazing World of Nature

Its Marvels & Mysteries

READER'S DIGEST

Our Amazing World of Nature

Its Marvels & Mysteries

THE READER'S DIGEST ASSOCIATION, PLEASANTVILLE, NEW YORK
THE READER'S DIGEST ASSOCIATION LTD., MONTREAL, CANADA

THIRD PRINTING

The credits which appear on page 320 are
hereby made a part of this copyright page.

© 1969 The Reader's Digest Association, Inc.
© 1969 The Reader's Digest Association (Canada) Ltd.

Library of Congress Catalog Card No. 69-10418
Printed in the United States of America

Contents

Part 1 The Miracle of Living Things

Part 2   The Life of the Sea

Part 3   This Planet Earth

Part One   The

Miracle of Living Things

Chapter One

Life in the Wilderness

Every wild plant, every freeborn animal is designed to fit some niche in the wilderness community where it can find food, fend off enemies, survive seasonal changes and produce young. The dazzling variety of adaptations that have evolved among the millions of species on our planet is one of nature's miracles.

HOW ANIMALS HELP EACH OTHER

Alan Devoe

A flash of bright blue in the green depths of the piney woods caught the eye of biologist Hilbert Siegler of the Texas Game Commission. Then a second spot of blue stirred, as another jay sailed on silent wings to the same branch. The newcomer, holding a morsel of food in its beak, hopped closer to the first bird. Turning eagerly, the first jay lifted its crested head and accepted hungrily the gift its visitor poked down into its throat.

Siegler was astonished. In fledging season, young birds often continue coaxing food from their parents even after they have grown up; in courting season, bird swains often bestow dainties upon the females they are wooing. But this wasn't the season for fledglings, nor was it courting time. This was the dead of winter.

Hastily the wildlife expert raised his binoculars and got the answer. The recipient of the bounty was an adult jay, a grizzled veteran. The lower mandible of its beak had been broken off nearly at the base. It had no way to pick up food.

This impulse to share and cooperate is familiarly awakened in creatures of the wild by members of their immediate families. But here seemed to be something close to the human ideal of brotherhood.

Nature's creatures often exhibit impulses of self-assertion and competition. But all through life's vast range, these instincts are balanced by another kind of drive. Nature does not implant in her children just the single message: "Take care of yourself." Ancient and universal, there is a second injunction: "Get together." It is as vital as the breath of life.

Every creature has a need for companionship as biologically important as food and drink. Testing tadpoles, zoologists have found that even these humble creatures are so deeply influenced by social need that a solitary tadpole can regenerate an injured part of its body only slowly, but if it is given the dimly sensed comradeship of fellow tadpoles its healing powers speed up almost miraculously. University of Chicago scientists have discovered that when mice are raised in contact with fellow mice they grow faster than mice reared on an identical diet in isolation.

Animals often develop teamwork into active patterns of partnership. R. M. Yerkes, an authority on apes, gave a chimpanzee a heavy box of fragrant delicacies with a complicated lid-fastener. Sniffing delightedly, the chimp tried to drag away the box so he could work at leisure on the task of getting it open. It was too heavy, so he sought out another chimp, tapped him on the shoulder, and gestured for help. Together, the two easily moved the box, worked jointly at opening it, and shared the feast.

A chimpanzee, given food when apes in adjoining cages were left unfed, has been seen to pass a share of his delicacies through the bars. Sharing sometimes extends to giving help. An ape with a sliver in his finger goes to another ape, and the "doctor" works as earnestly at the job as a human medico.

The coatis of Central and South America, long-nosed relatives of raccoons, swing through the jungle treetops in bands, hunting for small prey. A favorite delicacy is the iguana, the big arboreal lizard. But an iguana would be a tough customer for a small coati to tackle up among the twig tips, so hunting coatis split into two groups. One band goes aloft and scares dozing iguanas out of the branches. As the lizards fall, they are grabbed and overpowered by a contingent of coatis deployed on the ground.

Eloquent of the bond of inner unity is the fishing art of temperate America's great white pelicans. The pelicans come swooping down and form a wide semicircle offshore. Then, as if at a signal, the birds start wading toward shore. Shoulder to shoulder, beaks poised just above the water, they advance as a living net. Now and again all the birds join in a tumultuous

Baboons, like other primates, groom one another—not only for cleanliness but also as a means of maintaining friendly social contact. The amount of grooming an individual enjoys is an indication of his social rank.

thrashing of the water with their wings, scaring the fish into a smaller and smaller area near the shore. This beautifully coordinated drive ends with a tightly penned haul of fish imprisoned in the shallows of the shoreline. Then the birds fall to feasting on such a repast as no one of them could have secured alone.

A coyote can streak along over the prairie, in top bursts of speed, at about 35 miles an hour. But a jackrabbit can hit close to 45. Coyotes sometimes organize a relay race to defeat the challenge of such arithmetic.

Coyote No. 1, when his strength begins to flag, drives the rabbit on an angle toward a piece of cover. Out pops Coyote No. 2 to take over the chase, angling off on a new diagonal. Moving cross-lots at a leisurely pace, resting up and getting back his wind, Coyote No. 1 is presently ready to cut in again. This continues until the rabbit is exhausted.

Crows and ravens demonstrate the rewards of joining wits. Frances Pitt, British naturalist, owned a raven pair, Ben and Joe, whose teamwork in dealing with visiting cats was characteristic. Ben would approach the cat from the front, parading nonchalantly close. Fascinated by what looked like an easy meal, the cat would fail to observe that Joe was mincing around to the rear. A moment later a black beak like a pair of steel pliers would close on the cat's tail. Meowing in outrage, the cat would whirl around, to see Joe waddling away across the yard, while Ben seized the tail now presented to him. On a good day Ben and Joe could get a cat to turning circles like a frantic top.

I have seen a trio of crows work a team play of this sort so effectively with a great horned owl that the hulking killer fell off a branch.

Small alliances among animals grow into the bigger ones. The spirit of the flock can result in such an amazing performance as this—reported by the great

French naturalist, Baron Georges Léopold Cuvier.

A pair of swallows had built their mud nest under the eaves. The naturalist, hoping to observe the fledging of babies, was watching one day when the nest was invaded and taken over by an interloping sparrow. The bullying sparrow sat defiant in the nest, thrusting its beak angrily out the entrance hole, keeping the rightful owners at bay. Finally, the swallows flew off.

They returned with a swarming, chittering, aroused host of neighborhood swallows. With beakfuls of the wet mud they use for nest making, the birds converged on the invaded nest, deftly smearing, daubing. As they veered off, the watcher saw that the sparrow-held nest had been sealed tight shut. It had become its invader's tomb. Baron Cuvier felt that he had had an extraordinary look into one of the fundamental meanings of life itself.

Such group teamwork is not unusual among creatures of the same species, but scientists are now discovering that the sense of brotherhood can be trained to cut across species lines. The elephants in Ringling Brothers-Barnum & Bailey's Circus and the circus cat, Midnight, were as devoted to each other as if they were all kittens together. At the Philadelphia Zoo a few years ago the keepers had a problem with a surly, unapproachable rhinoceros, until they gave him the only available companion they could think of risking in the cage: a domestic goat. Almost overnight the rhino's disposition began to change. Before long he would take all the high-spirited butting the goat cared to inflict and come back for more. He had discovered fellowship.

This innate urge can cut across even the lines of supposedly "incurable" enmities. In a series of dramatic demonstrations a Chinese biologist, Dr. L. S. Tsai, would put a cat and a rat in a cage adjacent to a food compartment that had a transparent shutter. This shutter could be opened by pressure on two buttons in the cage; but both had to be pressed simultaneously, one by each animal. Again and again, rats and cats learned to put aside their wary distrust of each other and, faced with a common problem, worked successfully together to solve it.

This urge toward constructive cooperation touches first the individual, then expands to family, then widens to the flock, then at last in humanity becomes the shining ideal of universal brotherhood, carrying an incalculably heartening message of faith and hope. Wherever naturalists have peered deeply into the mysteries of nature's world, they have found the same moving message. Our human ideals are not visionary. They are good biology.

THAT ASTOUNDING CREATOR—NATURE

Jean George

A bird that eats feathers; a mammal that never drinks; a fish that grows a fishing line on its head to catch other fish. Creatures in a nightmare? No, they are very much with us as co-inhabitants of this earth. Nature has fashioned most animals to fit the many faces of the land—moose to marshes, squirrels to trees, camels to deserts, frogs to lily pads. Give nature an environment or situation and she will evolve a creature, adapting a toe here, an eye there, until the being fits the niche. As a result of this hammering and fitting, however, some really unbelievable creatures circle the sun with us.

One summer in Maine I saw a sleek mother horned grebe herding her three bobbing young to supper among the green pickerelweed. Suddenly I noticed through my binoculars that she was feeding her babies quantities of feathers from a deserted duck's nest. As she stuffed the dry feathers into the gaping mouths, she made two or three pokes to get each one down. Finally she worked a dozen or so down her own throat; then, sailing low on the water, she vanished contentedly among the plants. I later learned that 60 percent of the grebe's diet is feathers. When I asked why, a biologist from the U.S. Fish and Wildlife Service answered, "Because nature finds a use for everything. Feathers seem to act as a strainer to prevent fishbones from entering the intestines."

Australia has many strange beasts, one of the oddest of which is the koala. Perfectly adapted to one specific tree, the eucalyptus, this living teddy bear does not need anything else, not even a drink! The moisture in the leaves is just right for the koala, making it one of the few land animals that do not need water to supplement their food.

The creature with the fishing line on its head was created for the dark canyons of the sea. Here food is so scarce that the deep-sea anglerfish, which preys on smaller fish, grew a line and an appendage on the end that wiggles like a worm. This catches the attention of the occasional passerby. A fish approaches the bait, and the angler swirls up and swallows him.

The gigantic ocean bottom creates other problems. A male anglerfish could swim for years without meeting a female of his own species. Nature's solution to this problem is for the female to carry a dwarfed husband tightly fused to her body. Marine biologists believe that this nuptial begins when the eggs first hatch and there are many fry of both sexes. A male then grabs hold of a female with his mouth and hangs on until he has literally become a part of her. His mouth becomes fused to her stomach, and for the rest of his life the male remains attached to his mate, marking the most amazing union on earth.

Sound has shaped the bodies of many beasts. Noise tapped away at the bullfrog until his ears became bigger than his eyes. Now he hears so well that at the slightest sound of danger he quickly plops to safety under a sunken leaf. The rabbit has long ears to hear the quiet "whoosh" of the owl's wings, while the grasshopper's ears are on the base of his abdomen, the lowest point of his body, where he can detect the tread of a crow's foot or the approach of a shrew.

Sometimes food will determine an animal's appearance. Earthworms have shaped the woodcock, a snipelike bird of the forest floor. This creature has a long narrow bill that looks like a pencil and fits neatly into the burrows of the worms. But the bill has its disadvantages: With it buried deep in a worm hole the woodcock is vulnerable to attack from above. To counteract this danger, the woodcock has eyes near the top of his head. This singular device permits him to scan the trees for danger even when his beak is buried. A successful arrangement for longevity—but it certainly creates an odd-looking creature.

The need to catch elusive prey has evolved some staggering biological tricks. The sea anemone, a flowerlike animal of the tidemark, is usually riveted to one spot, yet it feeds on darting fish. A diabolically clever trap was necessary to catch them, so the anemone developed tentacles with bombs in the end of each. When a fish forages into these tentacles, the ends shoot a thin thread into the fish's body. The thread in turn explodes a paralyzing poison. The stunned fish is hauled in by the tentacles and shoved into the anemone's gullet.

Nature seems to have gone all out in creating preposterous gadgets for self-defense. The jacana, a bird found in the American tropics, for instance, is endowed with spurs that unfold like a switchblade at the bend of the bird's wings, and with which he can slash his enemies to shreds.

Lizards are professionals in the art of warding off attack. The two-headed skink, whose tail is shaped like his head, confuses his enemy. A hawk, upon attacking this fellow, anticipates that he will run in the direction of the lifted head and makes allowance for the movement. However, the bird usually strikes nothing, for he is aiming at the tail. The real head took off the other way.

In order to travel in a hostile world, the Portu-

The koala, about the size of a raccoon, sustains itself solely on the leaves of a dozen species of eucalyptus. It lacks the prehensile tail of some of its close relatives, but uses its long claws and rough-padded paws for climbing, and seldom descends to the ground except to travel from one tree to another.

guese man-of-war first mastered the art of floating. To do this, it evolved a purple bag and inflated it with gas from a special gland. As a crowning idea it also grew a sail! Launched, the man-of-war can blow away from enemies or approach food by putting its sail up and down. When severely threatened, it forces the gas out of the float and submerges.

There is hardly any environment, however hostile, that some creature has not mastered. Land is, of course, the nemesis of the fish. If they flop out on it they die. If their ponds dry up, they are helpless. Given this situation, it was almost certain that some fish would evolve a way to beat it; and so there is a lungfish. It is an air breather and must come to the

surface every 20 minutes or so; otherwise it drowns. When the ponds of Africa dry up in the arid season, the lungfish wrap themselves in mud and wait it out, sometimes for years. When the rains finally return, they resume their water life.

Just as nature adds things on creatures that need them, so she occasionally takes things away from those that don't. The adult mayfly, for example, has no mouth or stomach. Last year, by a northern New York lake, I found myself amid hundreds of thousands of these insects. I told the conservation officer with whom I was that I was glad they didn't bite. He replied that they have no mouths to bite with. "Adult mayflies live but one day," he explained, "and that day is devoted entirely to pleasure. They do nothing but dance and mate all their short lives, and so they do not need a mouth."

With all this elaborate evolution, it is not surprising that some of nature's inventions got out of hand. Into this category falls the speedometer of reindeer. A tendon snaps back and forth over a bone in the reindeer's foot, noisily tapping out the speed of his gait. Useless. And so is the nose on the stomach of the scorpion and the featherlike tongue of the toucan, a bird of Central and South America.

But probably the most dumfounding of nature's extraordinary creations is the horned toad of the Southwest. A herpetologist once invited me to observe one of these lizards right after it had molted. In a sand-filled glass cage I saw a large male. Beside him lay his old skin. The herpetologist began to annoy the beast with mock attacks, and the old man of the desert with his vulnerable new suit became frightened. Suddenly his eyeballs reddened. A final fast lunge from my friend at the beast, and I froze in astonishment—a fine spray of blood shot from the lizard's eye, like fire from a dragon! The beast had struck back with a weapon so shocking that it terrifies even the fiercest enemy.

Later I walked home, pondering the bizarre methods for survival with which evolution has endowed earth's creatures, sometimes comical, sometimes pathetic. I knew the biologists were right: If any adaptation is possible, nature has tried it.

Eluding one's enemies is important in the animal world, and nature helps by providing many creatures with specially placed organs that perform evasive tricks. With high-set eyes that see clearly in all directions, the woodcock (top) can spot enemies even while grubbing for earthworms. The horned lizard (bottom) has eyes that can squirt a fine spray of blood for several feet, distracting an attacker so the lizard can escape.

A TOOTH AND A CLAW

Jean George

Once in a clover-spattered meadow I watched two cows cracking their heads together with such violence that I winced and asked the farmer why he didn't separate the animals. "Cow fights," he drawled, "make for order and peaceful individuals. The sooner those two decide which is gonna be boss cow, the sooner I'll get a bucket of milk from both of them."

In his lifetime with cattle this farmer had seen what science is now establishing: that animal aggression is creative. A tooth-and-claw encounter is a positive adjustment to an irritating situation, just as sleep is an adjustment to fatigue, eating to hunger.

Since World War II, psychologists and biologists have been prying intensively into the stuff that makes a fight. In man this force can be expressed destructively in war and murder, or positively in murals in a Sistine Chapel. The human impulses that make a fight are precisely those that make a masterpiece.

One of the first clues that animal aggression has its constructive uses came to light in 1938, when psychologist C. R. Carpenter shipped several hundred rhesus monkeys from India to Santiago Island, off Puerto Rico, where he released them in order to study their natural society. When they were set free on the island, they swung into the trees—and fights started. Males battled until a leader emerged. Losers gradually took their positions under him. Now the females turned to the care of their young and to friendly relationships with other females. Once order had been established in the monkeys' society, they showed deeper feelings: Traveling groups moved through the trees at a pace to accommodate the old and infirm.

Almost all lower animals use fighting only to create order. In his study of birds, H. E. Howard, British businessman-ornithologist, found that the springtime song was actually a warning to other birds to stay away and avert a physical battle. Males sang from trees and posts to tell one another where their boundaries lay. Only rarely, when the warning song was ignored, did they clash physically, and then never to the death. More often a song was tussle enough. As the nesting season progressed and each bird became established in its territory with a mate, the loud songs died down.

There have been a number of recent experiments

to discover what sparks a fight. John Paul Scott, research professor of psychology at Bowling Green State University in Ohio, discovered in testing mice that one of the primary ingredients of a mouse battle is pain. He needed only to pinch a male mouse gently on the tail and it slashed its nearest neighbor.

Emotional torches also ignite animal battles. For some animals conflicts may arise over females (although much less often than we have been led to believe), threats to young and food scarcity. The most frequent battles, however, seem to relate to status and property. Every animal that has territory is aggressive against trespassers.

When status fights have established a hierarchy in a pack, herd or flock, fighting decreases. This can be observed in barnyard chickens, among the most pugnacious of all birds. At a Massachusetts experimental laboratory a group of five hens was tagged alphabetically according to the previously established rank. Then a dish of food, big enough to feed only one bird at a time, was presented to them. All the hens ran toward it—but A stretched her neck, lifted her head feathers and threw up her comb. Whereupon the others stopped short of the dish and let her eat first.

The researcher then removed this strong leader. B stepped up to the tray. Only when all the birds but D and E were removed was there a fight. Wings batted, feet clawed and beaks descended on heads. "Those two fight for status when the others are gone," said the researcher. "They need the dominance of the whole group to keep them from fighting."

Since the dominant animal, often the oldest and heaviest, is important to peace in some kinds of animal societies, the question of how dominance is achieved was studied by Dr. Scott at Jackson Laboratory in Maine. It was found not only that the dominant animal is often a winner but that a winner is made by winning.

Dr. Scott and his co-workers placed two male mice in a small cage, where the animals had no choice but to fight after a tail pinch. The winner was then pitted against a series of weaker opponents until finally he became so confident that he did not even bother with the warmup—tail rattling and hair raising—but simply charged and fought as soon as he was put into a cage. Fighters trained in this manner became so aggressive that they would tackle every mouse they encountered, including females and young—something that no normal mouse would do.

Many wild creatures have a psychological zone about them which, when an intruder enters, forces them to make a decision—to fight or flee. Jack Couffer, Walt Disney wildlife photographer, tells in his book *Song of Wild Laughter* about a bobcat that was confined to a cage so small that the people who came up to it were within the cat's fight-or-flight perimeter. Unable to attack them and yet having no room to retreat, the animal, once a docile house pet, turned viciously neurotic.

This comfort zone is very important in keeping zoo animals healthy. When tigers and bears retire to that distant peaceable corner, they are actually removing the irritation of their human audience.

The ways an animal expresses anger are different in various species. In birds it may be a song. Some frogs will leap heavily upon the back of an intruding frog. An angry ram will lower its head.

Not knowing what animals respond to can sometimes get people into difficult situations with pets. Not long ago my usually docile Newfoundland snapped at a three-year-old child. I was perplexed, because the dog is accustomed to children mauling her. Then I noticed that the little girl approached Tonka from the rear and put a firm hand on her shoulder. Tonka instinctively became aggressive, for unwittingly Patsy was going through the motions of dog aggression. Approaching from the rear, a paw on the shoulder, and a head higher than the other dog's is "bossing" in the canine world. We solved Patsy's problem with a few counteracting suggestions: Speak to the dog, let her see who's coming, and pat her gently.

When an animal is stimulated to aggression, blood rushes to its muscles, its heart beats faster, adrenalin flows. Violent action—fighting or running away—brings the body back to normal. But what happens if this body state can't be worked off?

Knowing that in man long periods of suppressing aggression often contribute toward such disorders as heart disease, asthma and stomach ulcers, psychologists put animals under the stress of unresolved aggression. A number of mice—males and females—were crowded together in a small cage. Afraid and worried by constant threats, many died of fatigue. Some lost weight. The overcrowding interfered with the milk production of the mothers and therefore subsequent litters were smaller.

Where is all this research into animal aggression taking us? I had an answer recently while walking the beach with a psychologist from Cornell University. I picked up a clamshell from the sand. "There's a beast that knows no rancor," I said. He gave me a tired glance. "A clam has nothing to fight with," he replied. "Give him a tooth or a hand, and even he will use it. Weapons have a way of being used."

The Uganda kob, a variety of African antelope, jealously defends his breeding ground. Here two males lock horns in a border dispute, the winner of which has prerogative over the females in his territory. Defender and challenger engage in vigorous sparring that looks fierce but seldom results in death or serious injury.

I paused, thinking of the weapons we have. The young Ph.D. tossed my shell into the water. "That's why we are studying the nature of fighting," he said. "If we know what it is, maybe we can do something about it—before it's too late."

ANIMALS CAN BE ALMOST HUMAN

Max Eastman

Hardly a week goes by that the daily paper does not contain one story about fabulous feats performed by animals. I have admired my animal neighbors all my life, but I confess that I find many of these stories a little too fabulous, others too sentimental, to chime with my feelings. I do not want animals to be supernatural; I want them to be natural. I am not half so much interested in tales of the intellectual prowess or moral heroism of some dog or cat or elephant as in learning about those traits of animals in general that are similar to ours and that give

us a sense of the kinship of all life on this planet.

Take the giving of gifts and love tokens. According to Edward A. Armstrong, author of *The Way Birds Live,* even the custom of "saying it with flowers" is to be found among certain birds and insects. The male empid fly, for instance, wraps up a flower petal or a bit of food in a web of fine silk that he weaves with his front feet, and presents it to his bride. "Starlings," says Professor Armstrong, "carry flowers into their nesting hole when the female is on the nest. A herring gull will pick up a shell or pluck a sea pink and, with great courtesy, lay it before the brooding mate."

Other birds come so near being human that they express their sentimental emotions by talking baby talk—a trick I cannot endorse in either species. According to Konrad Lorenz, an outstanding naturalist, "Every delicacy the male jackdaw finds is given to the bride, and she accepts it with the plaintive notes typical of baby birds. The love whispers of the couple consist chiefly of infantile sounds."

A more dignified example of similarity between humans and animals is the ceremony of betrothal.

Long engagements always seemed to me an unbiological affliction that man in a state of puritanical super-civilization has imposed upon himself. Among English robins, however, extended engagements are an all but inflexible rule. They pair up in late December or January, but do not mate or start housekeeping until the end of March. Among jackdaws and wild geese betrothal occurs in the spring following birth, although neither species becomes sexually mature until 12 months later. Indeed, nearly all birds that marry for life are betrothed for a time before they marry.

Another social custom commonly regarded as peculiarly human is the division of society into castes or classes, with the special privilege, the oppression, the cruelty and snobbery that go with it. You can see it in the henyard, where a definite social hierarchy, or "pecking order," is always established. Every bird has a wholesome fear of those above her in rank and also knows which ones are below her. It is not always by tests of strength that this order is established; energy, nerve and, above all, I think, self-assurance count, too. And, just as among men, this hierarchy of prestige is often prone to culminate in an oppressive dictatorship.

An equally human aspect of this ladder of prestige is the snobbery it entails. Dr. Lorenz describes how a jackdaw of high rank fell in love with a young female among the lower orders. Within a few days the entire colony knew that this little low-class upstart, whom 80 percent of them had been maltreating, could no longer receive a black look from anybody. She knew it, too, and made the fullest use of it. "She lacked entirely," Lorenz mourns, "that noble tolerance which jackdaws of high rank should exhibit toward their inferiors. She used every opportunity

From northern breeding grounds, Canada geese may fly 4000 miles south every fall, without cutting family ties.
They mate at two and remain paired for life. Both parents help raise each brood of five to nine goslings.

to snub former superiors. In short, she conducted herself with the utmost vulgarity."

Dr. Lorenz warns us against the sentimental notion that animals are morally "better" or "worse" than man. Moral judgments, he insists, are irrelevant where life is instinctive. In explaining the all-too-human sins of animals he relates the sad tale of the alienation of a swan husband's tender affections by a determined female. Swans are monogamous, and supposedly faithful to their mates for life. But one old male swan "furiously expelled a strange female who came close to the nest where his wife was sitting and made him proposals of love—and then on the very same day was seen to meet this new female on the other side of the lake and succumb to her charms without more ado."

Dr. Lorenz is disposed to find "human weaknesses" in nearly all animals. For instance, he says

that his dog Bully was an accomplished "liar." Bully would always run out to meet him with exuberant affection at the front gate, but he would also run out there to bark savagely at strangers. In old age Bully's eyesight grew dim, and one day when the wind was blowing the scent in the opposite direction, recognition failed and Bully barked fiercely at his master. When he got near enough to perceive his mistake, he stopped short, then rushed past him and across the road, where he pretended to be barking at a neighbor's dog who was not there.

Cats, too, are exceedingly vain of their poise and dignity. If by some chance—perhaps a slippery floor when they are in a hurry—they take a sideways slide, they will instantly turn to examine some object in the new direction, giving a careful smell to each detail of it, as if that had always been their intention.

"Women and children first," a precept of chivalry not invariably lived up to by the human race, is an instinct that can be relied on absolutely in dogs. The most ferocious dog terrorizing a neighborhood of canine males will never touch a female or a young puppy. If a neurotic spinster bitch should attack him, he is completely nonplussed. His pride prevents him from running away, but he cannot bring himself to give battle. And so he just stands around, shifting from foot to foot like a bewildered schoolboy.

Magnanimity to the vanquished, another high standard of conduct adhered to on occasion by civilized man, is a "law of nature" among wolves. When there is a fight between two timber wolves and the weaker is licked, he stands rigidly still, turning his head in such a manner as deliberately to expose his throat, the primary point of attack. It is a gesture of surrender, a plea for mercy, and the victor is unable to attack. The victim, so long as he holds that position, is safe. This same instinct of magnanimity—so to name it—is found among many kinds of dogs.

Pleasure in owning property is an instinct extending far down into the animal kingdom. It is this pleasure, most often, that birds are proclaiming when they sit on a high treetop and sing. They are shouting: "These are my real-estate holdings. Trespassers keep out!" Other animals deposit a proprietary scent along the borders of their private estates. The mongoose has a special gland that exudes a tiny spray which he uses for this purpose; if you wipe his markers away with a wet cloth, he will promptly come back and renew them.

Dr. William M. Mann, when director of the National Zoological Park in Washington, told me of his attempt to mate a pair of leopards. He kept them in two cages separated by bars until they had fallen quite madly in love. When, however, he admitted the female into the male's cage, the male's property sense overrode both love and lust. He snarled and struck her dead with one blow of his paw.

And so it was nature, not man, who invented the delight of owning a little piece of this planet we camp on.

ARE WILD ANIMALS REALLY WILD?

Andy Russell

After 20 years as a guide for big-game hunters in the Rockies, I have learned what I would never have believed before—that so-called wild animals are not really wild at all. Usually they do flee the presence of man, but only because they have learned from bitter experience that he is the most dangerous creature they encounter. Offered friendly treatment and respect, they will respond in a most extraordinary manner.

The bighorn sheep, for instance, is reputed to be one of the wildest of all living creatures. Hunters, aided by guides, telescopic sights and long-range rifles, often spend weeks trying to collect a single trophy—the most prized in the West. Yet I recently sat in the midst of a band of 16 bighorn rams, the nearest ones less than 20 feet from me. The story of how Dick and Charlie, my two oldest sons, and I achieved this unheard-of friendship may add something to man's knowledge of natural history.

I received an assignment from a Canadian foundation to record the life history of the bighorn (*Ovis canadensis*). When my boys and I first began stalking them with cameras in the heart of their range along the Continental Divide, the sheep were wary and suspicious. And even with telephoto lenses, it is necessary to get close for good pictures—much closer than normal rifle-range. The usual sly approach of the hunter simply did not work, for if the sheep chanced to see us sneaking from one bit of cover to the next, we were left looking at mountain scenery where sheep had recently been. Even if we got within desirable range, our best shots were of startled bighorns leaving in a hurry.

One day when I was resting in a canyon and pondering this problem, under the watchful eyes of a bunch of rams bedded on a mountain shoulder half a mile away, it suddenly occurred to me that we might be going about it the wrong way. I remembered that once, years before, I had taken a hunting party into a remote valley cradled among 10,000-foot peaks in southeastern British Columbia. We were rounding a cliff when we met a bunch of mountain goats face to face. Instead of running, they stood staring at us like children at a circus. Then, to our astonishment, three of them came toward us, obviously unafraid though nervous enough to stamp their front feet. My two hunters and I looked at one another, left the rifles hanging on their slings and began taking pictures. Hunting was one thing, but sheer murder was quite another!

So, I thought, perhaps the bighorn sheep would accept us in the same way, if we could convince them we meant no harm. Abandoning hidden stalks, the boys and I now resorted to patience and diplomacy, staying in sight of the sheep at all times. It was a slow, painstaking business requiring weeks of climbing. We schooled ourselves to move smoothly, for the sheep took instant alarm at any jerky motion. If, as we approached, we saw signs of nervousness, we turned our backs on the animals and wandered aimlessly about, admiring the flowers, as though bighorns were far from our minds. Above all, we avoided looking directly at them for more than a casual glance, for like all "wild" things, bighorns do not like to be stared at. (Even the birds and squirrels in the parks of big cities, where people are a part of their daily lives, usually take alarm at a direct stare.)

In time, our new methods began to show signs of paying off. We found ourselves getting closer and closer to the sheep. Then one day I was able to work my way right in among a bunch of bedded rams and sit down. It was one of the greatest thrills of an adventurous life to look around and study the characteristics of individuals as they casually glanced my way or, better still, looked past me down the mountain in complete acceptance of my presence. No experience hunting with a rifle had ever matched this!

Either the news circulated along the mountain grapevine, or our technique had been perfected, for soon we were at home with the bighorns over their whole range. Out of the many sheep we encountered, we came to know about 40 individuals. These and many more seemed to recognize us and often let us approach within a few feet, paying us no more attention than they would other sheep. Once I filmed a feeding ewe at exactly 12 feet. Charlie photographed a ewe's eye at less than six feet, obtaining a unique record of the rich, golden color and the distinctive rectangular pupil.

I remember watching Dick working with a bunch of ewes and lambs at the foot of a cliff. When they

The massive corkscrew headgear clearly marks this bighorn sheep as a ram; a ewe's horns are thinner and straighter. Once abundant from Mexico to western Canada, bighorns have been reduced in number by hunters, disease and competition for grazing land from domestic sheep. Conservationists now seek ways to safeguard this handsome species.

began to climb to the rims above, Dick fell in behind on all fours to climb with them. Then out of no-where came a magnificent ram. He took a brief look at the procession, and bounded up to take his climbing position directly behind Dick. I chuckled to think how Dick must feel with 60-odd pounds of ram horns so close to his hip pockets.

There was one huge patriarchal ram whose horns were the biggest I have ever seen—probably measuring 47 inches around the outside curls, and 17 inches in circumference at the bases. He was about three and a half feet high at the shoulder and weighed at least 400 pounds. His head alone must have weighed close to 70 pounds, and we often saw him take the load from his neck by resting a horn on the ground as he lay bedded. Time after time we climbed high, trying to come up to him, but he was too wary.

One day on my way down from a high peak I paused on a sunny ledge. At once, that sixth sense developed by chronic wanderers of the wilderness warned me that I was not alone. With infinite care I moved my eyes slowly to the side—to see the big ram not 20 feet away. He had let me climb down past him a little and now he was lying watching me with those magnificently keen eyes. For long minutes neither of us moved a hair. Then I saw a ripple rise

in his throat and he began calmly chewing his cud—sure sign he was unafraid. I had been accepted by the king ram of them all. But every scrap of film in my pack was exposed!

I am convinced that animals are not naturally afraid of human scent, for we found we could completely ignore the direction of the wind on approaching the sheep—though it was often noticeable that they did not enjoy our smell. The one thing the bighorns never would tolerate, no matter how well they knew us, was any quick movement. The accidental slip of a tripod leg or climbing boot would trigger instant flight. Once when I was working my movie camera on a bunch of rams, I dropped a glove. Instantly I was alone.

Perhaps the most fascinating of the habits we recorded were the bighorns' games—joined in by old and young alike. One evening after supper we were sitting in front of our camp when a mixed bunch of ewes, lambs and small rams appeared on the skyline high above us. Suddenly a dignified-looking old ewe ran down the ridge to a snowdrift pitched at a steep angle toward a formidable cliff. Without checking her speed, she launched into a reckless glissade straight down the icy drift. With the snow streaming over both shoulders, she seemed bent on suicide; but at the last precise instant she did a four-legged christie to run off on the naked rocks at the side. As she galloped back to the top the others followed her in turn, each making that hair-raising swing on the brink of disaster. We watched till the light failed, while they went blithely round and round in a bighorn version of follow-the-leader.

They also play a replica of king-of-the-castle. Once we saw five young rams busy at this game. One stood on top of a loose pile of rocks and his companions took quick turns trying to knock him off, while he whirled and danced, meeting all comers head on, until he was finally dislodged. Then the victor took his turn defending the castle.

Filming newborn lambs proved to be a problem, for the favorite lambing grounds are hardly chosen for their accessibility and the ewes are even more shy than usual. We followed one bunch for six weeks before we got close-ups. Yet before the lambing season these same mothers would allow us almost within reach.

Born in late May and June, the lambs weigh about four pounds at birth, and it would be difficult to find more attractive young animals. They can run when only a few hours old and we have seen them trailing their mothers before they were licked dry. In three days they can streak over incredibly rough ground like rabbits, and in a week they can jump clear over their mothers' backs, just for the fun of it. They are extremely playful and join in speedy games of follow-the-leader and general roughhousing on cliff faces that would give human mothers nervous prostration to watch.

Throughout most of the year the rams stay by themselves in bachelors' clubs under the leadership of the oldest and wisest individuals. But in late November each year they disperse to mingle with the ewes, and all camaraderie is forgotten in competition for the females during the breeding season, which lasts through December to early January. Squaring off with dramatic dignity, the rams batter each other in head-on engagements that set the mountains ringing. These collisions often leave them temporarily groggy and permanently scarred. Nearly all mature rams have chips knocked off their horns, and their hallmark is the broken nose reminiscent of professional prizefighters.

It was such a fight that I particularly wanted for the climax to our film. We had seen several battles from a distance, but our attempts at close-ups seemed fated to failure. Then, on a clear winter day, as I headed up into the sheep country, I had the feeling that luck was with me.

Stopping at a vantage point, I spotted a lone ram traveling across the front of a peak above the valley. Even at a distance of over a mile, he had that arrogance of bearing that goes with a questing male. I climbed quickly up a side canyon to intercept him. Near the top, I saw what I had hoped to see—another big ram escorting a single ewe. Scrambling on up the ice-draped rocks, I eased over the last edge just in time to film an epic battle.

The rams stood facing each other with heads held high and proud. Then both reared straight up with front legs hanging, to run toward each other on their hind feet. Two lengths apart, they hurled themselves forward to meet in midair, horn to horn, with a crash that rang for half a mile. The impact was so terrific that their bodies literally whiplashed and the arrested inertia jerked their ridiculous, short tails straight up. For a few moments they stood staring off into space, apparently dazed by the shock, before stepping back to resume maneuvering for position. Again and again they collided with shattering slams. Once I saw splinters fly, and a new scar showed up on a horn of the ram defending the ewe. Several times they came within six feet of me, paying me no more attention than if I were a stump.

Finally the defending ram had had enough; he broke off the engagement and headed down the mountain. The challenger followed him closely for a way, apparently to make sure he left for good. Then he turned back to claim his prize.

It would be nice to say that the proud victor returned triumphantly to the lady and that, together, they disappeared happily into the fastnesses of the peaks. But such was not the fact. The winner arrived back on the battleground just in time to see the cause of all the uproar disappearing over the skyline ahead of a young ram who had slipped in to steal the gal away. The victorious gladiator, too tired for pursuit, just threw a disgusted look in their direction and proceeded to feed. I passed him my unspoken sympathy and headed back down the mountain.

After 17 months of almost continuous living with the bighorns, I had completed my film. The job was done—now I could return to my guiding business. But somehow that prospect held small appeal. My experience with the sheep had opened up a shining vista of adventure with cameras instead of guns. I knew that I could never kill another bighorn.

So the sheep remain my friends. As a guide, I have been able to provide pleasure and thrills for the privileged few who could afford de luxe wilderness trips. Now, with camera and typewriter, I hope my boys and I can bring pleasure and a true knowledge of nature to many, many others.

Chapter Two

Microscopic Multitudes

*The microscope has given us a window on the vast world that stretches just beyond
our unaided vision—a world inhabited by countless billions of tiny creatures,
plants and strange beings that are half animal, half vegetable. Sparking this teeming
microcosm is the greatest unknown of all: the secret of the living cell.*

THE INVISIBLE HORDES IN YOUR LIFE

Rutherford Platt

Recently Prof. David Pramer of Rutgers University, using a powerful microscope, watched a thrilling drama. He saw a tiny, one-celled fungus plant lasso and strangle a ferocious nema worm. Out of its single cell this speck of a plant had grown a gossamer thread 1/200 of a millimeter in diameter but strong as steel. When the nema came charging in, the plant formed a loop at the end of its thread and gripped the monster around its middle. The loop then inflated like a rubber tire and strangled the victim. The fungus then devoured the carcass at leisure.

Weird battles like this are constantly being fought under your lawn and in the fields. In this strange, invisible world, fantastic beings are dueling, minute throngs are waging appalling wars for survival. These invisible hordes, the original forms of life, are giving up many of their secrets as modern microscopes penetrate deeper into their realms. The distinction between the plant and animal kingdoms disappears, and astonishing lines of evolution point all the way back to the time when nonliving elements combined to create the first living cell.

Nature used one-celled organisms as pilot models, so to speak, for big plants and animals. For several billions of years these basic organisms tried out different forms of living, moving, growing. They responded to light in ways leading to eyes. They "invented" eating, drinking and digestion. They perfected photosynthesis and a system of inheritance with genes. They initiated sexual reproduction. All the cells of your body reflect life processes developed by the invisible hordes. Their profound importance is not often honored because, since Pasteur, research has concentrated on germs—"gangster" microbes that throw human life off-balance. But the truth is that the invisible hordes are the mainstream of life.

How do these hordes get from place to place? To them the air is a magnificent transportation system which has enabled all their races to colonize the globe.

The fungi are the supreme aerialists. These microscopic specks live in damp, dark places on the ground, but break out by erecting mushrooms and puffballs to launch their spores into the winds. Astronomical numbers of spores are always whirling in the sky; they have been detected at 35,000 feet. Algae torn from their clinging places ride the winds, and clouds of bacteria are launched by coughs and sneezes.

But the chief homeland of the invisible hordes is the soil. An acre of typical farm soil (to a depth of six inches) has a ton of fungi, several tons of bacteria, 200 pounds of protozoa (one-celled animals), 100 pounds of algae and 100 pounds of yeasts. Soil is thus the highest concentration of life power on earth.

The frontier between this invisible world and the visible one is a millimeter, or 1/25 of an inch. This is about the smallest dimension that can be clearly seen by the naked eye. The living beings beyond this milestone are grouped in three categories according to size. The largest are the big protists, which average only 1/5 of a millimeter. These protists are mostly the "giant" one-celled animals called protozoa—amoebas, parameciums, etc.

The second group, the little protists (average size 1/200 of a millimeter), includes primitive one-celled algae and fungi. Algae are egg-shaped and have green chlorophyll. Fungi are slender threads with no green pigment.

Far smaller are the monerans of the third group, only 1/1000 of a millimeter in size. These most primitive of living forms include the bacteria and a mysterious form of life, the blue-green algae.

Single-celled evolution reached its limit with the big protists. Of these, the most developed and the most arresting are the protozoa, like, for example, the amoeba, an irregular blob with an elastic skin.

From any part of its body it pokes out a bulge known as a false foot that elongates and withdraws, giving this formless animal an uncanny method for creeping around.

Certain protozoa, the flagellates, or "whip-bearers," use very long hairs, made of many fibers twisted together, which they whip about to propel themselves in pursuit of food or a mate.

Most spectacular of the protozoa is the giant paramecium, which revolves among the smaller forms by means of spiraling rows of hairs that the creature uses like oars. Batteries of poison arrows are embedded in its skin, enabling this masterpiece of one-celled evolution with no sense organ, no muscles and no brain to rout its enemies.

Another protozoan, didinium, is shaped like a fat jar with a puckery snout as though it were whistling. The snout is surrounded by two circles of vibrating hairs that create whirlpools to suck its victim within range. Then didinium's mouth stretches enormously—and the prey is gradually devoured.

However, it was not the big protist animals that led the way in evolution toward beings of many cells. The individuals in this top level of one-celled life with the fanciest equipment represent a dead end of evolution, for such self-sufficient bodies could not fuse easily to form many-celled life, and did not have the urge to do so. Instead, it was the little protists—the algae—that unlocked the secret of sun power and with this energy carried life to higher and higher spheres.

The secret was the green pigment, chlorophyll, the magic ingredient of the photosynthesis process that catches the energy of sunlight. In a split second this energy is imparted to a molecule in which carbon from air and hydrogen from water are combined. We call the resulting product carbohydrate, or sugar. It is a nugget of energy that can be released later when it is digested, and it is the chief food of all living things.

The green algae had inherited this power to make food chemically with the help of sunlight from the ancient pigmented organisms, who first did it differently, with sulfur and iron and without free oxygen. Oddly, it seems that the green algae almost gave us our red blood. The complicated chemical formula of chlorophyll is the same as the red pigment of blood, except for a slight detail. If one atom of magnesium in a molecule of chlorophyll is replaced by one atom of iron, the substance turns into red blood!

With chlorophyll, the green algae multiplied enormously and created a great surplus of food energy, available to fungi and to the monerans below and the big protists above. The nations of the invisibles were energized in a tidal wave of carbohy-

In a drop of pond water or a grain of garden soil, fantastic creatures like those shown here live, reproduce and die in a world lacking distinctions between plant and animal. Though these microscopic multitudes seem insignificant, they form the basis of all higher life; we could not exist without them.

Amoeba   Paramecium   Fungus   Flagellates   Blue-green Alga (bottom)

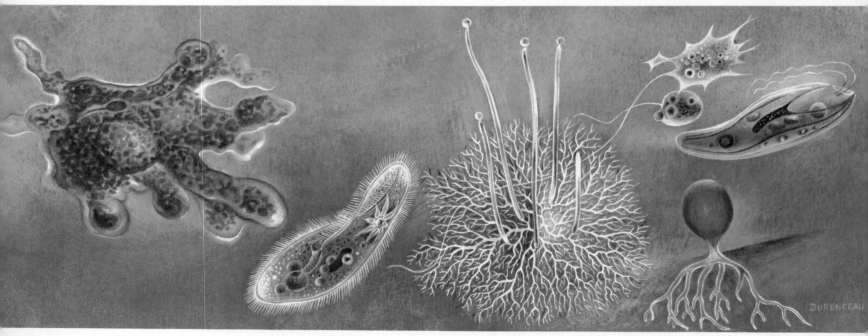

drates—and tremendous mergers of cells began that created big seaweeds, and then complex new species with skeletons, limbs and organs.

Oldest, tiniest and most primitive of one-celled organisms are the monerans, which include the all-important bacteria. Their shadowy silhouettes have three shapes—sticks or rods (bacilli), corkscrew spirals (spirilla), and plain ovals and spheres (cocci).

Another type of moneran is the mysterious blue-green algae—less complex forms than the green algae and ages older. They are even considered to be the ancestors of bacteria.

Some of these remarkable infinitesimal blobs do not obey the familiar laws of life. Quite independent of heat and cold, they can live on polar glaciers or in hot springs close to the boiling point. With no apparent way of moving they have mysterious motions —clinging together in chains whose tips bend from side to side as a colony glides forward and back with a revolving motion. They can live without breathing oxygen—yet shift to oxygen when that is available.

The blue-green algae represent one of nature's ancient "experiments" at one of the turning points of evolution. For some of these mysterious cells are red, yellow, orange, purple. Here is a veritable laboratory test of the effects of different pigments for photosynthesis, as it was made by the first living cells, around 2½ billion years ago. (Multicellular life began much later—around 600 million years ago.) Thus, Dr. Lawrence S. Dillon, biologist at Texas A&M, believes that at the base of the tree of life stand the blue-green algae, the oldest form of cell life known still to exist on earth.

In the light of these revelations about the domain of life beyond the millimeter marker, the line between the two classical kingdoms—the animal kingdom and the plant kingdom—has vanished. Some biologists today propose that the tree of life has a tall trunk that is all plant. This trunk rises from the blue-green algae at its base through the various green-algae forms culminating in the brown seaweeds at the top of the trunk.

Then two subkingdoms branch off. One is the subkingdom of many-celled plants, from which evolved the flowering plants. The other branch is the subkingdom of many-celled animals, with man at the top. This means that we share the same point of origin with the trees and flowers. The brown seaweeds are, in a sense, our relatives, and we are cousins of the trees.

Today the invisible hordes still dominate the earth. From their viewpoint, we are a minority trespassing on their planet. Dr. René Dubos of the Rockefel-

ler University estimated that the total mass of microbial life on earth is approximately 20 times greater than the total mass of animal life. The products of its activities can be seen on every hand. Trees and flowers rise out of the nourishing brews that microbes mix in the soil. Myriads of invisible beings coloring its waters gave the name to the Red Sea. The phosphorescence of ocean water is made by the jostling and tumbling of unseen hosts in the waves.

The invisible hordes are the waterwheel of life. By digesting raw elements, they lift them to a higher level of energy, so they can be used as vitamins and enzymes by higher forms of life. By eating dead plants and animals, they cause "decay," which releases locked-up elements. Thus they keep the three great cycles of life flowing—the carbon cycle for food energy, the nitrogen cycle for protein, and the cycle of minerals that sparkplug life. They live with us—and in us. Our whole world of visible plants and animals evolved from them and still depends on them. And, while our submicroscopic relatives could go on without us, *we* could not exist without them.

THE WONDROUS "INNER SPACE" OF LIVING CELLS

Rutherford Platt

They saw cells walking—and it was a fascinating performance. Cells separated from each other floated around inert and helpless, until one happened to touch the container. Then suddenly it began to climb the wall.

The time was about 35 years ago, and what the scientists were watching were early experiments with "tissue culture," a technique to keep cells alive outside the body by floating them in a nourishing fluid. From these experiments—and a host of more recent ones—came solid confirmation of what the scientific world had long suspected: that the billions of cells that make up a living body are far from being the simple, amorphous blobs of jelly they appear; they are vastly complex entities, each with a specific mission in life that it strives mightily to carry out.

A cell taken from the fresh, young skin of an embryo, for example, *bulges* when it touches, say, glass. The bulge elongates—like an arm reaching out in the direction it wants to go. The tip of the arm flattens and glues itself to the glass. Then the remainder of the cell material (protoplasm) flows into the pseudopodium, or "false foot." The operation is repeated as another bulge reaches out to another spot

Model of a Generalized Cell

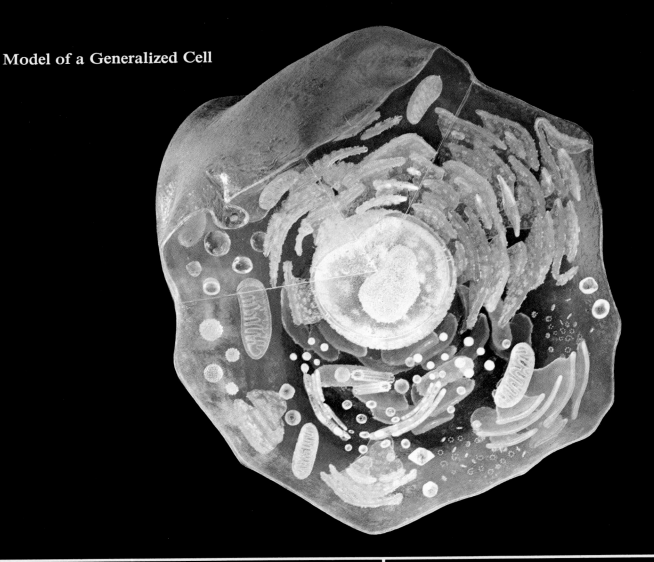

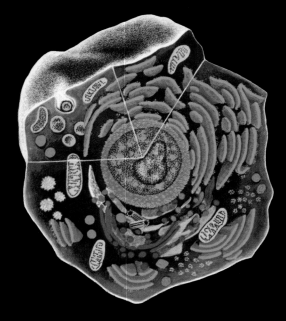

NUCLEUS

FOOD PARTICLES

CELL MEMBRANE

LYSOSOMES

MITOCHONDRIA

RIBOSOMES

GOLGI APPARATUS

ENDOPLASMIC RETICULUM

Nature's Vital Building Blocks

Mouse or man, earthworm or elm tree, each living thing is an intricate but orderly assembly of tiny cells. To meet the myriad demands of life, nature has evolved an almost endless variety of specialized cells, but nearly all contain the basic equipment shown here.

The NUCLEUS stores the substances called DNA and RNA, which make sure that proteins manufactured by the cell are the right kind. FOOD PARTICLES enter in solution through the CELL MEMBRANE. The enzymes in the LYSOSOMES digest the food particles; in the MITOCHONDRIA part of the digested food is converted to ATP, the cell's energy source. The RIBOSOMES manufacture proteins, the raw material for all living matter. In the GOLGI APPARATUS, dehydrated proteins are collected and shipped out of the cell through the ENDOPLASMIC RETICULUM.

on the glass. Thus the cell creeps steadily onward, hand over hand, just as, in a body, it travels up to the surface of the skin from the inner layer where it is formed. It seems—even in a test tube—to be trying to reach its assigned location in the body.

Such experiments heightened curiosity about the living cell. Obviously no mere droplet of formless jelly could perform such deliberate movements. As ever more powerful microscopes plumbed the depths of the cell, vague shadows and specks were seen; slowly these were brought into focus, their geography was mapped and the cell's amazing structure came into view.

One of the most astounding discoveries is about the outer surface of cells. This used to be thought of as a "semipermeable" membrane through which foods and minerals dissolved in water could slowly seep, while harmful materials were held back. Now it is clear that a cell's surface is no mere film; it is the face of the cell. It acts as though it has chemical senses of taste and smell and can swallow what it chooses, when it chooses.

According to one theory, the cell surface has four layers, two of lipids (fat) sandwiched between two of protein. The two lipoid layers act like a rubber lining. Complex proteins on the outer and inner layers work together to see that the proper supplies get pulled through the lipids.

Using powerful electron microscopes, scientists have recently discovered that a tiny droplet formed on the surface of the cell encloses a nugget of food. A dimple forms and then elongates inward, pinching off the droplet as it is ingested in the cell. In this way a cell gulps nutrients.

Another fascinating fact about cell membranes is that their outer surfaces teem with various chemical substances. Some are created by the cell itself and some have traveled from other cells. Many of these substances are enzymes, specialized proteins, each capable of modifying the speed of a specific chemical reaction.

The traveling substances are the voices of other cells calling across intercellular spaces, swapping information so that the millions of cells gathered to create body parts can act in concord in dividing and multiplying, taking their places and assuming special shapes. Many calls come from close neighbors, concerning local business in a lung, muscle, eyelid or whatnot. Their effect can be seen when cells from heart tissue are separated in a tissue culture. The heart cells appear listless at first. But after a few minutes some begin to throb slightly. Then they start to move toward one another. After several

hours clusters are formed—and the cells in each cluster are pulsing in unison! The messages that they pass among themselves seem to have reminded the cells, in complex chemical ways not fully understood, of their original unity and of their basic assignment in life—to create a heart.

Long-distance calls are handled by hormones, which ride the bloodstream to and from distant points, bringing orders to step up or slow down growth, digestion or some other vital activity.

"Protoplasm" has been science's catchall word for a jellylike substance inside cells. Only a few years ago it was considered to be just a kind of glop in which molecules swirled and collided at random. Then came the first hint that this wasn't so: a bit of netting was discovered near the nucleus of a cell. It was named endoplasmic reticulum, or "netting in the protoplasm." So dim and evanescent was it, even under the electron microscope, that its reality was questioned.

But then, six years ago, Dr. George E. Palade, at the Rockefeller University, New York, reported that the inside of a cell contains a vast labyrinth of incredibly fine tubes and chains of minute bags. His discovery was a milestone. It showed that protoplasm has one of the most complicated and beautiful structures in the universe. So elaborate are cells that one can say that nature had already done most of her job by the time she evolved them. After that it was merely a matter of putting cells together to build bees, fish, birds, horses, elephants—even human beings.

With the discovery of the nature of endoplasmic reticulum (let's call it ER), the "mixing bowl" concept of protoplasm was overthrown. Molecules do not collide haphazardly in a cell; the elements of life are propelled unerringly, in disciplined, coordinated patterns, through the ER labyrinth, whose tiny tubes and bags lead in all directions and connect every part.

Digestive enzymes are added to the droplet that has brought food into the cell. Subsequently the walls of the droplet are breached and its contents are released. The ER is also related to the synthesis and transport of protein and other substances destined for eventual transport outside the cell. As it carries on the business of the cell, it is constantly expanding and contracting, tearing apart and reconstructing itself.

The ER system is functionally continuous with the outside world. Its tubes lead indirectly to the cell's membrane—and out. The spaces between the ER channels are the true interior of the cell. They compose a large attic, for storage and many other uses.

This attic is a tortuous shape as it interlaces the ER labyrinth. Much of its space is occupied by vacuoles—reservoirs containing water, oil or liquid food. Also sprinkled throughout the interior area are many dark threads and grains called mitochondria, "thread grains." These grains have been pried open and found to contain high-powered generators that turn out a dynamic chemical fuel called adenosine triphosphate. ATP powers many of the cell's activities; the contraction of muscle cells, the constant building and rebuilding that keep the cell intact.

The vast, rambling attic of the cell is also the headquarters of the enzymes that facilitate much of the building work. Some of those in the cell are for home use. They are constantly peeling off from the lumps in which they are stacked and go coursing off to special assignments throughout the cell's interior. They bear instructions for the personal activities in their cell. One theory is that other substances are for export; they pass through the ER tubes—right *out* of the cell. These will be the voices of the cell talking to other cells.

What gives these proteins their instructions? It seems that they are at the business end of a long chain of command that leads back to a mysterious code of life in each cell's nucleus.

Over 15 years ago scientists first blasted their way into the nucleus of the cell and pulled out a thrilling trophy called deoxyribonucleic acid. The nucleus of every cell was found to hold a rolled-up coil of DNA's—exquisite tapelike molecules that carry the code of life on them the way a magnetic tape carries music.

DNA is the dictator of the cell. It regulates all the other chemicals in the cell. *All* forms of life on earth from bacteria to elephants, except certain viruses, have DNA in their cells, directing all their activities.

DNA rules through a marvelous system of "messengers" that create and guide the entire structure of the cell. Called ribonucleic acid, these messengers look and act very like DNA, except that they have an exit permit to leave the nucleus. First a portion of the DNA "double helix" separates, freeing each side to attract floating molecules, the order depending on the particular DNA, so that as the RNA is put together it automatically carries the imprint of the original DNA. Then the RNA rushes out into the reaches of the cell, where its code is finally translated to other proteins one after another. To each the code spells out instructions for doing a particular job: to go to work building something in the cell or to travel to other cells. It is through the RNA's that

DNA's in all the cells talk to one another. Somehow they agree to cooperate so that a great mass of a billion cells looks and acts like a dog or a horse or an elephant or you and me.

These discoveries hold great promise. When future generations look back to our space age, they may well regard the exploration of inner space—the depths of the living cell—as far more important to humanity than the spectacular achievements of the astronauts.

WHEN LIFE ON EARTH BEGAN

Rutherford Platt

Deep in a void of time, perhaps four billion years ago, Earth's infancy came to an end. The temperatures on the surface of our planet were now determined by sunlight. The raw crust, a metallic desert of lava, scoria and granite, was a battlefield of the elements, illuminated by the lurid glares of lava fountains, rumbling and shaken by earthquakes. Steam gushed out of vents until the atmosphere was saturated and black clouds blotted out the sun.

Then came a downpour that continued for centuries, until wide, low areas of the crust were filled with fresh water. When at last the clouds parted, the sun shone on blue, new oceans. Yet Earth was a very dead ball of rock and water. The elements vital for life were there, but none was accessible.

There was no free oxygen in the air, for example. (The atmosphere was a mixture of water vapor, ammonia and methane.) Earth's fund of oxygen was tied up with hydrogen (H_2O), or in iron ore, or in granite (which is half oxygen) and other rocks deep in the crust. The supply of nitrogen was in a similar fix. Carbon was gripped in the clenched fist of heavy metals (as in iron carbide), and buried under massive layers of granite and lava.

The lifeless Earth was now bursting with dramatic events—volcanoes thrusting up their cones, ultraviolet light bombarding land and sea, and great winds roiling the waters. Melted and torn loose by these upheavals, the vital elements began colliding in the volcanic fluids and gases, dissolving and mixing in the seas. Rain washed chemicals out of the air; rivers carved valleys and canyons, dissolving the salts out of the rocks. All this flowed into the seas.

The reservoirs of Earth's oceans were a unique milieu for chemical adventures. The sun's glare made land surfaces scorching hot by day, but the water at the surface of the sea was held at moderate temperatures by the circulation of cool water underneath. Here, chemicals washed out of the atmosphere reacted with salts washed from the rocks.

If we had been there to witness the coming of life, we would have looked for the first hydrocarbons, for they are step one in the chemical evolution of life. Molecules of hydrogen and carbon have unique powers. For one thing, they reflect a trait of living stuff in the way they can grow. Instead of being a finished speck of matter, a hydrocarbon can repeat its patterns and thus grow bigger and bigger.

For a long time chemists thought that the hydrocarbons, like other "organic" substances, could be made only by living cells. This posed a puzzling question. How could there be hydrocarbons without life, and how could life start without hydrocarbons? Today, laboratory experiments have demonstrated how the early hydrocarbons could have been formed when methane molecules in the air were bombarded by cosmic rays and electrical charges (lightning).

Even with the release of elements and the formation of certain chemical compounds basic to life, something else was needed—the stability of shape.

We do not have to look far to find the beginnings of form among the hydrocarbons in the pre-life sea. When a clump of organic matter is suspended in water, its molecules tend to stick together, forming a jelly. Chemists call this a colloid, a form of matter halfway between a fluid and a solid. (Colloids are familiar to us as gelatin, egg white and the scum on a broth.) If the colloid is shaken up in watery fluid, instead of dissolving it breaks into tiny drops.

Ultrasensitive instruments have detected a curious fact about these gel droplets. They have a whisper of magnetism on their surfaces that induces molecules of water in which they float to cling to the droplet in tight parallel ranks. This gives the gel droplet a peculiar skin of water, through which dissolved materials can pass in and out.

The myriad gel droplets in the sea were only mimics of protoplasm in living cells. But each droplet body fenced off a tiny, isolated portion of the sea, where chemical reactions gained some control and direction.

The curved transparent skins of the gel droplets acted like microscopic burning glasses, focusing light rays heavily charged with ultraviolet. Today, ozone in the upper air shields delicate protoplasm in living cells from ultraviolet rays. But in the Era of Creation there was no ozone and the ultraviolet light cooked the chemicals of life in the primeval ocean.

We cannot know how long it took for the tint of life to appear. There was no demarcation of time.

Through dim epochs, the gel droplets simmered and simmered in the tepid seas.

Gradually some giant molecules or clusters of molecules, complex descendants of the simple gel droplets, emerged until finally, after almost infinite time and infinite chemical combination, the incredible molecule we call protein was formed. We speak of this event as though it happened suddenly. But the fact is we simply discover protein in the void of time, and cannot know how it got there.

The new substance is something utterly different from rock, gas and liquids. A giant compared to ordinary molecules, composed of hundreds of atoms, it has tremendous chemical energy, and it can grow in every direction. It expands and contracts; elongates, shortens and flexes. It may become straight as a stick, wind into a ball, or coil at one end like a figure 6. Protein and certain other molecules called nucleic acids, also evolving in the sea, are together the wand of life. In the course of time they evolve to form protoplasm, enzymes, genes, insulin, hemoglobin; they organize into muscles and organs and coordinate their work; they will command the beating of hearts, the breathing of lungs, the vibrations of nerves and, ultimately, the flow of thought. But first, out of the flotsam of the ancient sea, they have to make a living cell. For these molecules, in all their glory, are not yet life.

In a single epoch, bridging millions of years, chemical trial-and-error fabricated the green pigment we call chlorophyll. The gels of the flotsam, equipped with chlorophyll and thus endowed with photosynthesis, could now make food within their own bodies out of light, air and water.

With this achievement, we have reached the mysterious threshold. Only one more crucial step remains: To be called life, the gel droplets and the complex molecules in them must be able to carry their banners across the horizons of future time by passing along their natures to descendants. Otherwise, this near-life stuff is doomed to be forever making a fresh start. The vital step was when protein and nucleic acid (with accessory substances) mysteriously joined to form the first protoplasm. The long-chain nucleic-acid molecules, rich in nitrogen and phosphorus, appear to researchers to be "blueprints"; thus the protein-nucleic-acid systems were duplicators that could strike other molecules at the right time and angle to break them up and reassemble them into their own likeness. So the magic of heredity became possible. And now, though the complex cells we know today were still far in the future, the threshold had been passed. Life had begun.

Chapter Three

The Ways of Insects and Spiders

*Watch a garden spider weave an intricate web with easy precision, or a male
firefly flash signals to a potential mate. Observe the bustling orderliness
of a beehive or an anthill. Intelligence at work? No, it is the incredible, instinctive
behavior that these joint-limbed, many-segmented creatures have evolved.*

THE MARVEL OF AN INSECT

Alan Devoe

A naturalist might conclude that God greatly enjoys creating insects, for our Earth so teems with the complex little creatures that no one knows how many different kinds there are. Nearly one million species have been classified. About 4000 new varieties are found every year. Awed entomologists predict that when all our Earth's insects have been discovered the final tally may be over ten million.

The members of this vast and amazing group of living things have assumed countless strange shapes and habits enabling them to cope with life under almost any circumstances. A drugstore beetle thrives in red pepper. There are insects so tiny and so intensely specialized that they live on the tongues of horseflies. There are others whose shimmering lives under the sun are so brief that they have neither mouths nor stomachs and never eat at all.

Despite this immense diversity, all insects have certain things in common. The lovely giant moths that enchant us when they come beating their beautifully patterned wings at our summer screens seem utterly unlike the pinhead-sized fleas hopping around in our dog's hair or the gauzy-winged mayflies whirling in a lyrical spring dance over a brook pool in the dusk. But basically they are all a similar kind of living machine. To learn about their make-up is to be introduced to extraordinary wonders.

An insect has no bones. It wears its skeleton externally. From man's point of view, it is built inside out and upside down. Its heart is on top near its back. Its legs are tubular sections of its skin-skeleton plate armor with muscles, nerves and soft tissues carried protectedly inside. The engineering of an insect's leg makes it, for its size, the strongest supporting device possible. In a recent experiment in which

an entomologist gradually piled tiny weights on a scarab beetle, he was able to get his little porter to move around under a load of 850 times its own weight without buckling. An average man, straining, can lift a little more than two thirds his weight.

This strong, pliable external skeleton provides even the most fragile-looking insects with astounding durability. Monarch butterflies, seemingly as insubstantial as blown thistle seed, make migratory flights from Canada to Florida and back again. Painted-lady butterflies, tagged for scientific identification, have been found to make a gigantic journey from North Africa to Iceland, although storm-tossed, lashed by rains and gales. They often reach their destinations with their wings in tatters.

With an outside skeleton there is no room for expansion. Growing insects must periodically molt. The horny casing splits and the insect creeps out in such a soft skin that temporarily it is almost "boneless." To make its new skeleton form in a suitably bigger size, the insect swallows air or water. Gulping and swelling until it is the required new size, it waits while its roomier skeleton hardens around it.

The insect's blood is not confined by any system of veins, as ours is. From its single great artery, which runs from the heart through the chest, the blood surges and seeps through the whole body. The blood is forced to the far tips of thread-fine extremities by little auxiliary hearts—pumping stations with sets of powerful muscles, located wherever there is a difficult booster job to be done. A cockroach has one in its head, to pump blood through its long feelers. Water insects have booster hearts to ensure perfect circulation in their legs.

For an insect, drawing the breath of life involves another remarkable process, because it has no lungs, nor does it breathe by mouth or nostrils. Along its sides are symmetrical rows of tiny perforations. Each of these is an air duct. Inside the body they link into two main trunk lines, which branch into hundreds of air lines running to every area of its

The face of every insect is designed to suit the life that it leads. The mouth of the queen hornet (top left) is adapted for chewing up nesting materials; that of the planthopper (top right) for sucking plant juices (red specks on the planthopper's legs are parasitic mites). Spines like those on the brush-footed butterfly caterpillar (bottom left) discourage predators; the beak of the robber fly (bottom right) is a weapon for impaling prey.

body. Thus the whole insect is continuously ventilated by a flow of air, which it controls by opening and closing its air ducts just as an organist pulls out stops.

Resting, an insect needs relatively little oxygen, but in flight it must breathe prodigiously. It must be able suddenly to call upon as much as 50 times the normal amount of oxygen. Its beating wings bring this about: as the wing muscles contract, they force out almost all the air in the system; as they relax, fresh air rushes into the ducts. The oxygenation provided to a flying insect is so pervasive that even in its wing muscles there occurs an almost complete change of air at every wingbeat.

No aspect of the dynamics of an insect's body presents more striking powers than its wings. A dragonfly, carrying its long body on wings thinner than fine paper, can hit 40 miles an hour. A mosquito, gorged on blood, performs the extraordinary aerodynamic feat of flying off carrying a load twice its own weight. To do so, it beats its wings more than 300 times a second. Such a furiously rapid wingbeat is by no means a unique performance. When we hear the high, thin whine of a midge—so small it is almost invisible—the midge's wings are beating more than 1000 times a second.

In insects that do not fly, the blaze of energy is concentrated in special adaptations that result in equally impressive displays of power. The little flea that hops aboard our dog is able to do so because it can make a leap of 100 times its own height. If man had the flea's jumping power, proportionately, he could jump over the Washington Monument.

Insects may look fragile, but their strength is as deceptive as the lacy engineering of a suspension bridge. Dr. F. E. Lutz of the American Museum of Natural History sealed bees and butterflies in a tube, then pumped out the air to make a vacuum. Even the insects' body moisture was sucked out of them. His "fragile" little prisoners survived unharmed even

A praying mantis feasts on a grasshopper that has strayed too close to its powerful, sharp-spined forelegs.
Much superstition is attached to this big, gangly insect: In various areas, praying mantises are known
as soothsayers, devil's coach horses and—in the mistaken belief that they carry a deadly sting—
mule killers. Despite the folklore, mantises are harmless to anything larger than their fellow insects.

when the tube was broken and normal pressure suddenly restored. The toughest elephant would have died instantly.

Insects have only rudimentary brains; they are guided through their lives by strange and lavish sensory gifts. They listen to life with two kinds of ears: delicate hairs sensitive to sound waves or tympanic membranes like our own eardrums; but these are distributed on many areas of the body, and are tuned to prodigies of special reception. Crickets have ears on their knees. Cicadas have ears in their abdomens. A water beetle hears with its chest. Katydids have been found to have supersonic hearing. Acute human hearing seldom ranges above about 20,000 vibrations per second. Katydids can hear 45,000. Many insects hear sounds outside our human range. Entomologists believe the whole outdoors may be ringing with an insect chorus of mating calls and interchanged messages when we think there is only silence.

Insects see by small eyes called "ocelli" on top of their heads, by great compound eyes at the sides and by a kind of allover "invisible eye," or light sense. With its eyes completely covered, a light-loving bug still moves unerringly toward brightness and a dark-loving one seeks the shadows. It literally sees through its skin.

With its compound eyes the insect sees a world of extraordinary composite vignettes. Several ingenious technicians have succeeded in taking photographs through an insect's eye. The world thus revealed is a landscape of finely patterned mosaic, each tiny piece of it caught by one facet of the eye. Fitted together, the pieces make a picture something like a stained-glass window. The eye of a dragonfly has more than 25,000 such facets.

In its capacities to taste and smell, an insect achieves perhaps the most remarkable sensitivity of all. It has taste organs in its mouth, but it also has the power of taste extended in unimaginable other ways and to an incredible keenness. Butterflies and bees can taste not only with their mouths but with their feet. The insect's detection of even microscopically slight traces of edible material amounts to a sensory miracle. The extreme limit at which human taste can detect sweetness is in a solution of one part sugar to about 200 parts of water. Some moths and butterflies can detect the presence of sugar when it is one part in 300,000.

As with taste, so with scent. An insect experiences the world as a "smellscape" of titillating vividness. Some male moths are able to catch the scent of a female nine miles downwind.

In addition to such sense powers—which, fantastic though they are, fall within our theoretical understanding—insects show signs of other sensings, the nature of which has not been fathomed. Experiments have been made with beetles to try to discover how they find a hidden bit of meat. With every known sense organ put out of action, and with shellac applied all over their bodies, legs and feelers, the beetles still make their unerring way to the hidden treasure.

To know something of the wonder of insects is to contemplate a little of the miracle of life.

THAT ASTONISHING ANIMAL: THE BEEHIVE

Jean George

The tiny honeybee dived onto a red rose, braked on a petal and walked into the flower. Glistening on her back as she drank the nectar was a red dot, placed there by a scientist. After her drink the bee turned her eyes toward the sun, took a bearing on it and started home. At her hive a quarter of a mile away the scientist was waiting, for this honeybee might well add another bright chink in an extraordinary mosaic of new and awesome bee research.

Today the beehive is no longer thought of as a mere collection of insects; it is considered a single organism of many glittering parts. An infant when it is swarming, the hive progresses from adolescence to maturity, gives birth to new swarms, finally subsides into the quietude of winter. A wounded, starving or plundered hive can actually suffer, moan in agony, and then, in its drive to live, repair itself by a healing process like that of any other feverish creature.

This concept is founded on a set of extraordinary discoveries. Any single bee, it is now known, can grow old quickly or, more unbelievable, grow *young*! The sterile can lay eggs; the senile can rejuvenate glands that have atrophied. A single bee can, in short, do the "impossible," in order to maintain the wholeness of the hive.

To understand the new bee research we should look into a typical wild hive that has lodged inside a hollow tree. There is always a main entrance with several combs of lustrous waxen cells hanging inside the door. Some combs contain honey, others hold pollen. A third type of comb, the brood comb, contains the larvae—unfledged bees in the wingless and footless state. Each hive has one queen, a large bee

Although they prefer the shelter of a cave or hollow tree, wild honeybees may build hives in the open, as in this mulberry tree. When a hive becomes crowded, the queen and most of the colony swarm nearby while scouts seek a new site and report back by dancing. The swarm checks these reports, selects the best site and follows the scout to the new home.

that lays up to 3000 eggs a day. There are also a number of drones who exist only to mate with the young virgin queens as they hatch, during the hive's sexually productive time of life.

Most of the other 20,000 to 40,000 bees in an individual hive are "workers" who perform a variety of specific tasks. One is nursing: feeding protein-rich "bee milk"—formed by special glands in the nurse bee's head—to the queen and the larvae. Making wax is another. In this process the bees eat honey, which is converted by special glands into beeswax. With the spines on their hind legs, they pick up wax scales protruding from pockets on their abdomens and pass them to their mouths. Then they chew and fashion the wax into six-sided cells which form the combs. The workers also forage for pollen and nectar. The nectar is fed to "receiver" bees who mix it

with the secretions of special glands and store it in the comb, where in two days it ripens into honey.

Some workers act as hive "guards," admitting only foragers that belong to the hive—they are recognized by odor, scented through the 12,000 scent organs on the antennae. Strange bees are killed on the spot. Air conditioning the hive (by standing inside the entrance and fanning their wings), building cells and cleaning the hive complete the list of duties.

As apiarists watched all these jobs being done year after year, the question arose: How did the bees know what to do? What intelligence told them that the hive needed more brood cells or a new guard detachment?

In 1925 a German scientist, G. A. Rösch, had a hunch that the age of the bees had something to do with their work. He daubed with paint a group of bees as they emerged from the brood comb. No sooner had their twinkling wings hardened than they started cleaning the cells, then moved toward the oldest larvae in the combs and began feeding them bee milk. Rösch examined one of the marked bees under the microscope to see if her physical development correlated with her job. It did; she had enlarged pharyngeal or bee-milk glands that lie in front of the brain. She was physically a "nurse."

In a few days, the marked nurses abandoned their original charges and began to feed the youngest larvae. After repeated studies, Rösch was convinced that young nurses fed the older larvae, old nurses the younger.

As days passed, the marked bees gave up their nursing duties and began taking nectar from the foragers and storing it. Examination showed that their bee-milk glands had begun to degenerate, and the honey sacs in their bellies were filled with nectar. Their mean age was 11 days.

Around the 15th day, these bees began making wax. The microscope showed that their bodies had changed once more to fit the job—their wax-making glands were highly developed. On the 18th day, the bees did guard duty; after the 21st day, their wax glands ceased to function. Now the bees became foragers. Rösch found that worker bees died when they were around 38 days old.

With the publication of Rösch's findings, other scientists joined the investigation. In Munich, Dr. Martin Lindauer noted certain variations in Rösch's time schedule—he had watched a marked bee stand guard duty for an unheard-of nine days. In Russia, Mrs. L. I. Perepelova announced that she had several precocious bees—one two-day-old was making wax, ordinarily a job for the 15-day-olds. Obviously a beehive was extremely adaptable. Jobs could be done earlier if the well-being of the hive demanded it.

Bee students everywhere set out to discover just how adaptable bees were. The most spectacular experiments were performed by Mrs. Perepelova. She removed the queen, larvae and eggs from the hive and watched to see what the workers would do. For several hours the hive did not miss the queen. Then one of the attendants lifted her antennae and began to circle. She exchanged food with a nearby wax maker, and the wax maker drummed her wings. She approached and exchanged food with others. The cluster moaned. The moan spread through the hive, and the whole group began to throb as if besieged by fever.

Several weeks passed. Then Mrs. Perepelova noticed some workers rushing over the empty brood cells and thrusting their heads far down into them. Then came the impossible, the supreme effort to heal the wound—a few "sterile" workers began to lay eggs! Nurses clustered around the egg-laying workers, feeding them bee milk. Slowly, laboriously, the workers gave forth eggs—six to eight a day, as compared to a queen's 2000 to 3000. Mrs. Perepelova's conclusion: "When the queen is gone, some inhibitory factor that prevents the workers from laying is missing from the hive."

Around the world, bee experts pressed on to find what else a hive could do to heal itself. Mykola H. Haydak, now of Minnesota's Agricultural Experiment Station, removed the brood comb from a hive and isolated it. Then he put upon it newly emerged bees. There were no nurses, hive cleaners, guards, wax makers, foragers. He waited.

The adjustment was violent! The entire developmental process was speeded up so dramatically that three-day-old bees took survey flights from the hive while others of this age built cells, a job normally reserved for the 16th day. On the fourth day the bees collected pollen. After a desperate week, the premature hive began to function as usual.

With the publication of Haydak's findings, experts wondered whether bees could also reverse their development. In Yugoslavia, Mrs. Vasilja Moskovljevic placed 503 marked foragers, all about 28 days old with dried-up bee-milk glands, onto an isolated brood comb with the queen. The bees would either have to produce bee milk or let the hatched larvae die. Days passed; no brood was reared. Then one afternoon Mrs. Moskovljevic noticed a forager leaning into a cell. The scientist looked closely. A glittering drop of bee milk was deposited near the mouth of a hatched larva. Quickly Mrs. Moskovlje-

vic placed the forager's glands under a microscope, and there was the proof. The old dried glands were swollen and filled with bee milk! The impossible had been achieved: youth had been regenerated!

Meanwhile, in Austria, zoologist Karl von Frisch discovered a "language" used by foragers to tell others the distance and direction to sources of pollen. A bee that had found some flowers returned to the hive and performed a dance for her fellow foragers. A vigorous figure-eight dance meant that the flowers were near. A feeble tail-wagging dance meant the flowers were far away (distance, near or far, could be spelled out explicitly in meters by the observer). If the bee's body was pointed vertically up on the comb, the flowers were in the direction of the sun. The body pointed down on the comb meant that the flowers were in the opposite direction to the sun. A bee dancing at a 60-degree angle from the vertical was telling her coterie to leave the hive at 60 degrees from the sun. The kind of flower was communicated by a taste of the forager's nectar or pollen.

Next, Martin Lindauer discovered that this dance language was also used by forager "scouts" to inform a swarming hive of the location of a new home—on several occasions he noted the angle and the rapidity of the dance movements and was able to get to the new location in time to observe the bees' arrival!

The final question: What stream of intelligence flowed through the hive that told its separate parts what to do?

England's bee expert Dr. C. R. Ribbands tackled this one. He noted an aspect of hive life that no one had seriously studied—the constant circulation of food in the hive. Food moved steadily from nurse to queen, from nurse to the wax makers, to the cell cleaners, to the receivers, to the foragers, and back from the foragers to the receivers, the cell cleaners, the wax makers, the nurses and the queen. Ribbands became convinced that each stage of bee development contributed a distinct glandular secretion or an enzyme which, if all were present and in sufficient supply, would tell the individuals that the hive was balanced.

Dr. Ribbands kept coming back to Mrs. Perepelova's remark: "Some inhibitory factor," preventing workers from laying eggs, was missing when the queen was gone. He also saw that it took the hive several days to make the adjustment—the time necessary to circulate the food with the missing ingredient and lift the inhibitions. Could the food be a kind of circulatory system, a bloodstream of sorts?

Thus Ribbands conceived the idea of the hive-animal of many individually functioning parts, controlled by the essence of a hive—its golden food. Much study remains to be done; the chemical properties of the food ingredients, for instance, still need to be isolated and identified. But most bee researchers today agree that the concept is sound.

I realize now that many years ago I was present when a wild hive died. It had lived in the kitchen walls of our summer home in Pennsylvania, humming gently and giving birth to new swarms for 12 years. Then, one September day, there was a hum in the walls different from anything we had ever heard. We ran outside to see what was the matter. A few bees dropped from the hive doorway to the ground. Then there was silence.

Next spring the bees did not come out. A year later when the walls were opened to make room for a picture window, my uncle described what he had found. "A little dried queen in a circle of attendants, some of them close against her, as if to keep some vital lifeblood going."

A beautiful golden creature had stopped breathing. We had always spoken of "the hive" as a single thing, but none of us realized how close we were to the truth: Something with a thousand sparkling parts had lived and died among us—the humming, life-giving hive, without which the earth would be a less fruitful place.

THE WACKIEST ORCHESTRA ON EARTH

Jean George

The musician drew his thigh over the teeth of a saw and began to bow a six-beat phrase. Another instrumentalist came in on a belly drum, amplifying a low tattoo into a sirenlike wail. A third snapped his head against a wooden board, and a fourth, lying on his back with his feet in the air, made music by arching his spine.

Some far-out combo performing in a Greenwich Village loft? Not at all. Most of this group can be heard around the summer world in every field and hedge, for the musicians are a grasshopper, a cicada, a death-watch beetle and a click beetle—all members of the wackiest orchestra on earth.

The conspicuous soloists of this orchestra are crickets, grasshoppers, katydids and cicadas, but you can listen to a fuller ensemble on any summer night on the stage they prefer—hot grass, dry earth and, for good measure, an August moon quivering in a sea of heat. Many of them (there are nearly one mil-

lion kinds of insects, representing 80 percent of all animals on earth) reach a jazzy pitch that marks the high tide of their breeding season.

I have long been an admirer of this orchestra, but I did not become a true fan until a physicist, Prof. George W. Pierce of the Cruft Laboratory at Harvard University, compiled his book, *The Songs of Insects.* Dr. Pierce started out to analyze the loudest animal noises on earth (some insects have been known to transmit a mile) for U.S. Navy acoustic engineers, but he soon became fascinated by the kooky insect instruments and way-out sounds. Thus his study has been useful to entomologists as well as to Harvard graduate physics students and to Naval officers in their acoustics research.

Studying the insect chorus is nerve-racking, for the all-male chorus (females don't sing, although a rare few can creak) creates a cacophony most people tend to hear only as background music on a summer night or day. Because this orchestra of trillions is so disorderly, students of their music usually isolate individuals in laboratories. But adding to the difficulty of studying them is the fact that insects are among the most adaptable of all creatures.

A katydid in Dr. Pierce's laboratory, for instance, nearly upset the professor's theory that insects can be identified by pitch and rhythm. This katydid learned to count and thereby change his usual two-beat rhythm. During one experiment, a laboratory assistant imitated the katydid sound, a shrill "zeep-zeep," screeching three beats. The katydid answered three beats. The assistant tried four. So did the katydid. They worked up to five. Then the insect lost count, and began to improvise on the numbers he had already learned. At seven he sulked and quit.

The katydid is a handsome, brilliant-green creature, with long, graceful antennae. He makes music by lifting his wings and running the edge of one over some 70 sawlike points on the other. Katydids have another characteristic interesting to the physicists. In the base of their wings they possess a miniaturized amplifier, less than one eighth of an inch in size, composed of chitin, the stuff from which the strong outside skeleton of the insect is made. Thinner than paper, yet stronger than a comparable thickness of steel, this tiny disk-shaped device can amplify an almost inaudible scratch into a crackling "zeep" that, according to Dr. Pierce, will carry a mile. The physical proportions of this amplifier were diagrammed by Dr. Pierce and his associates for the Anti-Submarine Laboratory at New London, Connecticut, where the Navy applied some of the principles to its sound-signaling program.

Two midnight musicians meet face to face. The katydid makes a loud chirping call by rubbing together two roughened areas of his front wings. The tiny tree frog produces a birdlike trill with his vocal cords and resonant throat sac. Both creatures have the same objective: to attract females of their species.

Familiar to almost everyone are the crickets with their fat bodies, long antennae, big heads—and their endearing habit of singing from the hearth and doorstep. Crickets sing with a distinctive "creeeak, creeeak," produced by rubbing a scraper on the left wing against a file on the right. Cricket songs have meaning. Some are love calls, others are danger signals and still others are simply "here I am" ditties.

The tree cricket blasts forth one of the most shrill and persistent songs of all insects—a repetitive "trill" that goes on endlessly. This is a mating call. However, it's a rather peculiar love song, because the female is deaf, having no sound-receptors on her body. But while the male rubs his left wing over his right in a series of two, then three and four harmonic frequencies, a small gland is exposed which emits fluid. The odor of this fluid *does* get to the female, who crawls up on the male's back to drink, and is then quickly inseminated.

Grasshoppers, known in the Bible as locusts, bow with their thighbones. A grasshopper, standing on his "hands," lifts his big back legs until the femurs

rub against a line of small stiff pegs on the wing. This produces that dead-battery sound in the summer meadow. The grasshopper also has a flight song. As he takes off, he snaps his two big top wings against the smaller inside ones and produces that familiar crackle of grasshopper jumps.

The loudest members of the insect orchestra are the "drummers" that literally beat one object against another. The cicadas are the classical drummers. Those with the two-year life cycle are about an inch and a quarter long, chunky, often with beautiful crystal wings. When the brood emerges from the ground, the cicadas leave their crisp brown coats on trees and plants. The sounds they make are courtship calls, a buzz saw high in the treetops that begins softly and rises to a frantic, earsplitting climax.

Entomologist S. W. Frost calls the cicada's noise-making instruments "the most complicated sound organs found in the animal kingdom." The cicada has not only drumheads that he vibrates by pulling them with powerful muscles, but an amplifying system that makes the katydids' megaphones mere toys.

*The seventeen-year cicadas require a long
metamorphosis. After living underground for years as
nymphs, cicadas crawl up plant stems and burst from
their larval shells, winged and ready to mate.
They die within a few weeks, after laying their eggs.*

The sound organs are small pits on either side of
the abdomen just under the wings. Two large plates,
which can be raised and lowered to control the volume, lie over them. The drumheads, or timbals, are
in these cavities, together with the amplifier—a folded
membrane, a so-called mirror, or sounding board,
and a pipe that lets in the air to be trembled. The
muscles vibrate the timbals slowly at first and shake
the air inside the cavity. The vibrations expand within the folded membrane and then bounce off the
mirror for more intense magnification. Meanwhile,
the plates are opening, letting out a sound that is an
air-cracking fanfare.

Of all the drummers, however, the death-watch
beetle is the most astonishing, for this is the musician that hits its head on wood to beat a tune. He
does this inside his burrow in woodwork and old
furniture. These clicking concerts can go on for
years. I recall the morning my father, a former entomologist for the U.S. Department of Agriculture,
told me to listen to the top of his oaken desk. I was
amazed to hear snaps and clicks. Then he pointed
to a little volcano of sawdust. "The beetle's been
getting closer to the surface for the last few days,"
my father explained, "and so I have been keeping
an eye out for him." Presently a slender, quarter-
of-an-inch beetle stepped out of the sawdust. "I'll
miss him," my father said. "He's been keeping me
company for twelve years."

In addition to the insects that sing deliberately to
communicate, there is yet another group of noise-
makers—the "incidental musicians." These are the
flies, bees and mosquitoes that make sounds as they
go about their daily chores of gathering food and
defending the hive. They have not been ignored by
the physicists. One study of the housefly revealed
that it whines the note F in the middle octave, by
vibrating its wings 21,120 times a minute.

When I mentioned this to a friend who is a musician with absolute pitch, she listened to a housefly
and said, "You're right." Three weeks later, however, I had a call from her. "Two flies in my studio
are driving me crazy," she reported. "They're off-
key. Flat!" I suggested she turn up the heat, for the
warmer insects are, the more active they become.
Later she called back to say that the heat had
worked, stepping up the wings' vibrations. "The flies
are on pitch now," she said happily, "and I can
work again."

Bees and wasps also use their wings to create
sounds, but the tones they make are an expression of
their moods. They hum while peacefully gathering
food, "pipe" when calling to mates, and "roar"
when attacked. But of all the fiddling, drumming,
vibrating insects, the click beetle is my favorite
musician.

I came upon one while I was working in the garden
recently. He was a narrow shiny beetle and he had
fallen on his back as click beetles are wont to do.
When I leaned down to watch him, he suddenly
arched his spine as he pressed head and tail against
the ground. At the same time, a section of his thorax
pulled out of a groove in his abdomen, and he
seemed done for. However, with a loud click he
shoved himself together again. This gave him such a
jolt that he rode 18 inches into the air, where he
turned over and came down on his feet.

As I watched him scurry away, a passing bee
hummed out the peace of nectar-gathering, and a
grasshopper cracked out a ditty of flight. From nearby came the drum and roll of a cicada. In the soft
August sun, the band played on.

THE MYSTERY OF THE FIREFLY

Robert Gannon

The hunt begins as dusk turns the sky from rose to gray. With butterfly nets, or stockings stretched wide by tennis rackets, with baseball caps or simply with cupped hands, the children of Oak Ridge, Tennessee, stalk the quarry. They're catching fireflies for science.

In the last few years, while unraveling secrets of the miniature lamp-bearer's illumination, scientists have also been discovering surprising things about the firefly's private life. It begins as an egg secreted in the earth. But, in many species, the egg may already show a touch of luminescence—just a wisp, glowing, like a promise.

In about three weeks, the eggs hatch into larvae that look something like sow bugs, those multi-legged, turtlelike creatures found under damp boards. The larva is a voracious predator—paralyzing, then eating, such things as snails and cutworms. At this stage, too, many species glow. Tiny spots on the underside softly shimmer like view holes in a furnace door. Such shining larvae are called glowworms. (The one in the song, however—"Shine, little glowworm, glimmer, glimmer"—is not a larva but the adult of an English species, a steadily glowing, wingless female whose winged mate is lanternless.)

The most familiar U.S. larva type, *Photuris,* lives one or two years underground, then in late spring builds a marble-sized mud house around itself and changes to a pupa. In ten days or so, it breaks out and flies forth to add its stardust to the summer night. Now its life-span is short, only a few days.

Fireflies are true beetles, and there are 60 or more luminous species found in North America. Seen from above, the adult looks commonplace. Typically, it has a rectangular brown or blackish back, a pair of nervous segmented antennae, a half-dozen legs, and a head that looks like a space helmet. But turn it over, and you'll notice a difference. The whole lower end of a male firefly's abdomen is yellow; a female has a smaller yellow splotch. It's from these marks that the living light comes.

If a firefly is under stress—caught in a spider's web, for instance—its taillight glows brightly. Even the shock of a firecracker or thunder may cause a field of fireflies to flash once in unison. But, ordinarily, the signal is used to find a mate.

Dr. John B. Buck, chief of the Laboratory of Phys-ical Biology of the National Institutes of Health, has been studying fireflies off and on for 30 years and, along with other naturalists, has worked out a typical firefly courtship pattern. It begins on any warm, humid evening—preferably moonless—from June through August. All day the male insect has been snoozing among moist grass roots. Now he crawls out, raises his hard, tough wing covers, unfolds and spreads his gossamer flight wings, and whirs off, searching. He flies with his body at a 45-degree angle, holding his hind legs high and close to his sides so the whole world below can see his debonair undercarriage.

Some species emit a signal that looks like a row of periods in the night. Others give only infrequent blips. The common eastern U.S. firefly, *Photinus pyralis,* traces out a bright "J" or check mark. In his slow, roller-coaster-like flight, he flips on his light—as much as .02 candlepower—toward the end of a steep dip, keeps it burning while he pulls out and nears the apex, then turns it off before he begins another dive.

Down on the ground, meanwhile, the female waits. She recognizes a firefly of her species primarily by the length of his flashes. When she sees the gleam she's looking for, she sends out an answering blink. Her light isn't as bright as her beau's, but his compound eyes have more facets and are keener.

Some years ago, Dr. Buck spent a series of nights in the fields of Maryland, squatting in the grass and blinking a flashlight at passing fireflies. By the end of three weeks, he had broken the firefly recognition code and could fool amorous male fireflies into approaching and plumping down alongside his flashlight. The male's recognition of the signal of a female of his own species, he determined, depends not on the color or intensity or length of the female's flash but on how long after his flash it comes.

The pattern of flashing between the sexes is as fixed and characteristic as the songs of different birds. One eastern female, *Photinus ignitus,* on a relatively cool night (the warmer the weather, the faster the exchange), waits 5½ seconds, then emits a single short flash. At about the same temperature, the female of a Florida species, *Photinus collustrans,* waits one second, then holds her flash for a full second.

The lamp of a firefly is a lighting engineer's dream. An ordinary light bulb has an efficiency of about 10 percent; the rest of the power is lost in heat. The firefly turns *92 to 100 percent* of his lantern energy into visible light. The secret lies in two chemicals: a compound called luciferin, from the Latin meaning "light-bearing"; and a complicated enzyme called luciferase.

In the 1880's French physiologist Raphael Dubois extracted these two chemicals from solutions of ground-up firefly lantern, shook them together in a test tube, and found that they lighted up in the presence of oxygen from the air. In 1942 a graduate biochemistry student at Princeton, William D. McElroy, identified another essential ingredient: a substance called adenosine triphosphate, or ATP. This acts, he discovered, as the vital "energizer," allowing the firefly to renew its light again and again. Without it, not a glimmer.

Biochemists had known that ATP was the chemical that supplied energy to muscles and performed a few other cell functions in animals. The work of McElroy and others showed that ATP is found in many more places—in fact, that it is the closest thing we know to the spark of life itself. "You might call it the universal source of cell energy," says Dr. McElroy, now director of the McCollum-Pratt Institute of Johns Hopkins University. "It's the primary chemical required for any process that utilizes energy in a biological system." In fireflies or human beings, ATP is the mysterious substance that allows food to be turned to energy, causes cells to grow and multiply, sores to heal, brains to think.

In 1948, to continue his studies of luminescence, Dr. McElroy offered to pay 25 cents a hundred for fireflies. By the end of the summer, 85,000 fireflies had been delivered to his office—many simply stuffed into envelopes and squashed in the mail. Today, McElroy enlists an army of children to do the gathering. He pays central "coordinators" a half cent each for fireflies in quantity (5000 or more), quick-frozen after capture and sent to him in insulated containers. He hopes to gather at least a million.

Why not breed and raise fireflies in a laboratory? Nobody yet knows how. Other mysteries remain, too. The switch for the firefly's beacon, for instance. For years, scientists thought that the firefly's nervous system simply opened tiny air valves to let oxygen into the cells whenever it wanted to flash. It is now suspected that the firefly nerve endings, like those of many higher animals, secrete adrenaline. This depolarizes the light cells, allowing the luciferin and luciferase to mix and so produce light.

Meanwhile, an extract of firefly tail *minus* the ATP makes an efficient measuring tool. Mix it with any tissue, and the resulting light gives an exact reading of the amount of ATP present. If the tissue lights up, something has recently been alive.

In this time exposure, two trails of light record the movement of a Pyrophorus *beetle along a leaf. A Central American relative of the familiar firefly,* Pyrophorus *carries light-producing organs on its shoulders instead of in its tail. In one species, less than an inch long, the light given off by three or four beetles is bright enough to read by.*

In Project Firefly, at the Goddard Space Flight Center in Greenbelt, Maryland, research scientists are developing a system to look for traces of life in space. Balloon flights have brought back tiny bits of living matter—spores, pollens, mold—from 15 or more miles out. In September 1965, an Aerobee rocket soared aloft to bring back dust from 35 to 100 miles out. Unfortunately, an air leak in the lower atmosphere contaminated the experiment, but another try will be made.

Later, when the first unmanned spacecraft soft-lands on Mars, an extract of firefly lantern may be aboard. A pair of mechanical fingers will reach out, pick up a pinch of Martian dust, and mix it with a bit of firefly extract, while a light-sensitive device watches. If the dust holds even a single cell containing ATP—which means life as we know it—the mixture will light up, and from the essence of a hundred firefly tails, word will be winked back to a waiting Earth.

THE WIZARDRY OF WEBS

Jean George

From rock to grass, from twig to petal, the Earth is strung with signal lines, traps, love nests, nurseries and railroads as some 40,000 species of spiders talk to each other, express fear and desire, hunger and anger through their complex and beautiful webs. Largely unnoticed by humans, thousands of spiders are working on every acre of countryside.

The tons of spider silk, for which the Earth is a mere spindle, comprise hundreds of varieties and weaves to meet the multiple needs and crises in the spiders' lives. Where one thread suffices for dropping over a cliff, another tension, a different weave, is required to fasten webs to leaves, and still another to send warnings or receive messages from a stuck fly or courting male. Webs of spiders are, in fact, their eyes, ears, voice and fingers.

Spiders are such a different form of life that we cannot say they have a head and body; after all, their legs are attached to the front part, a head and thorax, while silk glands lie in their belly. Seven different kinds of glands, not all present in all spiders, lead out to the spinnerets. Most spiders have three pairs of complicated spinnerets tipped with many minute spinning tubes. These move like human fingers. They card, pull, weave, twist as they turn the fluid silk coming from the glands into precisely the right kind of thread to suit the particular situation confronting them.

The first need in a spider's life is to get away from home in order to avoid being eaten by parent or sibling. To this end, the spiderlings fly on a silvery thread over field and mountain. And they take off on this voyage like expert circus performers.

Last spring I watched a hatch of grass spiders emerge from their egg case and crawl down silken avenues to disappear in the garden plants. As they went they trailed behind a veil of threads that heaved and rippled between the leaves of the iris and ferns. One spiderling eight-footed its way to the top of a dried chrysanthemum stalk, where it circled until it faced the wind. Then it threw up its hind legs and stood on its head like an acrobat. In this position it spun out two or three feet of ballooning thread, a dry and wide strand. Then it let go of the stalk, grabbed the silk with its front legs, and in the best circus tradition went flying through the air. Aided by the wind, it guided itself around the elm in the yard by pulling in on the streamer and then letting it out. The wind bowed it. As it billowed away it struck the edge of the house and was stopped. There the spiderling reeled in its slender balloon and hurried to the porch roof to take off again. In this splendid manner it sailed out of sight.

During the spring and autumn when spiderlings go ballooning, as this is called, the sky is filled with tons of dragline, known as gossamer. In some places it will fall to earth with the rain in such abundance that the grass is swathed in white silk. In Yosemite Valley, California, it is periodically trapped in sheets between the stone arches. When the sheets are thick enough the wind carries them off like glittering laundry and wraps them over the trees, until the forest is eerily shrouded in silk, like furniture in a deserted mansion.

Gossamer and trapping threads are perhaps the best-known webs, but some of the lesser known are more exciting. There are the "wild threads," for instance. These fine, almost invisible strands can surround a simple sheet trap—that flat, silver platform between grass blades—with a sunburst of trip lines. As clear as air, these lines are nevertheless tough enough to trip a flying insect and send it tumbling onto the sheet below.

The swathing band is the most dramatic production of the spider because of its size and quantity. It rolls out in broad ribbons and is composed of strong parallel threads that come from the lower spinnerets, plus a crisscross of finer silk from the upper spinners. So instinctive is the production of this band that anyone can induce a spider to produce it by tossing an insect onto its web. Before the thread appears, however, the insect must struggle on the web, a rhythm that impels the spider to rush forward and sink its poison fangs into the prey. It is the activation of the poison glands that sets off the spinners. Next the spider's legs turn the insect so that the river of silk is spread evenly until the prey is completely engulfed.

Some spiders use their webs as trophy walls when the meal is done. Because they "drink" the insect, by turning its interior into liquid with powerful digestive juices, the insect grows smaller as the feast goes on. Usually a mere dot remains, swathed in silk.

The most beautiful combination of threads is the famous orb of the garden spiders. Walking one day in a garden, I saw a spider among the phlox. She had just built a triangular frame for her web. Now she began the laborious task of constructing the orb. She walked to the middle of the top thread and dropped on a vertical line to the bottom. Back she climbed to the center of this line, and, establishing a hub, she spun out spokes, using a dry, hard thread. Then, circling outward from the hub, she built a scaffolding for her wheel. Next she spiraled back again, leaving behind a line with gobs of fluid on it. To space this shining glue perfectly she gave the line a quick flip as she secured it. The line vibrated, spreading the fluid evenly. When the thread lay still, it was hung with droplets of equal size, nearly equally spaced. How, I wondered, had her race learned and passed on this wisdom?

Spiders are predators, the best insect killers known; in fact they will even kill one another if there is no communication between them. So spiders, too, must be careful of others' webs, for most of them work in the dark of night, are nearsighted and have no ears but their threads.

Under these conditions it is no wonder that their means of reproduction is the most complicated on earth. For the reason that every advance toward a female is fraught with danger, the males have evolved a strange narcissistic love. They make love alone, to a web, before they carefully hand their cells of life to a female.

The tarantula's method is particularly spectacular. He spins a sheet in which there are two holes, one large, one small. Between the holes he leaves a narrow band of strong silk, different from anything else he spins. He steps through the large hole and, hanging below, strengthens its edges. As he does this, his body touches the exquisitely woven band. The sensation induces him to release a drop of sperm fluid. He crawls back to the top, and, reaching around the

weaving, draws the fluid into bulbs in leglike attachments near his head, to be handed to his mate later.

The male spider then destroys the web and sets out upon the risky task of courting and mating. Almost invariably the female, who matures later than the male and is usually larger, is not ready to receive his gift. She gives him a bad time, charging and threatening, and sometimes eating him.

Because of the danger, the tarantula male uses caution. He approaches his mate. She rears in hostility. He jumps and pets her. She opens her fangs to bite and poison him; but in a quick maneuver he grabs her fangs with hooks on his front legs and hangs onto them while he deposits the sperm in a pocket in her abdomen. Now he can walk away safely.

There are as many ways of subduing a female as there are kinds of spiders. One of the most intriguing ways is that of the crab spider. He ties his mate down with strong threads. Approaching her gingerly, he crisscrosses her body with threads, until, when he is done, he has staked her to the ground with a veil of silver. This special piece of craftsmanship is known as the "bridal veil" of the spiders.

With the renewal of the species—and it does go on in spite of the dangers—the female spiders now weave the most important webs of the spider world: the cases for the eggs. Some are golden silk, tough, windproof, waterproof and resilient, while some are merely poorly constructed bags. The eggs are laid in the sac. Some species lay as many as 3000, some lay only one, but all of them spin around their precious offspring a beautiful thread that is carded and twisted by the last spinnerets. The egg cases may be glittering baskets or dense whorls of hard thread.

The silk of a spider egg case is so beautiful that a Frenchman in the 18th century wove it into stockings and gloves. The gleam of the cloth impressed the Academy of Sciences of Paris, and it commissioned an investigation into the commercial possibilities of silk from spiders' egg cases. It was found impractical mainly because spiders, unlike silkworms, are loners. They will not live close enough together to produce easily gathered egg cases.

Most spiders spin certain traps and designs, then stop. But not the grass spiders. They add to their webs all year until, when the frost forms, there may be yards of huge white sheets in the fields. We call autumn erroneously the time of the spiders. In truth it is the end of the time of the spiders, for most live, as mature spiders, only eight or nine months, and the white sheets are their shrouds.

Of all the weavings and webs—the funnels and

A golden orb spider advances on her victim, a grasshopper trapped in her sticky web. Before killing it, the spider will expertly roll the grasshopper in the web and spin many strands of silk around it to prevent its escape. The intricate web, usually about two feet across, is repaired each time it is damaged or disturbed.

snares and trip lines, the sperm webs, the draglines, the orbs—the one whose creator has the most faith in nature is the fishing line of the bolas spider. It is a single line with a sticky ball on the end. It is swung from a limb of a tree, back and forth, back and forth, as the spider fishes the night for a passing insect.

I met a bolas spider recently while sitting out at night under the apple tree. I was struck on the cheek by something sticky; and, as I tried to wipe it off, my finger became caught in the line. I turned my flash-light on, and at the end of the line was a fat bolas who looked more like a bud than a spider. She was balancing on a web trapeze and reeling up her line that had struck so noble a bite.

I jiggled her line again. She lifted her fangs and reeled in faster. Then I leaned toward her, looming into her world. At that she crept off into the leaves, and I did not see her again. I often wonder how she felt, in the limits of her spider brain, about the "big one that got away."

Masters of Mimicry

In the world of insects and spiders, things are not always what they seem. A katydid looks like the lichens on a tree trunk, a walkingstick like a twig, a grasshopper like a dried leaf. Such disguises, designed to fool the eye of a predator, have played a vital role in these small creatures' evolutionary struggle to survive. Nontoxic insects and spiders are virtually incapable of protecting themselves from larger, more voracious forms of life, but this very size limitation may be what has made them masters of mimicry. Some have developed patterns and colors that help them blend into their natural backgrounds. Others have been able to alter their shape and coloration so they resemble parts of the plants they live on. To scare off foragers, distasteful creatures tend to advertise their distastefulness, while more edible creatures try to imitate the distasteful ones. Thus, as in the photographs below, a harmless caterpillar may look like a poisonous snake and a defenseless moth like a sting-bearing bee. Mimicry is known to birds, reptiles, mammals and fish, but insects and spiders outstrip all other animals in the variety and effectiveness of their disguises.

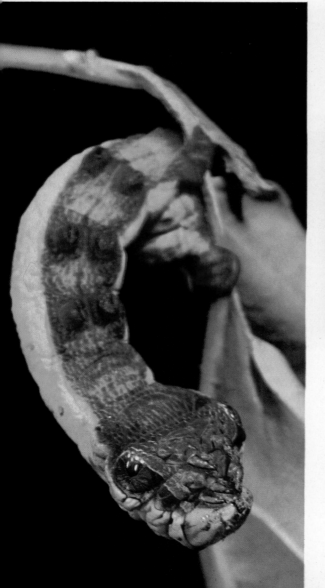

This hawkmoth has the clear wings, fat body and short black antennae of a bumblebee—a disguise that warns real bumblebees to look elsewhere for food.

When threatened, this caterpillar flips over, pulls its legs into its body, flashes a pair of false eyes—in convincing imitation of a deadly pit viper.

The Indian leaf bug is a mimic in both looks and behavior. It is flat and veined, and rocks back and forth like a leaf being blown by the wind.

During the day, stick insects rest alongside twigs, which they resemble to perfection. After dark, they crawl slowly about, feeding on leaves.

Treehoppers, which suck juice from plants, look like thorns along the stems they feed on. This disguise is good enough to fool the birds, their enemies, even when the plants they cling to have no thorns.

Perched among these lichens is a cricketlike katydid. Its camouflage is extended even to its long antennae (which are obscured by black and white bands).

Short-horned grasshoppers have protective coloration that blends with their environment. This one looks like a dead leaf; others resemble green leaves or even pebbles.

The dune wolf spider is doubly safe. It lives in a tunnel, and when it emerges its markings so break up the contours of its body that it blends into the sand.

The pattern of this sphinx moth's wings makes it indistinguishable from tree bark. As added protection, the moth can startle an enemy by flashing bright-colored underwings.

Chapter Four

Cold-Blooded Creatures

It is not heartlessness but heatlessness that marks a creature as cold-blooded. Lacking the built-in heating systems of birds and mammals, all reptiles, amphibians, fish, and the multitude of lower animals must regulate body heat by physical activity (or inactivity) and by choice of environment.

NOBODY LOVES A CROCODILE

Gordon Gaskill

The most feared beast in the world is its largest reptile, the crocodile. Many experts believe crocodiles kill more human beings than do lions, tigers, leopards and snakes put together. Each year Africa alone loses an estimated 1000 victims, mostly women and children.

The croc's domain includes central and southern Africa, the warmer parts of Asia, tropical Pacific islands, and northern Australia. He also inhabits the warmer parts of the Americas but is here far outnumbered by his cousins, the alligators. The differences between crocodiles and alligators are many and technical. The most obvious one is that, with jaws closed, the alligator's teeth are invisible while in the crocodile the long fourth tooth on each side of the lower jaw fits into a notch on the outside of the upper jaw, giving the crocodile a deceptive "grin."

Except for a few tiny chameleonlike lizards, the crocodile is the only reptile with a true voice. He can emit a loud, eerie roar, "like distant thunder or the roll of a big drum." His dental arrangement is marvelous: if he loses a tooth, another one quickly grows in its place, and this goes on all his life. He will eat almost anything. His digestive juices are so strong with hydrochloric acid that they have dissolved, within a few months, iron spearheads and six-inch steel hooks that have been swallowed. Even so, he doesn't seem to need a great deal of food. In captivity, crocodiles thrive on less than a pound of meat a day.

The crocodile has two deadly weapons—terrible jaws and terrible tail. A murderous sidewise blow of the tail can knock down and break the legs of the largest buck. But the crocodile's classic attack is to drift in unseen in the murky shallows, and then, without the slightest sound, to submerge entirely and make a swift lunge to seize his prey in viselike jaws.

Nature has equipped him well for this method of attack. The crocodile, like a submarine, has a "periscope" and a "snorkel" breathing tube: elevated eyes and nostrils. They peep just above the water, almost invisible, while all the rest of the body is submerged. Like a submarine, too, the croc has a marvelous system of valves that automatically close when he dives, to protect nostrils, ears and throat from water. Imbedded in his eyes are thousands of tiny crystals that collect all possible light, giving him amazing sight under water, even at night.

The crocodile is one of few animals in the world that deliberately and regularly attack human beings. In places where crocodiles are considered sacred and are fed, or in lakes that swarm with fish, they almost never attack. But wherever the crocodile's natural prey has been largely depleted, it soon acquires a taste for human flesh. Most victims are women who are bathing, washing clothes or drawing water, and children who splash in the shallows. Many Africans are careless because they rely on some anti-croc charm a witch doctor has sold them.

In Tanzania some years ago, a tribal chief told an Englishman that crocodiles had, in one month, taken five women as they drew water. The Englishman suggested that the women use large tins tied to long bamboo poles to draw water. The chief shrugged and said, "Tins like that are hard to find and very valuable."

When a crocodile catches a large animal such as a buck or a cow, he keeps it off-balance with savage sidewise yanks of his head and pulls it into deep water to drown it. The crocodile can then feed at leisure—but he has problems. Impressive as his great jaws are, his teeth are not made for chewing. They serve mostly as clamps. He can therefore eat at once only something he can swallow whole: Small dogs are among his favorite tidbits. If his victim is large, he tows it away to rot and thus become soft

Protruding teeth identify this big fellow as a crocodile; an alligator's teeth cannot be seen when its jaws are closed. In the water the croc is swift and agile, holding its limbs close to its body and swimming by sinuous movements of its tail. On land, too, this sluggish-looking reptile is capable of startling bursts of speed.

enough to tear apart easily. Often he takes his prey to a tunnel-like den that has a below-water entrance that slants up above the waterline, underground, and has an air vent in the roof.

Perhaps the strangest escape from a crocodile was that of a native who was seized and pulled under water within sight of friends. By enormous luck, the croc's den was only a few yards away. The victim regained consciousness to find himself inside a dim cavern full of decaying carcasses—and with the croc lying beside him. Soon the reptile went back to the water, and the African seized the chance to enlarge the air hole above him and escape. It was a long time before his family would let him into his own house; they were sure he was a ghost.

Most widespread of the several species of crocodile is the Nile crocodile of Africa and Madagascar. The Nile crocodile mother lays her three-inch-long eggs (averaging about 60 per clutch) near the water's edge in sun-warmed sand, covers them with more sand, and waits for them to hatch—a period of about three months. Her job is to protect the buried eggs from predators: mongooses, pythons, hyenas, monkeys and big monitor lizards. (People sometimes eat crocodile eggs, too, despite their rather strong fishy flavor. Theodore Roosevelt once found 52 eggs inside a crocodile he had shot; he ordered them made into an omelet and pronounced them "bully.")

At hatching time a miracle occurs. The baby crocodiles cannot dig away the foot or so of earth above them; therefore, while still inside their shells, they begin calling for mother, who has been listening for just this SOS. At the first peep, she begins to dig away the earth. This instinct is so strong that, when scientists tested it by building a fence around a sand nest, the frantic mother tore it to pieces.

The newborn baby is about ten inches long and, from the first moment of life, aggressive. It snaps at anything near it. With unerring instinct it heads for the nearest water to find shelter; for lots of animals, including storks, cranes and mature crocodiles, find the wriggling infants even tastier than the eggs. With all these hazards, some experts estimate that not more than 1 percent of the eggs laid ever become mature crocodiles.

Recent wholesale shooting makes it less and less likely that a given crocodile will live to any great age —and thus to great length. Asiatic-Pacific species are *said*, meanwhile, to reach nearly 30 feet, but in the past few years no Nile crocodile over 19 feet has been shot.

Since World War II a tremendous feminine desire for crocodile-leather shoes, handbags and luggage has spurred widespread crocodile killing. Although prices are rising steadily, demand, particularly from Paris, rises even faster. Today a croc hunter may get

$100 for a high-quality belly-skin—the only part of the animal with commercial value. A portion of this skin, tanned and made into a smart handbag, may bring up to $550 in a retail store.

Such prices lure hundreds of men into shooting crocodiles almost everywhere they exist. In one seven-month period some hunters in Australia made $15,000 each. Croc populations dwindle quickly under such pressure. Many lake and river spots which only a few years ago were packed with crocodiles are now bare of them.

Dr. Hugh B. Cott of Cambridge University, England, an expert on the Nile crocodile, fears that the croc may soon become extinct. "It would be a grave loss to science and posterity," he says, "if these saurians, which have survived for over 100 million years, were to be sacrificed to fashion's demands."

Few others share this worry. There is a widespread belief that many crocodiles have retreated to places less accessible to hunters. "After two or three days," one hunter told me, "they learn that a spotlight or an outboard motor means danger—and they move away." Several nations have now placed some restrictions on crocodile shooting.

"The protection they receive in parks alone," says one game warden, "will preserve all the crocodiles science would ever want—or that tourists would ever want to see."

WHAT SNAKES ARE REALLY LIKE

Alan Devoe

Our fellow creatures on this earth include about 2500 *species* of snakes. To understand a snake's life is to encounter some of the most amazing adaptations in the world of nature.

A snake never closes its eyes; it has no eyelids. A snake can engulf prey far bigger than its mouth; giant snakes such as Asia's pythons are capable of swallowing a deer. Some poisonous snakes, like the African mamba, are so deadly that men have died from a bite in less than one minute. The harmless snakes of our fields and gardens have such odd endowments as a stomach that can digest bones and a yellow eye lens that gives sharpened vision by filtering out ultraviolet rays.

It is hardly surprising that creatures so curious and startling should be the subject of more myths and misunderstandings than any others under the sun —or moon, for many snakes are most active at night.

It is not true that snakes are "slimy"; their skins are dry and exceptionally clean. No snake has a poisonous sting in its tail. No snake rolls like a hoop or hypnotizes birds. Snakes' flicking, "wicked-looking" tongues are harmless. Killing a snake will not bring its mate seeking vengeance. It is not true that a mortally injured snake retains life until sundown. Nine tenths of all species are harmless. Few are aggressive toward man. They don't suck milk from cows. And they are not charmed by snake-charmers' music; snakes are deaf.

The real facts about snakes are more remarkable than any fables. Everything about a snake is designed around the key fact that it has no arms or legs. Yet it is not a primitive or simple being like a worm (to which it is unrelated), but a highly developed, complex one. It breathes by a lung. It has a three-chambered heart. Its internal processes involve an intricate physiology of liver, gall bladder and kidneys. And it must catch prey, defeat or evade enemies, reproduce its race, while confined inside its own elongated skin, like a man straitjacketed and hobbled. To meet this unique problem, nature has given it an array of specialized equipment and some peculiar skills.

A snake lives in a world of silence. Since it has no ears, it "listens" with its sensitive underside for ground vibrations. The eyes can focus in delicate adjustment to near distances, like a precisely calibrated microscope. A night-foraging snake has eyes like a cat's, with vertical pupils.

A snake's tongue is both an exquisitely sensitive "hand"—used for delicately touching and feeling every strange object it encounters—and a means to super-smelling. The fine forked tips pick up microscopic particles from the air, earth and water. Drawing in the tongue, the snake inserts the forked tips into two tiny pits in the roof of its mouth. Lined with keen sensory cells, these pits give the snake the scent and feel of its immediate environment.

From nose tip to tail tip the snake's body is covered with convex, overlapping scales, affording a tough covering so continuous that a portion of it which is transparent covers even the snake's eyes.

Special adaptations enable this garter snake to swallow a cricket frog whole. The snake's mouth can expand enormously because its upper and lower jawbones are unjoined and both halves of the lower jaw are connected by an elastic muscle. The snake's teeth point backward, enabling it to grasp its prey firmly, and its stomach juices are so potent that they can even dissolve bones—which means that the snake has no need for chewing.

The water moccasin (above), *one of the few venomous North American snakes, is among a small number of species that give birth to living young. The bull snake* (below) *illustrates the more common form of reproduction: It is laying a clutch of from 10 to 24 tough, leathery-shelled eggs that will hatch in about eight weeks.*

The backbone is engineered for tremendous suppleness. Its vertebrae are articulated by perfect ball-and-socket joints. To each vertebra is attached a pair of ribs. (Some snakes have more than 300 pairs.) There is no breastbone; instead each rib is joined by a cartilage and a set of powerful muscles to one of the scales on the snake's underside.

In the glide a snake angles its ribs forward, hooks the ground with the attached scales on its underside, then gives a backward rib-push. The smooth flowing glide of a snake is a beautifully synchronized, many-footed walking, all done from the inside.

For faster speed, snakes supplement this action by undulating laterally in a wriggle that takes advantage of every projection in the terrain. Where purchase is poor, a snake may thrust its head forward, hold it firmly to the ground, then pull up the rest of its body.

Snakes achieve prodigious acrobatics. Blacksnakes

can race through the tops of shrubbery as fast as on the ground. I have watched a pine snake climb straight up a tree trunk, just pressing its underside against roughnesses of the bark.

A snake becomes sexually mature usually in its second or third year. Only a few naturalists have been privileged to see the ritual of courtship. Among water and garter snakes, the male fondles his chosen female by rubbing his chin gently upward along her back, in a series of gliding caresses. Blacksnakes and other racers engage in a courtship dance. Weaving, bobbing, rearing with heads almost touching and then whirling in a new arabesque of challenge and response, the two courting snakes are whipped into a flashing crescendo of excitement.

About three fourths of all snakes hatch from eggs; a minority are born alive from their mothers' bodies, sometimes in immense broods. A garter snake has been known to produce 78 babies in a litter. Egg clutches, deposited by the mother in a sheltered spot such as an old stump or buried in the sand, vary in number from a few to over 70.

A snake's egg is not brittle, like a bird's egg, but slightly malleable. An extraordinary fact is that it increases in size after being laid. It may grow as much as one third before hatching. Some eggs hatch within four days, others take as long as 90. In temperate climates most snakes lay their eggs in early summer and the babies hatch in August or September. Research has recently disclosed that a mother snake may lay fertile eggs even though she has not mated for several years.

The baby snake gets out of its egg by means of a temporary egg tooth, as a chick does. From the moment of hatching it is ready to cope with its world. Among poisonous species a newly hatched baby is already venomous and knows instinctively how to use its equipment. A rattlesnake two minutes old can coil and strike expertly.

During its first year a snake more than doubles its length and may triple it during the second year. Then the rate of growth slows, but it never stops entirely as long as the snake lives. And the life-span of a snake may be long. A water moccasin has lived to be 20, a boa constrictor 23. Even a little garter snake, contented in captivity, has reached 11.

Since a snake grows steadily, it is obliged to change its tight and hampering skin, which does *not* grow, at an average interval of six weeks (except during hibernation in northern climates). New skin forms under the old. As the old skin begins to loosen and slacken, the snake rubs its head against a twig or rough-edged stone until a hole is worn through the skin. It works its head free. Then, contracting its muscles rhythmically, pushing, pulling, thrusting against the ground, the snake slips the old skin off backward, inside out like a peeled glove, emerging gleaming in fresh color and agile again in a right-sized suit.

Because the snake may be able to catch prey only at undependable intervals, nature has ensured that it can swallow a bulk that will keep it going through a fast of more than a year. A snake has six rows of teeth: two in its lower jaw, two above, two more in the roof of its mouth; they grow in a continual succession of replacements. Needle-sharp, the teeth all curve inward, making it almost impossible for a small animal that has been seized to pull away.

All the movable bones of the snake's head are loosely articulated. The bones of its lower jaw can be separated from the upper. Each side of the jaw can be worked independently, the two halves being connected only by elastic ligament. As a result, a snake can perform eating feats that seem mechanically impossible. Some snakes can engulf large birds' eggs without breaking them. A slender garter snake has been known to eat 30 tree frogs in succession. To digest its big, unchewed meals, a snake is equipped with gastric juices potent enough to break down fur, feathers, even teeth.

In the venomous species, one or two pairs of teeth are lengthened into fangs, grooved or hollow, and connected with sacs of poison in the snake's cheeks. At the moment of biting, the snake gives a powerful squeeze to these sacs and squirts a jet of venom into the victim. The coordinated speed of a poisonous snake's lunging strike, bite, poison injection, and return to normal stance is one of the most startling feats of agility in nature. The whole operation may be completed in less than half a second.

Venom helps in the capture of food, making it possible for our limbless, handless hunter quickly to paralyze small creatures that might otherwise get away. A venomous snake employs its poison against big animals or human beings only rarely, and in self-defense. The rattlesnake basking on a sunny rock ledge, the copperhead stretched at ease on the checkered forest path, want nothing so much as to be let alone.

American and Canadian deaths from snakebite total under 100 per year. Scientists agree that widespread knowledge of these simple rules would keep this figure still lower:

If bitten, keep calm. Don't run. Don't drink spirits. Snake poison spreads relatively slowly, but panic, excitement or alcohol will accelerate its action.

Most snakebites occur on the legs or hands. Apply a tourniquet above the bite, but not too tightly. (You should be able to insert a finger under it.) Loosen it for a few seconds every ten minutes.

With a knife or razor—sterilized with a match flame if nothing else is available—make a cross-cut (X) one quarter inch deep over each fang mark. Suck the wound to encourage bleeding and draw out as much venom as you can.

Get to a doctor as promptly as you can *without rushing.*

FISH IN LOVE

Konrad Z. Lorenz

I am familiar with the behavior of animals in the wild ecstasies of battle and of love, but, with the exception of the wild canary, I know of no animal more hot-blooded than a male stickleback, a Siamese fighting fish or a cichlid, all of them suited to the aquarium. No animal becomes so completely transformed by love, none glows, in such a literal sense, with passion as a stickleback or a fighting fish at mating time. The sides of the male stickleback turn transparent with glowing red, its back becomes an iridescent blue-green and its eyes glow a brilliant emerald.

In the fighting fish this marvelous color is not so continually present, for the little brown-gray fish lies with folded fins until another of his kind approaches him. Then they both light up in all their incandescent glory and the fins unfold like ornamental fans. There follows a passionate dance of life or death which may lead to mating or to bloody battle. Fighting fish recognize the sex of a member of their species not simply by seeing it but by watching the way in which it responds to the severely ritualized, inherited movements of the dance.

After a mutual self-display in which every luminous color of the wonderful fins is brought into maximum play, the female lowers the flag by folding her fins, and the love ceremonial begins. But when two males meet face to face orgies of self-glorification take place, the idea being to intimidate the opponent and to stimulate each dancer to a state of fearlessness. There is a striking similarity between the war dance of these fish and the corresponding ceremonial dances of Javanese and other Indonesian peoples. In

A male Siamese fighting fish builds a nest of air bubbles, linked by mucus he secretes, inside half a plastic cup (left).
Heavy with eggs, the female is lured beneath the nest (right) *for the dancelike spawning ritual with the male.*

As the ritual ends, the female is upside down; the male is bent over her, fertilizing the eggs she releases (left).
The eggs sink; the male catches them and takes them to the nest (right). *Driving off his mate, he tends the nest alone.*

both man and fish the minutest detail of every movement has its own deeply symbolic meaning.

On account of their beauty and the ritual character of these long preliminaries, fighting fish appear less malevolent than they really are. One of these fish will attack, when stimulated to that point, by opening its jaws so wide that all its teeth are directed forward and, in this attitude, it will ram them into the side of its adversary. After this it is often only a matter of minutes before one of the combatants lies on the bottom, mortally wounded.

The fights of sticklebacks are very different from those of fighting fish. The basic principle of the stickleback's fighting is, "My home is my castle." It is only when he has founded his home that the stickleback becomes physically capable of reaching a state of full sexual excitement; therefore, a real stickleback fight can only be seen when two males are kept together in a large tank where they are both building their nests. And, owing to the extreme toughness of the stickleback's skin, their battles are absurdly harmless.

At the nest itself, the stickleback is a raging fury, and there even the smallest male will defeat a large one that has entered his territory. The vanquished fish invariably flees homeward and the victor chases him furiously. The farther the victor goes from home, the more his courage ebbs, while that of the vanquished rises. Arrived at his nest, the fugitive dashes at his pursuer, and off goes the chase in the opposite direction. The pursuit is repeated a few times, swinging to and fro like a pendulum. The line at which the fighting potentials of the two fish are equally balanced marks the border of their territories.

Though stickleback and fighting fish are different in fight, as parents they have much in common. In both species, it is the male that undertakes the building of the nest and care of the young, and the future father only begins to think of love when the cradle for the expected children is ready.

The stickleback digs his nest in the sand at the bottom of the tank, but the fighting fish builds his on the surface of the water. The castle in the air of the fighting fish consists of a little pile of air bubbles that are coated with spittle and are very tough. While building, the male already radiates gorgeous colors. When another fish approaches, like lightning he shoots forward and, glowing, halts. If it is a female and she is prepared to accept him, she colors herself modestly with light-gray stripes on a brown background. Then with fins closely folded she swims toward the male, who, trembling with excitement, expands all his fins to breaking point and presents the dazzling brilliance of his full broadside to his bride. Next, as a beckoning gesture, he swims off with a sinuous movement in the direction of the nest. In this way the female is enticed under the bubble nest, and now follows the wonderful love play that resembles, in delicate grace, a minuet.

The male always exhibits his broadside to his partner, but the female must remain at right angles to him. If he gets so much as a glimpse of her flanks, he will immediately become angry and unchivalrous; for standing broadside means, in these fish, aggressive masculinity and elicits instantly in the male a change from hottest love to wildest hate. Therefore the male moves in circles around the female, and she follows by keeping her head always turned toward him. The colors become more glowing, the movements more frantic, the circles ever smaller, until the bodies touch. Then, suddenly, the male slings his body around the female, gently turns her on her back and, quivering, both fulfill the great act of reproduction. Ova and semen are discharged simultaneously.

The female remains for a few seconds as though benumbed, but the male has important things to attend to. The minute, glass-clear eggs are heavier than water and sink at once to the bottom. Gently releasing the female, the male glides downward and gathers them, one after the other, in his mouth. Then he blows them into the nest, where they miraculously float, coated now with buoyant spittle. He has to hurry, for not only would he soon lose the tiny globules in the mud, but, if he should delay, the female would wake from her trance and, also swimming after the eggs, would swallow them.

Much more highly developed is the family life of the beautiful and courageous fish of the cichlid group. Here both male and female care for their young, and we see a type of behavior that human beings consider highly moral: Male and female remain in close partnership after reproduction is completed, and even after the care of the brood necessitates it. Really personal ties exist between the male and female; they are the only fish that live in a "lifetime marriage."

Anyone who has watched cichlid parents fanning a continuous stream of fresh water toward their eggs or small babies lying in the nest, or relieving each other of duty or, when the brood has learned to swim, leading them carefully through the water, will never forget these scenes. The prettiest sight of all is when the children that can already swim are put to bed. For every evening until the age of several weeks the young are brought back to the nesting hollow, where the mother stands above the nest and gathers them about her with signals of her fins.

These details of cichlid behavior are particularly developed in the gorgeous jewel fish. When the female is putting her babies to bed, she jerks her red dorsal fin up and down, making its brilliant blue jewel spots flash like a heliograph. At this the young congregate under the mother and obediently descend into the nesting hole. The father, in the meantime, searches the tank for stragglers. He inhales them into his roomy mouth, swims to the nest and blows them into the hollow. The babies sink to the bottom and remain there.

One evening I saw a father jewel fish perform a deed that astonished me. As I approached the aquarium to feed the fish, most of the young were already in the nesting hollow over which the mother was hovering. She refused to come for the food which I threw into the tank, but the father, who was dashing backward and forward searching for truants, allowed himself to be diverted from duty by a nice hind end of earthworm. As he was chewing it, he saw a baby fish swimming by; he started as though stung, raced after the baby and took it into his mouth.

It was a thrilling moment. The fish had in its mouth two things, one of which must go into the stomach and the other into the nest. What would he do? I must confess that I would not have given two cents for the life of that tiny jewel fish. But the fish stood stock-still with full cheeks and did not chew! If ever I have seen a fish think, it was at that moment. For seconds he stood riveted. Then he solved the conflict: He spit out everything, and both the worm and the little jewel fish fell to the bottom. The father turned resolutely to the worm and ate it up, without haste but with one eye on the child. When he had finished, he inhaled the baby into his mouth and carried it home to its mother. Some students who had witnessed the scene started to applaud.

THAT REMARKABLE CREATURE, THE SNAIL

Oscar Schisgall

It can exist on the tops of mountains, buried in deserts and hidden forests. Both constructive and destructive, it serves admirably as a menu item and in medical research, while producing havoc in vegetable gardens. Land snails originated millions of years ago and since then have made their way over most of the world, dividing into some 18,000 species.

In many ways, the everyday snail—or *l'escargot*, as the French call him—is a phenomenal creature. He is without an internal skeleton and is practically all muscle. Although small and fragile in appearance, one species, *Helix pomatia*, the *Bourgogne* of gastronomic fame, can easily carry 12—and pull 200—times its own weight.

In spite of such feats, the snail has a predilection for sleep. In addition to several months of winter hibernation, he crawls into his shell at the least sign of hot sun, which dries him out, or heavy rain, which waterlogs him.

He can take short naps or spend days huddled in his bedroom behind a thin curtain of mucilage. Desert snails carry the sleeping habit to miraculous proportions, dozing off for as long as three or four years.

In motion, a snail is a thing of graceful beauty. His sinuous body—varying in color from gray to silver—glides along without visible effort on its "suction-cup" underside. Tiny muscles contract in a rhythmic succession of waves, and thus the fragile body is propelled forward.

Wherever they go, snails lay a protective carpet under themselves, leaving behind a colorless, sticky discharge that sometimes shimmers silver in the light. So effective is this coating that snails have been induced to crawl along the sharp edge of a razor blade—without a trace of a cut.

In the everyday life of a snail, moisture is the ruling factor—moisture to keep his body supple, moisture for his silver path, moisture to nourish the young sprouts he dotes on. Come mid-April, when temperatures turn milder and spring showers bathe the countryside, the snail wakens, his tiny silvery head appears, his tentacles dart here and there to learn what the world has to offer. The upper pair of antennae, which can elongate themselves to three quarters of an inch or more, are topped by the eyes; in the lower two, much shorter, are extremely sensitive organs of touch.

As *Helix pomatia* seeks out his first meal, his body, which may be three inches in length and a quarter inch thick, stretches out from the shell. He is woefully nearsighted, but his strong sense of smell helps him zero in on new greens. Then his tiny mouth goes to work. Although no larger than a pinprick, it is equipped with 25,600 infinitesimally small but incredibly effective teeth. Put a snail in a cardboard box, and he will eat his way out to freedom. If he wears down the teeth, he replaces them as easily as he repairs a broken shell.

Usually the snail forages at night, but cloudy and drizzly days become uninterrupted day-long orgies

The soft, juicy fruit of a blackberry is an ideal meal for a land snail. With its tiny, tonguelike radula, covered with rows of hooks and horny teeth, the snail pierces the fruit, scraping portions of it into its mouth.

of eating. The rest of the time he hides from the sun's drying rays.

Twice a year, in spring and fall, *Helix pomatia* suddenly stops eating and takes to wandering restlessly about. He is in love. His antennae reach out, probing restlessly. Suddenly he sets out at top speed.

The love quest ends when the snail meets its chosen mate face to face. During the ensuing courtship, which may last for several hours, they first bite each other, then prod around the right side of the neck, where the genital orifice is located. The two hermaphrodites—each snail possesses both male and female organs—eventually unite at the neck and one leaves the other pregnant.

Twelve to 15 days after mating, the pregnant snail picks a moist spot at the base of a tree or amid grass roots close to a potential food supply, and there digs a nest—a hole about three inches deep. For over 12 hours, it carefully drops as many as 26 tiny eggs, one by one, into the hole. It then covers up the traces and abandons the eggs to their fate.

In three or four weeks, the eggs hatch into near-perfect miniature *Helix pomatia*, with paper-thin shells. As soon as they hatch, the young snails are fully able to cope with life—to crawl out of their nest, provide themselves with food and find shelter.

Every year the snail adds about a tenth of an inch to its shell, depending on climate and diet. In France, where snails are regularly harvested, two years is the average life-span and thus size is limited. There are, however, giants that have been shipped to France from lands where they were allowed to age much longer.

Émile Dhumerelle, one of the best-known snail dealers in Paris, exhibits one shell as big as a tennis ball.

But big or little, the snail attains his greatest stature at the end of a fork. From the days when housewives had to spend tedious hours washing, cooking and elaborately preparing them, *les escargots* have become today one of the quickest and easiest dishes on the French menu. Some 40 large "snail preparers" see to it that housewives can always find a ready supply of the two species of snails considered the most succulent by the discriminating palate: the tantalizing *Bourgognes* and the slightly smaller *petits gris*. Some 250 million of them are swallowed every year in France alone. In the United States, a growing army of *escargot* devotees annually devours 24.8 million snails, most of them imported.

And the snail may prove to be more than a gastronomic delight. Every spring the faculty of medicine at the University of Paris buys several hundred pounds of snails. These are kept alive at a low temperature for the use of a staff of some 100 technicians. According to the laboratory heads, the gastric juices the snails secrete are invaluable in the study of sex and adrenal hormones, known as steroids, attached to other molecules in the human bloodstream. Thanks to a discovery made in 1952, the chemical properties of this secretion have made it possible to isolate steroids without damaging them. By studying their concentration in blood or urine, we may possibly detect the presence of certain types of cancer. There's no telling where the snail's silver trail may lead.

Chapter Five

Winged Wonder

What inner compass guides the arctic tern each spring as it travels to its nesting grounds across 11,000 miles of empty sea? Why does a cardinal fiercely guard an invisible line that marks its own home territory? Science has yet to explain the mysterious migratory instincts and nesting habits of even our most familiar birds.

THE MIRACLE OF BIRDS

Alan Devoe

"**A** bird is to me as wonderful as the stars," said ornithologist Elliott Coues. To learn something about that winged marvel is to make acquaintance with one of nature's breathtaking miracles.

In the making of a bird, every step was as with a single thought in mind: the thought of flight. Here was to be a creature of incarnate air, a "grace for the sky." Here were to be lightness, buoyance, arrowing strength, a sight to lift man's spirit as if on wings itself.

A bird is "bird-brained" because it needs prodigious eyesight for flight. Because only a small part of a bird's eye is visible to us, we're not likely to realize what a gigantic organ it is. A bird's eyes are actually so big that there is barely room in its skull for them. Many hawks and owls have eyeballs bigger than yours and mine. These immense eyes force a bird's brain to be a relatively insignificant organ, squeezed to the rear of its skull. In many birds, the eyes weigh more than the brain. In some, each eye does. And for these eyes there is a third eyelid—to be drawn back and forth as a "windshield wiper" as the bird rushes through the high sky.

Other marvels? An owl scans the dark woods with eyes ten times as sensitive to faint light as ours. A hawk may have vision so piercing that as it perches on a lookout tree it can see small prey more than a mile away. To extract grubs from trees, a woodpecker has a tongue so long it curves over inside the bird's head and is rooted in front of its eyes. Many coastal birds have a built-in sense of time so precise that after inland trips they can return to shore for feeding at the hour when the tide is right. The commonest little finch in our shrubbery is such a fabulous quiver of life energy that its tiny heart races at

500 beats a minute. Some birds' body temperatures are as high as 110 degrees.

Ruskin was using only slight poetic license when he spoke of a bird as "but a drift of the air brought into shape by plumes." A bird inhales a draft of air more deeply than just into its lungs. A bird's lungs connect with as many as nine additional air sacs, some of which have elongations extending into the bones. A mammal bone is heavy, dense. A bird bone is hollow, filled with a spongy network engineered for air capacity. As a bird breathes, it is inflooded with air to its marrow.

Even the skull of a bird is designed to help this airy insubstantiality. Skull bones become lightweight plates and struts. To lighten the living flying machine at its "nose," nature took away birds' teeth —teeth need heavy jaws and muscles. For lightness aft, birds' tail feathers are borne on one short bone.

Feathers are the strongest structures for their size and weight known in nature. A feather may seem to be only a central shaft with projections on either side. It is much more. Each projection (called a vane) from the feather stem is composed of numbers of parallel rods, the barbs. A barb is itself virtually a complete miniature feather, with extremely fine side-projections called barbules. Look still closer with a lens, and it is revealed that on these barbules are tinier barbicels, and on these are almost infinitesimal hooklets. The hooklets mesh the barbs; the whole vane is one light, perfect interweave. Barbules and barbicels on a single feather may number over a million.

To make its streamlined body a perfect flight machine, a bird's framework is the most rigid in the animal world. Vertebrae of its backbone are fused and united, to make an immensely strong axis. Backbone, ribs and breastbone form a "cage" of incomparable strength. The bird's ribs are lashed together by tough ligaments, fastened to both its backbone and its breastbone. Its two powerful shoulder blades are braced together across the front by collarbones

In flight, the American egret retracts its neck into an "S" and thrusts its legs out straight for balance. Lazily flapping 54-inch wings, it achieves an effortless buoyancy that seems to defy gravity. Even on the ground, as it wades through quiet shallows in search of food, this dazzling white bird has a regal dignity.

that fuse in its wishbone. Down the middle of this runs a tremendous ridge, for attachment of the great pectoral muscles that work its wings. In many birds these muscles constitute more than one fourth the bird's whole weight.

As a bird beats its wings in downstroke, it may seem to be pushing itself forward as if rowing through the air. High-speed cameras show it isn't. A bird is a natural miniature airplane. On the downstroke, each wing moves forward, the inner half held almost rigid, its fore edge slightly sloped like a plane wing, its upper surface arched by a curve of feathers. The outer half of the wing moves separately, activated by the bird's "wrist," located about halfway along the wing's length. During wingbeat, the primary feathers at the bird's wing tips flare out almost at right angles to the wing and become propellers. The inner half of the wing, curved and tilted, is meanwhile the plane wing providing steady lift. On landings and takeoffs, the bird avoids stalls by means of special feathers at the front edge of its "wrist." It raises these to make a "slot" between them and its main wing, providing a perfect auxiliary airfoil.

A bird's flight feats can be nearly incredible. A big Cooper's hawk is streaking in pursuit of a quail. Sud-

denly the quail, from a height of only five or six feet, drops like a rock to a clump of bushes. In the instant before its body can hit that shelter, the hawk shoots under it, turns upside down in full flight, catches the falling body, rights itself and zooms on without a second's slackening.

A sparrow hawk, flying at top speed, saves itself from crashing into a sudden obstruction by performing a perfect Immelmann turn. An African eagle, swooping down at a speed of better than 100 miles an hour, brakes with such stunning skill—spreading wings and tail in an aerial skid-stop—that it comes to a dead halt in the space of 20 feet.

A bird cushions its landing with its legs, which consist of three single rigid bones with joints that work in opposite directions. This is probably the most effective shock-absorbing mechanism in nature.

As a male bird utters his song, to claim territory and invite a mate to it, he uses an extraordinary vocal organ called a syrinx. In this song box is a bony band to which attach structures of outstretched membrane under control of intricate muscles that can exquisitely tighten or relax the valve as the ecstatic bird forces air from its lungs.

The songs of springtime lead into courtships

For a sea bird, the puffin of the North Atlantic has surprisingly small wings and an unusually plump body. It has difficulty in taking off from either land or water but once airborne, flies rapidly. An excellent underwater swimmer, the puffin collects several fish in its improbable bill during one dive, possibly anchoring the catch with its tongue.

stylized by instinct into some of nature's strangest and most touching rituals. Even a common little nuthatch, mousy visitor to winter window sills, is possessed of unexpected grace in wooing. He selects choice sunflower seeds and flies to his female with them. If she persists unwon, he resorts to a further charm: He shucks each seed before presentation! Courting lapwings hold a wing-waving fiesta, cranes dance, a woodcock climbs the sky in a spiral while he "winnows" by letting air whistle through his outer primary feathers in an unforgettable love call.

Birds' nests are often so elaborate that it is almost impossible to believe such skill can be instinctive. But it is. Science has recently proved that for at least five generations the nest skill can survive in perfection independent of experience. Four generations of weaverbirds were bred under artificial conditions in which they never saw a nest or nest material. Then the fifth generation was freed. At once the birds began constructing with unerring skill the complex woven nests of their ancestors.

After baby birds, using a temporary "egg tooth" that nature provides, have tapped their way free of their shells, they become prodigies of almost unimaginable appetite. One infant robin eats as much as 14 feet of earthworms a day. A wren whose feeding trips to her youngsters were counted between sunrise and nightfall visited the nest 1217 times. A young black tern, weighing 31 grams, consumed daily 48 grams of food. To survive, every bird must eat at least half its own weight in food each day.

By late summer bird families have been raised and the parents, withdrawing to deep woods, stilling their song, have molted. Worn feathers are replaced in a change so delicately gradual that the first lost feather must be partially regrown before a second feather drops. The whole refeathering follows this pattern, so the bird's flight is never impaired. In the case of vivid birds—tanagers, buntings and the like—their bright summer dress is completely replaced by a travel suit of dull drab.

In autumn migration, the birds fly at heights ranging up to 5000 feet or more above earth, and cover distances nearly beyond belief. A tiny blackpoll warbler, nesting in Canada, wings 4000 miles to Brazil. A golden plover travels from the edge of the Arctic Ocean to Argentina, almost 8000 miles. Champion migrant is the Arctic tern, which summers at the north-polar land limit, winters in Antarctica. Its annual round trip: 22,000 miles.

How do they find their way? Naturalists have recently proved that birds can expertly calculate geography, and probably time, from sun slant. But there remains a mysterious "plus" in birds' pathfinding through the trackless skies, often at night.

The whole miracle of bird life must remind us of what the great naturalist Charles Waterton put into four words of simple eloquence: "We can but bow."

BIRDS LIVE IN NATURE'S INVISIBLE CAGE

John and Jean George

"Free as a bird," we say; yet nearly all bird watchers know how mistaken that saying is. The conduct of birds is so rigidly fixed that they are prisoners to the land they fly over, slaves to the air they fly through. Once we watched a bird go to his death because he was not free to fly a mere 700 feet to safety.

We were returning home along the Huron River near Ann Arbor, Michigan, where we were studying birds and mammals, and stopped to visit a cardinal we had named Red Click because of a special clicking note he used at the end of his song. We found him stranded on the piece of property where he lived; the land had been scalped that day by bulldozers so that only a few stumps and roots remained. As we watched, Red Click flew about 400 feet, then suddenly back-winged as if he had hit an invisible wall. After flopping to earth he flew off in another direction, only to smash into another invisible barrier.

"What's the matter with that crazy cardinal?" Jean asked. "He'll be killed by a hawk or an owl if he doesn't fly to the woods."

"He can't fly to the woods," John said. "His 'territory' is in the middle of the cleared land. The bulldozers have taken away his trees, his bushes, his grasses, but the boundaries of his home that he and his neighbors carefully established in their bird minds are still there and he can't fly through them."

"Perhaps we could carry him to safety," Jean suggested.

"And turn him loose on some other cardinal's territory? He's a prisoner precisely because he is more terrified of intruding on another male's land than he is of remaining here without shelter."

A screech owl called from the wood lot behind us. "Hear that?" John said. "That will probably be the last chapter in the biography of Red Click."

Next morning, at the roots of a maple sapling in the wasted field, we picked up the blood-red feathers of our cardinal.

This devotion unto death to a piece of ground is probably more intense in birds than in any other vertebrate. Strongest during the breeding season, the territory fixation serves to aid in the formation of pairs, to provide shelter for the young and to ensure perpetuation of the species by spreading its population over a wide area.

By simply walking behind chickadees, pushing them around their property in the spring, we were able to map some 200 of their territories in the woods near Poughkeepsie, New York. The chickadees would fly to the extremities of their lands, then circle back around the edges, revealing their unseen fences. Sketched on a map, a chickadee community looks like an exurbanite settlement of people, with the size of each property varying according to the "social standing" of the occupant; the older the male, the bigger, the stronger he is, the more land he gets.

Birds which are year-round residents tend to retain the same territory for life; migrants have both summer and winter properties. The birds that stay around your home all winter may seem to be in flocks, and therefore trespassing, but they are not. They are a well-ordered bird society made up of old-timers and young, complete with a leader or "boss bird." In these winter societies the defense of the breeding territory has given way, in certain species, to the common defense of a community territory against neighboring groups of the same species. Birds will tolerate trespassers of a different species on their land, since they are not competing, but not intruders belonging to their own.

Birds' property lines are established by song. If a male bird, returning in the spring, can sing from a tree without being challenged by a neighbor, he has it as his own, to mark the limits of his real estate. If, however, another male comes winging at him and puts him back a tree or two, he knows that this land is already claimed.

By taking the best land he can and as much of it as he is able to defend, he assures for himself not only a good food supply but also a mate. Female birds pick their mates by their attractive voices (each bird's voice is as distinctive as your own) and by the quality of the nesting sites in the land they have staked off. The weaker males and the late-comers, pushed into submarginal land, often go through the season as bachelors.

A bachelor song sparrow we called Mike sang so beautifully that Jean couldn't understand why the girls would not set up housekeeping with him. John said, "Your friend's territory is very small and in the woods. Song sparrows like some open fields and brush borders on their property. Getting a female to nest on Mike's territory would be like asking a debutante to live in Siberia."

Territory varies with different species from several square miles, as in the case of the horned owl, to only a square foot or so around the nest, as among the colony nesters such as terns and gulls.

Once boundary lines are settled, the feelings of the bird toward his territory mount with the progress of his nest, until he seems to do desperate things particularly near the nest site. Flying at windows and the shiny grillwork of automobiles is not bird hara-kiri. It is territory defense. His reflection in a window or grille is another male on his property, and he will fight this adversary until exhausted.

Territorial disputes, though constant in the bird world, are normally resolved by singing duels, almost always between males of the same species. Sometimes a disputed territory touches off a breast-to-breast battle in the air; the battlers seem to be rising and sliding down an invisible wall. The fight will usually be brief, and afterward each contestant will fly to a tree limb on his side of the property line and click in agitation. Usually there is a compromise and both birds will sing, in a full and exuberant song.

The female ordinarily stays within the boundaries established by her mate, but occasionally a blundering or frivolous wife can cause trouble. One season we observed a tragicomedy in a community of vivid indigo buntings. A little female, a first-time mother, had by error built her nest on another male's property. She would fly happily to her nest, expecting her husband to usher her home, only to find that he had stopped at the edge of his territory. There he was, turning around in circles, torn between two powerful impulses: to follow his mate, and to stay off his neighbor's property. Apparently property rights proved stronger than family love. He never once crossed the barrier during the nesting period. When the young hatched, the father would catch insects for the babies, call his mate and give her the offerings. Taking them eagerly, she would return to stuff her bottomless young. We were all (including the frustrated father) greatly relieved on the day the little mother coaxed her fledglings over the border to their father's estate.

A territory boundary is not the only restraint in a bird's life. Even within their own property birds do not fly around their land on any random course, but stick to routes, or "sidewalks." A bird will take the same path daily from his night roost to his feeding spot, from his nest to a certain singing post. We once saw impressive evidence that birds can map the fixed routes of other birds in the interest of safety.

A Cooper's hawk in our Michigan area staked off two square miles and soared elegantly around to attract a mate. The presence of this bird-eating intruder threw the small birds into a dither. But soon things quieted down and we wondered what adjustment they had made to the predator. In time we discovered the answer.

The big hawk, too, was a slave of habit. He nested in their woods, but always hunted in a far wood lot. Each morning he took an aerial sidewalk to the wood lot, returning home along another fixed path. The small-bird population figured out his habits, for they used fewer and fewer alarm notes to announce his coming and going. They knew he stayed on his sidewalks and never dipped down into their woods for food.

These invisible sidewalks can easily be noted in any backyard where there is a feeding station. A bird will come to the station every day about the same time from the same direction, and by way of the same sticks and twigs. There is generally a sidewalk in and another one out. We once put up a post on a bird's sidewalk, and he almost struck it, he was so confined to his route.

Each night the bird returns faithfully to his bedroom, or roost, which he picks as carefully as his nesting site. In a world teeming with enemies, its loss can mean his undoing.

A woodpecker roosted in a hole in an apple tree outside our window. He went to bed at the same time every night, depending on the amount of light. As the days grew shorter, our clock showed him returning two minutes earlier each night, but our light meter registered exactly the same light value. On cloudy days he came to roost early.

One night a white-breasted nuthatch went into the woodpecker's bedroom a few minutes before he was due home. The woodpecker performed his night rituals according to his heritage. He squawked from the top of a maple. He defecated in the same spot he had used for months; he flew to the apple tree, spiraled up it and winged into his hole—where he hit the intruding nuthatch head on.

Out they both tumbled and fought briefly. The nuthatch departed, with the woodpecker in pursuit. Sometime later we caught a glimpse of the woodpecker. It was late, but probably he could still see to get into his hole. However, he had to repeat the rituals of retirement all over again and so he went back to the maple tree. The night grew cold but the woodpecker never returned. Now it was very dark, well below his accustomed level of light. He squawked but did not fly to the apple tree. One twilight a few nights later the nuthatch cautiously investigated the empty hole and moved in. He had finally won the contest, probably because he upset the woodpecker's evening retirement habits, and the woodpecker, unable to change, was literally left out in the cold.

Almost all birds live and love and die behind the bars of nature's compulsions. They are captives in cages of their own instincts, from which they cannot—and have no desire to—escape.

THE CONTINUING MYSTERY
OF HOW BIRDS NAVIGATE

Max Eastman

While our top physicists study how to navigate interstellar space, top scientists in another field have been trying to figure out how birds navigate right here on earth. How, for example, does an Arctic tern, born within ten degrees of the North Pole, leaving home at the age of six weeks, find his way to the antarctic pack ice 11,000 miles away and, after wintering there, fly back to the same northern nesting place for the summer? That his heart and wings are equal to it is miracle enough, but how does his tiny brain solve problems in navigation that stumped the human race for thousands of years?

The compass is thought to have been invented in the 12th century, and 300 years later Columbus managed to cross the Atlantic. But birds had been cruising confidently all over the planet millions of years before that! I don't want to disparage mankind, but we really have been pretty dumb about this matter of navigation. Even now we haven't any complete understanding of how the birds do it.

The Greek philosopher Aristotle noticed that robins disappeared for the winter but redstarts did not, and concluded that robins turn into redstarts in the autumn and become robins again in spring. Pliny, the Roman naturalist, endorsed this general idea, and it became the expert opinion in Rome that swallows turn into frogs. The fact that gave rise to these wild ideas is that a great many birds, especially the small ones, migrate at night. They are here in the evening, and in the morning they are gone. Everybody knows that birds don't fly in the dark, so what has become of them?

It was not until the 18th century that ornithologists began to realize that birds do fly at night, and in enormous numbers. In 1898 a bird watcher at Washburn Observatory in Madison, Wisconsin, estimated that at the height of the autumnal migration birds passed across the night sky at his point of observation at the rate of 9000 per hour! Such reports awakened scientists to the navigation problem involved in bird migration, and they never went to sleep again.

Closely bound up with it, of course, is birds' "homing instinct," another hereditary gift which has been known and employed by man ever since Noah sent out a dove over the waters. Probably the world's record in finding the way home was established by a small seagull-like bird called a Manx shearwater. Many of these birds live in burrows in a cliff on the coast of Wales. One was banded and taken by air to Boston, Massachusetts, then released there on June 4, 1952. One June 16 at 1:30 p.m., 12½ days later, it crept into its burrow in Wales, 3050 miles across the trackless ocean!

While facts like these have been collected for the last century, it is only in the last 25 years that a determined effort has been made to find out how the birds do it. What do they steer by? The North Star? The sun? The moon? The winds? The climate? The earth's magnetism? What gives them their sense of direction?

A step toward real understanding of bird navigation was taken by a German ornithologist named Gustav Kramer, who devised a way of testing the idea, tossed off casually at the turn of the century, that birds guide themselves by the sun. Noticing that birds in a cage hop around restlessly when the time comes for migration, he put some caged starlings in a circular pavilion with windows through which only the sky could be seen. He then made a record of the positions the birds assumed and found them constantly oriented in the direction they wanted to migrate. When he darkened the windows, they lost their orientation and began hopping in all directions. Then he rigged an artificial light to imitate the sun, but had it rise and set at the wrong place and time. The birds oriented themselves for migration again, but in a direction determined by this artificial sun. He thus established strong evidence for the sun theory and left only one unexplained mystery: How can a bird guide itself by the sun, day and night, in fair weather and foul?

The complexity of so using the sun, even in broad daylight, becomes apparent when you reflect that the sun's position changes with the time of day, with the time of year and with every stage of the

Against the silhouette of Mount Shasta, mixed flocks of ducks and geese rendezvous at Tule Lake. Literally millions of birds use Tule and other northern California lakes as way stations in their twice-yearly migration journeys. How birds navigate across thousands of miles remains one of nature's intriguing mysteries.

journey. It would require, among other things, a time sense in the bird's constitution almost equivalent to carrying a watch.

The English biologist G. V. T. Matthews, formerly of Cambridge University, has set forth the difficulties of guiding a flight by the sun's passage through the sky. His demonstrations involve so much mathematical calculation that you would think only an IBM machine on wings could get anywhere with such a shifting point of reference. Nevertheless he is con-

vinced that migrating and homing birds are equipped by instinct for such a feat.

The one thing he could not adequately explain, when he summarized his results in 1955, was how the theory applied to migration by night. "The direction of the night's flight could be determined from the sun during the day," he suggested, "and maintained as well as possible throughout the darkness with possibly some guidance from the moon and star pattern."

compass" in the direction of its habitual migration. Even when he tried to turn the birds away by rotating their perches, they stubbornly turned back to the preferred direction.

Dr. Sauer next placed his warblers in a planetarium —under a dome, that is, with an artificial replica of the starry sky. Again they took up the correct position for a flight to their winter quarters in Africa. And, when the dome was rotated so that the stars were in a false position, they made the corresponding mistake!

There is poetry as well as science in Dr. Sauer's attitude toward the adventurous little birds he studies. "When fall comes," he says, "the little garden warbler, weighing barely three quarters of an ounce, sets off one night on an unbelievable journey. Without being taught, all alone, never in the collective security of a flock, it unerringly wings its solitary way southward to its distant goal in Africa."

Dr. Sauer had a favorite lesser whitethroat warbler named Johnny. From Germany the lesser whitethroat normally travels southeastward across the Balkans and then turns due south, flying along the Nile to its winter home in central Africa. Johnny knew nothing of this, for he had been born and spent all his life in a cage. Nevertheless, when the migrating season came and his cage was placed in a planetarium showing him the German sky, he took up the normal flight position heading southeast. Moreover, as the planetarium was rotated to correspond to the flight route of his species, he shifted his position gradually toward the south, until in the region of the Nile he set his course due south! With Johnny's help, Dr. Sauer has made it very certain that warblers can guide themselves by the stars as well as by the sun.

How such elaborate instincts can be inherited remains a mystery—"one of the crucial mysteries of biology," to quote Dr. Matthews. Moreover, as he reminds us, expert study and experiment in this branch of science are little more than begun. Dr. Sauer now has in mind to find out, by subtracting the constellations one by one from the sky of his planetarium, just which stars are essential to the warbler's nocturnal migration. Suppose it should be, after all, only the North Star!

Whatever may still be learned, those who for the last 25 years have been devoting intense study to the problem of bird navigation are agreed about this basic fact: Some apparatus exists in each migratory bird's tiny brain at birth that, by putting him in complex relation to the lights that pass across the sky, makes him at home on the earth as man, with all his inventions, will never be.

This rather hazy suggestion was unsatisfactory to another ornithologist, E. G. F. Sauer of the University of Freiburg, Germany, whose prime interest is in the tiny warblers that fly long distances, mostly at night. Sauer tried a series of night experiments. During the migrating season he placed a group of caged warblers where only the starry heavens would be visible to them. He found that at a glimpse of the night sky the birds began to flutter, and each would take up a position pointing "like the needle of a

OF SPRING
AND AN EGG

Jean George

On pine bough and willow limb, in woven basket and ground saucer, millions of birds' eggs lie hidden in springtime across half of the earth. They vary in shape from the nearly round egg of the screech owl to the pear shape of the plover; in size from the ponderous two-pound egg of the ostrich in the zoo to the 3/100-of-an-ounce egg of the hummingbird in the apple tree. But all have two things in common: They start as a gold and crystal cell within the female, and they maintain an unbroken pattern of growth that has existed since the beginning of bird history more than 140 million years ago.

This pattern is an amazing sequence of events that renders meaningless the question of which came first, the chicken or the egg, because a newly hatched female has already within her body the germs of a greater supply of eggs than she will lay in her lifetime.

The real question is: What *is* an egg? In his book, *The Avian Egg*, Dr. Alexis L. Romanoff, professor emeritus of chemical embryology at Cornell University, has brought together many of the new findings. It has been established, for instance, that both the process and the timing of egg formation inside the female are the same for domestic and wild birds.

An egg starts as a single cell, a spark of life. Still in the mother's body, it grows in size and complexity as layers of yolk, albumen, membrane and shell form around it. But it remains a single cell. It may or may not be fertilized by a male sperm in the process of its formation. If it is, it still must wait until it has been laid and incubated by the mother before a chick begins to form.

Thousands of closely timed microscopic studies reveal that the first coating of yolk is formed around a germ cell in the young chick when she is at least three months old. Moreover, they show that an egg yolk is made up of six rings, each having a white and a yellow layer, laid down to a strict rhythm determined by the position of the sun: During the day and up until midnight, the yellow yolk is formed; the white yolk forms between midnight and sunup.

The final layer, however, requires a more subtle alarm than the passing of nights and days to set it off —it needs the presence of a male bird. His just being there in a springtime tree triggers a hormonal change in the now mature female that creates the final layer. Most wild birds cannot lay if there is no mate, but this is not true of domestic birds—barnyard chickens, ducks and pigeons. One leghorn hen laid 1515 eggs in eight years, and never saw a rooster.

When the lustrous yolk sac is completed, the egg ruptures from its mooring and falls into the oviduct. This event is triggered by the courtship dances of the male bird. Each species has a different expression of affection. The woodcock, for instance, flies high in the air and flutters straight toward the earth. The pheasant jabs at the ground and fans his tail into a heart-shaped shield. The blue bird of paradise hangs upside down and shakes his iridescent feathers into a blue mist. The American egret displays his plumes and gives his mate a present of a stick.

Then mating takes place, and as the egg proceeds down the funnel-like oviduct, it encounters a male sperm. Immediately after fertilization the egg goes on a precise schedule. It stops in the oviduct for 20 minutes while it gathers albumen or white. Like the yolk, the albumen is a series of layers. The first is a thin covering; the second is dense, elastic and tough, a shock absorber to protect the spark of life in the center during the plunge to the nest and the tumbling it gets during incubation.

The egg spirals down through the oviduct, and this motion forces the third layer of albumen—a light, watery fluid—through the denser second layer, up against the golden yolk. In this waterlike fluid the yolk floats. The original tiny cell, which scientists call the "blastoderm" (and which is the white speck you sometimes see in a fresh egg), buoys to the top.

The spiraling serves also to twist the albumen at either end into the visible milky rope that every housewife recognizes. These "ropes" later break, in the incubation stage, so that the mother must rotate the egg in order to keep the yolk in the center.

Next on the schedule is the formation of the two white sheets of tough membrane found under the shell of the breakfast egg. This takes an hour and ten minutes. Then the egg drops into the shell-secreting area of the oviduct and remains there for 19 hours while the shell accumulates in four porous layers. During the last of these hours, the shell is colored. (There are approximately 9000 bird species, and most have distinctively marked or colored eggs.)

Eggs are always laid during daylight hours, usually between sunup and noon. For ten minutes after it is laid, a bird egg lies like a shiny gem in the nest. The shell is covered by a glistening film. This film hardens, and the egg waits for warmth. Air is entering the pores in the shell, and a breathing pocket is forming at the blunt end. Here, two weeks after incubation begins, the chick's head will lie.

The mother bird will lay more eggs—one a day, until she has filled her quota for this nesting. Then the eggs in her nest take complete control of her life, starting her on a schedule of brooding and turning. So delicate is the feeling of the mother for the eggs that some birds don't start to incubate until the right number of eggs lie in the nest. A female flicker, for instance, must sense four before she is triggered to brood. An ornithologist who removed one egg a day from a flicker's nest so detained the female that she laid 71 before she gave up.

It is the heat of the mother's body that triggers the explosion of life within the egg. As soon as the temperature at the center of the egg reaches 99.5° F., the cell development begins again. On and on the chain reaction goes until within the shell there are lungs, a heart, liver, eyes, all the requisite organs of a living chick.

Last Easter, in order to observe this miracle, I purchased six bobwhite eggs and a globe-shaped plastic incubator from a quail farm. I placed the eggs in the incubator and turned on a seven-watt Christmas-tree bulb. I knew that after 12 hours at 99.5° the germs of life would be racing around the centers of the gold and glasslike world and that on the fifth day these germs would determine whether the embryos were male or female.

But it was the 23rd, the hatching day, that I waited for. Then, as I hovered over the incubator, a crack, like the beginning of a minuscule earthquake, shattered the side of one egg. I lifted the egg and heard a voice within—thin, high, fragile. During the night I watched as bits of shell were torn and knocked away. As the night passed, the other eggs cracked.

At dawn, when the sun illuminated the yellow-green buds of the apple tree and the white crocuses on the lawn, the first tiny bird fell out of the shell into spring. It rested for several hours while, one after the other, its brothers and sisters fought for freedom. Then dry, fluffy and bright-eyed, it got up on its feet, as though in a hurry to keep some mystical appointment with the eternal life it harbored.

This Louisiana heron chick has just used its egg tooth, a small, temporary protuberance on its upper bill, to crack the shell of its egg. Having pipped a window in the shell, the chick takes a look at the world outside. The time required for a young bird to free itself ranges anywhere from several hours to several days.

Avian Architects

Birds' nests rank high on any list of wonders of the natural world. They range in size from a hummingbird's nest, no wider than a quarter, to that of the bald eagle—an agglomeration of sticks that often gets to be nine feet in diameter and two tons in weight. Nests can be casual lodgings—the Arctic tern simply scrapes out a saucerlike depression in the sand—or extraordinarily complex creations like those of the weaverbirds. For some species the work of nest-building belongs solely to the male, or to the female; for others it is a task to be shared. A number of birds do not build nests. The emperor penguin protects its single egg with its leathery feet and downy belly; the burrowing owl appropriates the dens of ground squirrels; the cowbird lays its eggs in the nests of other birds and leaves the raising of its young to foster parents. But whatever form nesting behavior takes, its purpose is always the same: to protect the incubating eggs and to get the developing young through their first crucial weeks of existence.

Trees provide nesting sites as well as nesting materials for many birds. The red-bellied woodpecker (below, left) *generally chisels out its nest holes in the trunks of live trees. The fish-eating little pied shag* (below, right), *an Australian cormorant, builds large stick nests on the ground or in trees.*

*Using tree bark, weed stems, grass or leaves, the yellowthroat
(above) builds its cup-shaped nest close to the ground in
shrubs, tall grass or clumps of flowers, like these black-eyed Susans.*

*A ruby-throated hummingbird (right) feeds its young in an inch-
deep nest made of spider webs, lichens, moss and plant fiber.*

*Cliff swallows nest in colonies under eaves of barns or on cliffs
(below). Their gourd-shaped nests are made of mud
pellets reinforced with straw and lined with feathers or grass.*

A white pelican protectively straddles its hatchling on a shallow nest of weeds and sticks built upon the ground.

A red-necked grebe carries its downy baby piggyback to a floating nest of plant debris occupied by its mate.

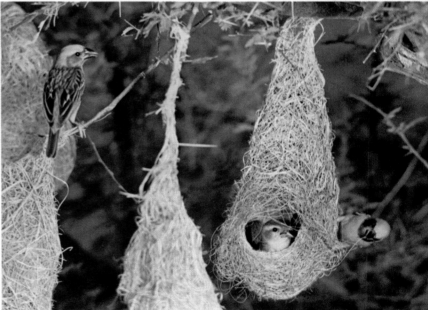

Having lured a female to his half-built nest of woven grass, the male baya weaverbird at right will now complete his home by adding a long sleevelike entrance tube.

Standing on a nesting mound made of mud and guano, a New Zealand gannet (left) feeds a young bird food regurgitated from its stomach. Gannets nest on small sea islands in colonies of as many as 15,000 individuals.

Chapter Six

Meet the Birds

*More than 8500 species of birds are spread across the face of the earth. They
nest everywhere from the polar ice packs to the equatorial jungles;
they eat everything from seeds and insects to fresh fish and carrion; they fly,
they run, they swim—and they never cease to stir man's imagination.*

HERE COME THE ROBINS!

Jean George

During a few weeks each year a shawl of birds lifts from the palmettos and avocado leaves of the Gulf states and fans north in America's most jubilant rite of spring—the migration of the robin. Like a rising tide, more than a billion robins plunge up the Mississippi flyway, chirping and thrumming out wing sounds, moving irrevocably toward their ancestral breeding grounds. Soon they will be seen in almost every garden, park, woods and yard in the United States and in parts of Canada, a range few other songbirds begin to approach.

This mark of the season is familiar to millions of us. When the frigid winds of February and the bitter blasts of March scream on, we impatiently wait to hear the robin's "cheer-up, cheer-cheer" ring out over the snow. And we excitedly report the first arrivals in fields or meadows to local newspapers. Yet most people know very little about this beloved harbinger of spring.

The American robin is misnamed. He is actually a thrush, but his red breast reminded homesick Pilgrims of the British robin (a bird in fact more closely related to our bluebird), and the name stayed with him. He also resembles the British robin in character and spirit. Like him, he is warm and friendly and involves himself with people. City building construction has been stopped while robins nested on girders; telephone booths have been closed while bird life went forward on top of the dial box.

But what robins are most famous for is their ability to pull worms from lawns. No other bird is as slick at this operation. We don't know how they do it, and every effort to duplicate the trick results in only half a worm. People are not the only ones who recognize this talent. One day I watched a starling follow a rob-

in all over the yard. Every time the robin pulled a worm, the starling ran up and snatched it.

Robins seem to accept this kind of thievery in friendly spirit. They are primarily fruit and berry eaters, and worms make up less than 4 percent of their diet. But they also eat caterpillars, beetles, weevils, flies, snails, spiders, termites and wasps. If one farmer is ready to shoot a robin for wiping out a cherry crop, another is blessing the birds for attacking the weevils and saving the cotton crop.

The robin migration moves as slowly as the reluctant pulse of spring. It has been theorized that the length of daylight gives the birds the signal to start north; from that time on they move up the continent with the thaw. If the temperature plunges, they may move back to warmer areas.

In the beginning the robins average from 17 to 32 miles a day, stopping off and on to gather sow bugs and weevils in the fields of the South. By the end of the migration, however, those headed for Alaska are often covering from 100 to 200 miles a day, flying faster as they near the homeland.

The migration is awe-inspiring. One day in late February, crossing a Louisiana meadow, I noticed the sunlight flickering at my feet. I looked up to see a throbbing mass of robins drumming resolutely north, their wings chopping endlessly up and down, with never a glide to rest them. The birds came on and on for hours—thousands and thousands of them, a ribbon of life extending from horizon to horizon. They made only soft "here I am" noises with their throats, but their wings sounded out like the crackle of a distant fire.

Some delicate birds, such as the warblers, flycatchers, orioles and buntings, go north by night. But the robin goes by day, right out in the open, sometimes only 100 feet over houses and trees, past hawks and owls, for he is a strong, vigorous flier.

The big migration of the robins moves up the Mississippi. Those born in the west or far north follow the Missouri out across the plains to the Rockies or

A mother robin holds a morsel in her bill while her youngsters wait to be fed. These fledglings are about two weeks old—too small to fend for themselves, too big for the nest and always hungry. Keeping them stoked with food is a job that the male will have to assume when the female is busy with the next brood. Surprisingly, robins were once considered game birds. Audubon said they were "fat and juicy" and afforded "excellent eating."

on to Canada and Alaska. Those raised in New England take the Ohio River valley east and north. And along the way, a robin drops off on State Street here, or Elm Street there, as a homing male spots his own backyard.

The old males arrive first and go to their old homes. Next the young males arrive, taking over the territories of those who succumbed to predators or to winter. All stake out their homesteads with dynamic energy in anticipation of the next wave of the migration—the arrival of the females.

Even before the females reach home, the males have established one of the most spectacular but little-known institutions of birddom—the robin roost. All day the males sing for their land, fight off other males

and enlarge their holdings. Then when night comes they sing a final serenade from their favorite tree, drop into the shadows and wing to a spot in the lowlands.

In spring this roost—often located in young, dense maple trees—consists of as many as 50 to 100 male birds. In the summer, when the mothers and juveniles join the father robins at the secret roost, its population may grow to thousands.

In many areas the robin is the first bird to announce the dawn and the last to sing with the setting of the sun, reason enough to love this old friend. And his song is one of the rare and beautiful ones—a highly evolved musical composition, not just a note or phrase like that of most birds.

Construction of the robin's nest usually takes about

six days and is done chiefly by the female. She makes the mud cup with her beak and shapes it with bill, feet and breast, hammering and beating and thumping until it seems as if the bowl would burst. She lines it with grass rootlets, lets the clay set, and then an egg is laid every morning for several days. Nestled in the tan grass these four—or sometimes five—sky-blue eggs are a beautiful, familiar sight.

Seeing a complete clutch, the female grows "broody," and wants only to sit. The eggs rule her behavior. While a broody robin incubated at my Pennsylvania home, we could gently lift her wing or touch her beak, and she would not come out of her strange open-eyed sleep. However, one "click" from her mate would awaken her, and she would fly off the nest to feed. About the 12th day the actions of the mother robin express news. She jerks, her eyes widen, and she actually seems annoyed and surprised. This is a sure sign that her eggs are pipping.

The hatching of a robin's egg can be a 20-hour suspense drama. Inside the shell the chick wobbles its head. As it does, the egg tooth, a tough bit of horn that sits up like a rose thorn on the beak, wears a groove that weakens the shell. As the growing bird shifts his position, the weakened shell cracks open. But this is only the beginning. Hour after hour the feeble little bird breaks off pieces of the shell while the mother robin looks on. With one blow she could have him out of there—but she never directly helps. Finally the shell falls back, and the wet, stringy-necked young thing flops exhausted on the grassy nest lining.

Young robins' beaks are large and swollen, their mouths and bills bright yellow—a sight that inspires action in a robin heart and sends both male and female out hunting worms. They are forced, almost without recourse, to feed these vibrating yellow targets.

Baby robins are endearing and charming; they wear the breast spots of the thrushes from which they came. Usually they stay in their nests at least ten days; if disturbed, however, they will hop overboard before they can fly. Fortunately robins nest quite low down. Almost every year in June and again in August—the time of the two broods—some small friend brings me one that has fallen out of the nest. I usually tell the children to return the young robins to the spot where they were found. They will be all right in most instances, for they will hide in the bushes and be fed by their parents.

When you watch the robins travel north, stopping in the neighborhood to run and hop in their distinctive manner—most other birds either walk or hop, not both, like the robin—you may be looking for your own particular one, your own harbinger of spring. To you they all look alike, dark heads, bright eyes, red breasts, bold manner. But to the robin every valley, road and landmark of your area is well known. Your very elm or maple is imprinted like a dream in his bird head. One fine morning you will awaken to discover that one of the billion has dropped out of the migration and stayed behind—your own special robin, home at last.

CONSIDER THE FRAGILE FLAMINGO

George S. Fichter

It was from an airplane that I got my first look at flamingos. Below us that day, on a broad mud flat at the southern end of Andros Island in the sun-bathed Bahamas, I saw a seething patch of pink rising and falling like the wind-whipped waves of a stormy sea. Even from half a mile above, I was awed by the brilliant beauty of this nesting colony.

Fortunately, our pilot, intent on maintaining his course, did not come in low for a closer look. During World War II many airmen were less thoughtful. Time after time inquisitive pilots buzzed nesting colonies in the Bahamas and the islands of the Caribbean, the cradle of the "American" flamingo, and left disaster in their wake.

For flamingos, while calm and stately in outward appearance, are highly nervous creatures. A plane zooming over a nesting group stirs them to frenzy. Frantically they race helter-skelter, bumping into each other in wild stampede. Many are left wallowing in the mud, their fragile, stiltlike legs splintered. Days pass before the confused, milling flock is settled again—by which time the nesting urge is gone. It would be impossible to calculate the World War II toll of flamingos in their native islands, but only a few thousand can now be found.

Meanwhile, this singularly gorgeous creature has become the most famous bird of the state of Florida, an area to which it is not even native and which it seldom visits! Every winter flamingo postcards move northward from Florida in a steady pink flow. The bird has lent its name to countless Florida hotels, motels, bars, grills and shops.

The main reason for this flamingo-Florida association in the public mind is that from a single Florida source each year almost a million flamingo cards are sent out by visitors. This is Hialeah racetrack near Miami, as well known the world over for its 430 flamingos as for its winter-season horse races.

Its pink feathers help identify this exotic bird as a flamingo, even from a distance. But close up, a more unusual attribute is apparent—a bent and boxy bill that has a remarkable series of sievelike structures along each side. This long-legged bird feeds by raking the tip of its bill back and forth in brackish coastal shallows. It scoops up mud by a pumping action of its throat. Water and silt are strained out through the edges of the bill, leaving the animal matter and small plants that are the basis of the flamingo's varied diet.

Flamingos may plunge into water as high as their bellies and can swim with the aid of their webbed toes, but they are less likely to swim than to wade. And, being gregarious, they tend to wade together. In chorus they make honking noises like geese. They also make sputtering sounds when they are filtering mud from their bills.

To the late Joseph E. Widener goes the credit for making Hialeah a mecca for flamingo lovers. When he bought the track in 1930, he proposed introducing a flock of flamingos to highlight his elaborate landscaping of the 200-acre park. Thirty birds, each with its legs folded close to its body and wrapped in newspaper, were flown in from Cuba. That evening the birds paraded about the center of the track like small pink clouds floating in the dusky greenery. But next morning they were gone. No one had remembered to clip their wings. Immediately, Widener ordered a new flock, making certain this time that the birds could not fly.

Seven years later came a surprise: One bird decided to build a nest. From the egg she hatched came the first flamingo ever born in captivity—a memorable event that brought an ornithologist scurrying from the Smithsonian Institution in Washington. Unhappily, that first fledgling lived only 14 days: Nobody knew how to care for it, and if the mother remembered she was too fussed by the commotion around her to do anything about it. Since then, with coddling, hundreds of flamingos (an average of 65 young per year) have been hatched and reared at Hialeah, providing birds for a number of zoos and wildlife exhibits all over the United States.

It was at Hialeah, not far from my home, that I became interested again in the flamingo. Related to the heron, stork and ibis, this bird is at once graceful and grotesque. Full-grown it may measure four feet in height. Whether in motion or standing on one leg with its head tucked under a wing while it naps, it is a picture of poised dignity. Yet it is weird-

ly assembled indeed. Its long, skinny legs look like two toothpicks sticking out of a ripe cherry, and you could never find knobbier knees if you searched Miami Beach all winter. Its slim, rubbery neck writhes like a serpent. Color contrast is provided by its outer flight feathers and beak tip (jet-black) and its small, beady eyes (crystalline-yellow).

Flamingos would have long since been slaughtered out of existence by plume hunters were it not that their handsome feathers fade to white soon after they are plucked. Even live birds in captivity soon become colorless if they are not fed a proper diet. This has long been a problem faced by curators, who feel obliged to show their public really "pink" flamingos. (And when they succeed, they are often accused of spraying them with paint!) Crab shells, ground-up shrimp and similar seafoods can generally suffice to keep the birds in color, but the pastel pinks thus achieved can hardly match the riotous, rosy hue of a wild flock.

In their native state almost all flamingos live near salt water. The largest known American colony consists of around 14,000 birds on the Inagua islands in the Bahamas. Second is a colony of about 4500 on Mexico's Yucatan Peninsula. Even flamingos found at a 15,000-foot altitude in the Andes live on a salt lake. It is true also of the African flamingo, which, though abundant, is not so colorful.

At Hialeah recently I went with Julius Barber, the keeper of the flamingos, while he fed his birds. "Don't expect them to come rushing over to us like hungry chickens," he warned me as we approached their island by skiff. "Flamingos don't get that tame." At our approach they clustered together on the other side of the island, a pistonlike neck shooting up occasionally and craning in our direction.

As we dumped the "shrimp chop suey" into the feeding troughs I asked Barber, "How can you tell a male flamingo from a female?"

"I don't believe anybody can tell," Barber said, "except another flamingo. Early in the spring the males do a lot of dancing and strutting and spreading their wings in front of the females. Then, after a few days of that, they pair off, and I try to coax them to build nests. I pile up mud and shape a nest or two, hoping the birds will do the same."

I looked at several nests the flamingos had built. The birds roll the mud into little balls with their beaks, then tamp it into place with their feet. Each nest was a conical mound, rising about 18 inches above the ground, with a saucer-shaped depression in its top to hold an egg. The female lays a single, chalk-white egg, about the size of a hen's egg, but slimmer. (Rarely, she lays two.) Then for about a month she and her mate incubate the egg.

A newly hatched flamingo bears small resemblance to its parents. Covered with soft, white down, it has a straight bill, short legs, and it looks much like a young goose. A week passes before its bill begins to acquire the flamingo's characteristic downward hook at the end, and its legs start stretching. From the minute it pips its way from the egg, however, it is almost always hungry. It commences by eating the shell from which it hatched. Then the mother takes over and provides a regurgitated fluid from her crop.

The flamingo has a strange way of eating. Unlike most birds, the *top* half of its beak is hinged. When it eats, it turns its head upside down, using the movable upper half of its beak as a scoop. Water and fine particles are squirted or rinsed out the side of the beak through the sievelike grill formed by its serrated edges. Early reports indicated that the wild flamingo subsisted solely on a diet of mud. A good quantity of ooze does slip into its gullet, but along with the mud go small shellfish, crustaceans and other plants and animals.

Every February, when the purple bougainvillea is in full bloom and the flamingos are reddest, Hialeah stages its famous Flamingo Stakes. Though this is a horse race for leading three-year-olds, on this day everything is keyed to the flamingos. Pink banners fly from the packed grandstand; racing forms are printed on pink paper; officials drive pink cars.

Herded off their island, the flamingos are started around the track. At first their gait is slow and graceful; they lift their legs high like prancing horses seen in slow motion. But as they arrive in front of the grandstand the men behind them begin to shout so that the birds break into a run. Those that do not have their wings clipped (roughly half of the flock nowadays—and they stay at Hialeah voluntarily) take to the air. Half of them running and the others in majestic flight, the flock passes before the grandstand like a massive wall of pink feathers.

VULTURE COUNTRY

John D. Stewart

There are three essentials for vulture country; a rich supply of unburied corpses, high mountains and a strong sun. Spain has the first of these, for in this sparsely populated and stony land it is not customary or necessary to bury dead animals; where there are vultures such burial would be a waste of labor. Spain has mountains, too, and the summer sun is hot throughout the country. But it is hottest in the south, in Andalusia, and there the vultures hang in hordes in the roofless sky.

The summer sun dries up every pond and lake, and almost every river. It kills the food plants and wilts the fig trees over the heads of the panting flocks. All animals weaken in these circumstances, and the weakest die. The unpitying sun glares down on the corpses, rotting the hide and softening the meat, to the vulture's advantage. But the sun plays a still greater part in the vulture's life. Its main and vital function, for him, is the creation of thermal currents in the atmosphere, for without these he would be helpless.

In the dawn of any day, in Andalusia, you may see the eagles, buzzards, kites and falcons already on the wing, quartering the plain fast and low, seeking reptiles and small game. But the vulture sits on a crag and waits. He sees the sun bound up out of the sierra, and still he waits. He waits until the sunstruck rocks and the hard earth heat up and the thermal currents begin to rise. When the upstream is strong enough he leaps out from the cliff, and without one laborious wingbeat spirals and soars.

By the time the vulture reaches his station, a half hour later and maybe more, the sun is blazing down on the plain. He cocks his head from side to side and checks the positions of neighboring vultures, his colleagues and competitors. There they hang, dotted across the clear sky at intervals of a mile or so—at the corners of one-mile squares. Now, circling slowly on his invisible support, the vulture begins his vigil.

At first glance, from below, this griffon vulture appears as one great wing, slightly less than seven feet from tip to tip and two feet broad. His tail is square and very short, for there are no sharp or sudden quirks in his flight that would call for a strong rudder. His movements are premeditated and leisurely, for his energy must be conserved at all costs.

The vulture's head and neck, too, protrude very little in front of his wing plane—and this distinguishes his flight silhouette from the eagle's. His neck is, in fact, some two feet long, but since it is covered only with light down he folds it back into his collar to keep it warm. His head is like an eagle's; his yellow feet, which never kill and rarely carry, are shorter and not so strong. His plumage is a uniform sandy color, relieved only by a whitish ruff and the broad black primary wing feathers fingering the air.

The vulture sails in silence (he croaks, growls and whistles only in his family circle and at his feasts). His head is in constant movement. He swivels it from one side to the other, bringing each eye in turn to bear on the earth. Then he bends his neck to right or left to check on one of his neighbors to north, south, east or west. The whole vulture network is interdependent. One bird falling, or the resultant hole in the sky, calls "Come here!" and his colleagues are relentlessly drawn by this signal.

Many other birds have telescopic eyesight too, so it is not surprising that the vulture can see a small animal from a great height. But a mystery remains: How does he know that the animal is dead? No book, no expert, could answer this question for me, and I carried it through the vulture country for years. Then, one hot afternoon, I lay down beside an old swineherd in the shade of a cork oak on the foothills overlooking the great plain of La Janda. For 50 years, he told me, he had watched pigs on that plain—the pigs, yes, and the vultures. I put my problem to him.

The swineherd's theory is not to be proved, but it is a wise one. All herds and flocks, said the old man, lie down together and at one time to rest. When a vulture sees an animal lying alone and apart, he is bound to notice it. He marks it, and waits and watches.

The next day the animal is still there, so he circles a little lower, his eye riveted, seeking the slightest movement. He sees none, but he continues to circle, said the old man. It takes him two days, at least, to confirm death. The other vultures note his behavior and every time he falls they move over a little in the

sky. Now he is very low. He seeks the heaving of the flanks or eye movements; he sees neither. Then he falls quickly, landing heavily at a little distance from the corpse.

The swineherd and I watched the first vulture land. We watched him sidling and circling the dead goat, standing erect to see better, wing tips trailing, neck stretched to the full, head swiveling rapidly, peering intently. If he could smell even as well as we, his doubts would have been over. But he stood there irresolute, famished yet fearful, with his bill open and his wings ready for use.

A shadow swept across the brown grass, a tall column of vultures wheeled overhead. He hopped to close quarters, stretched forward, pecked the corpse and leaped back. He watched for a second more; no movement. Then he croaked once, as though to bless himself, and threw himself on the body.

Almost immediately there were eight more vultures at the corpse. Watching them thrusting their long necks deep into the belly cavity, I saw why those necks have no feathers. Yes, said the swineherd, that is the one part the vulture cannot reach to clean.

Now 16 more vultures swept down, landing heavily in their haste and flap-hopping to the feast. The corpse was submerged in a heaving, struggling mass of broad brown wings. A new column wheeled above us, circling lower. There should be 24 up there, I reckoned. There were 23. The latecomers landed on nearby trees, including our own, and their weight bent thick limbs to the ground. At the height of the carnival I counted just short of 100 birds.

A mule lasts two hours, said the old man, and an ox three. This goat became bones in the sun in half an hour.

As the hundred fed, or hoped and waited, many more vultures circled high above, assessing the situation and treasuring their altitude. When the feasters scattered and exposed the small skeleton, the watchers drifted wearily away to resume their distant stations. But they had fulfilled their function. They had marked the spot and drawn the Egyptian vultures and the kites.

Now the little Egyptian vultures landed daintily and dodged nimbly through the throng of giants. The dirty work has been done; now the long and delicate beak comes into play. The Egyptian vultures attack the skull, the large joints and the crevices of the pelvic girdle—all parts inaccessible to the griffon's heavy beak. They dodge out through the encircling griffons with their spoils, gobble them swiftly and dance back for more. The griffons, gorged and panting in the sun, pay them scant attention.

Finally, when all but the whistling kites have left, comes the great solitary bearded vulture, the fierce lammergeier. His whole head is feathered. He lives aloof from all the rest of the vulture tribe; but they serve his interests, so he keeps them within sight. The lammergeier seizes the largest bones in his claws, carries them high, drops them on the rocks. Then he swoops down and rakes out the marrow. After his work has been done, nothing will remain except an empty skull and some small bones, which the ants and carrion beetles pick and polish.

Our griffon, first on the scene, will not be the first to leave it. Crop, throat and neck distended, he squats back on his tail, with his wings spread to steady him and his beak hanging open; it is an hour, maybe, before the meat subsides in him.

When he is ready, the griffon runs and leaps across the plain, thrashing heavily with his big wings, and labors into the air. He finds a thermal, circles in it to his altitude, then slips sideways and sweeps gently across the sierra to his distant nest.

The female griffon rarely leaves her nest from early March, when she lays her rough white egg, until August, when her huge poult is fledged and flying. The father has to feed and carry for all three. And the voracious chick alone will demand up to eight pounds of meat every day.

When the male vulture arrives at the inaccessible mountain nest he settles on a nearby ledge, vomits, and sorts out the result with his beak. The female feeds herself hungrily on the larger relics. Then she offers her gape to her cowering, whistling infant. The chick gobbles madly. With vultures it can never be "little and often." The birds, young and old, must gorge to the neck when opportunity offers. That is their instinct and their nature.

Now that his load is delivered and eaten, the male is likely to be the hungriest of the family. This, too, is as it should be, for the hunger sends him out and up again, however little daylight may remain, to circle in the sky until the sunset reddens the sierra.

Dominated by the constant panic for food, the vulture leads a competitive and anxious life. But vultures have strong forces for survival, as is proved by their numbers.

At times, lying on my back on the plain with binoculars trained on the sky, I have seen vultures circling in two or three layers, each one high above the other. What can this mean? A hungry duplication, or triplication, hopelessly covering the same feeding ground and using the only available thermals? Or the opposite—well-fed reserves idly standing by?

No one can tell me. But here in the vulture country there are no birds more spectacular, more fascinating to watch and to study. In time we may find out the last of their secrets. I lie on the plains and keep on watching them. And they, I know, keep on watching me.

This griffon vulture has nearly finished its meal of red deer. Since its beak is not strong enough to pierce the deer's tough hide, it was unable to feed until another animal had torn open the carcass or until the hot Spanish sun had softened the skin. As fewer and fewer dead animals are allowed to remain unburied, and as wilderness areas continue to shrink, the range of the griffon vulture is becoming more and more restricted.

MY WAR
WITH THE OSPREYS

John Steinbeck

My war with the ospreys, like most wars, was large-ly accidental—and it is not over yet. The coming of winter caused an uneasy truce, but hostilities may soon reopen, although I can find it in my heart to wish for peace, even friendship. I hope the ospreys, wherever they may be, will read this.

I shall go back to the beginning and set down my side of the affair, trying to be as fair as possible.

Some years ago I bought a little place on a beau-tiful point of land near Sag Harbor, which is quite near the eastern tip of Long Island. Sag Harbor is a fishing town, inhabited by people who have been here a long time. Though we are outlanders, still I believe that the people of the village have accepted my wife, my two sons and me as citizens. With the ospreys, however, I have not only failed to make friends; I have, on the contrary, been insulted, have thrown down the gauntlet and had it accepted.

In the upper branches of a half-dead oak tree on the very tip of our point, there was, when I took possession, a tattered lump of trash that looked like an unmade bed. "That's an osprey's nest," a native of the village told me. "They come back every year. I remember that nest since I was a little boy."

"They build a messy nest," I said.

"Messy, yes," he said, "but I doubt if I could de-

*Too young to leave its nest, this osprey flaps
its wings to test them. Catching fish is as
natural to ospreys as flying, but young birds often
miss the first few times they plunge for prey.*

of seaweed. One of them, so help me, brought a piece of two-by-four pine three feet long to put into the structure. They weren't very careful builders; the ground under the tree was strewn with the excess stuff that fell out.

I mounted a telescope on the sun porch and even trimmed some branches from intervening trees, and from then on those love-driven ospreys didn't have a moment of privacy.

And then one morning the ospreys were gone. I walked out to the point and saw, sticking halfway out of their nest, the shaft and feathers of an arrow. Now Catbird, my younger son (he was eight at the time), was the archer of the family. I ran him down and gave him what-for in spite of his plaintive protests that he had not shot at the nest.

The birds did not come back. They were across the bay. I could see them through the telescope building an uneasy nest on top of a transformer on a telephone pole where they were definitely not wanted.

I got a ladder and climbed up to the nest on our point, and when I came down I apologized to Catbird. For in the nest I had found not only the arrow, but my bamboo garden rake, three T shirts and a Plaza Hotel bath towel. Apparently nothing was too unusual for the ospreys to steal for their nest.

Now I must admit I had been pleased and a little proud to have my own osprey nest. I had planned to observe the nestlings when they arrived. The empty nest on the point that summer was a matter of sorrow and perplexity to me. I went to my Audubon, and it told me the following:

"Osprey (fish hawk), length 21 to 24 inches, wingspread 4½ to 6 feet, weight 3½ pounds. . . . Provided they are not molested, ospreys will nest wherever there is a reasonably extensive body of clear water and some sort of elevated nest site. The birds are excellent watchdogs, driving off crows and other birds of prey. For this reason platforms on tall poles are often erected to encourage them to nest about homes and farmyards."

It was in February that I asked myself: If people put up platforms on poles, why not build a nest so attractive as to win back my own birds? (The power company had meanwhile torn their nest off the transformer.)

In late winter I went to work. Climbing the oak

sign something the winds wouldn't blow out. It's darned good architecture from a staying point of view."

Toward the end of May, to my delight, the ospreys came back from wherever they had been, and from the beginning they fascinated me. They are about the best fishermen in the world. They would coast along, hanging on the breeze perhaps 50 feet above the water; then, suddenly, their wings raised like the fins of a bomb and they arrowed down and nearly always came up with a fish. I became a habitual osprey watcher.

In time, two of my ospreys were nudged by love and began to install new equipment in the great nest on my point. They brought unusual material—pieces of wood, rake handles, strips of cloth, reeds, swatches

Caught by a camera's high-speed shutter, a male osprey is seen just before he lands on the nest he shares with his mate. His wings are fully expanded, and his primary feathers are spread like fingers.

tree, I cleaned away the debris of the old nest. Then I firmly wired in place horizontally a large wagon wheel. I cut dry pampas-grass stalks and bound them in long fagots. With the freezing blasts of winter tearing at my clothes, I reascended the tree and wove the reeds into the spokes of the wheel until I had a nest that, if I had any oviparous impulses, I should have found irresistible.

After that I had trouble with the novel I was writing, since I had to rush constantly to the telescope to see whether my prospective tenants had returned. Finally June 1 came and school was out, and I put my boys on watch.

One morning Catbird charged into my study. "Ospreys!" he shouted. "Come running—ospreys!"

I rushed for my telescope. There were the ospreys, all right. But they weren't settling into my beautiful nest. They were tearing it to pieces, lifting out the carefully bound reed pads, carrying them across the bay and propping them clumsily on top of the power company's transformer.

Of course my feelings were hurt. Why should I deny it? But on the heels of injury came anger. Those slipshod, larcenous birds, those ingrates, those—those ospreys. My eyes strayed to the shotgun that hangs over my fireplace, but before I could reach for it, a Machiavellian thought came to me.

I wanted to hurt the ospreys, yes. I wanted revenge on them. But with number-four shot? No. I ached to hurt them as they had hurt me—in their feelings, psychologically.

I am an adept at psychological warfare. I declared the garage off limits to everyone. My novel came to a dead stop. Daily I worked in the garage, using pieces of chicken wire and a great deal of plaster of Paris. Then I asked my neighbor, Jack Ramsey, a very good painter, to come to my workshop.

At the end of two days we emerged with our product: a life-sized replica of a nesting whooping crane. It was my belief that there were only 37 of these rare and wonderful birds in the world. Well, this was the 38th.

Chuckling evilly, I hoisted the plaster bird up in the tree and wired her firmly in the nest. Her blinding white body, black tail and brilliant red mask stood out magnificently against the sky. I went back to the sun porch and turned my telescope on the ospreys, who pretended to go about their nest-building on the transformer just as though nothing at all had happened.

I knew what must be going on over there, though. Mrs. Osprey was saying, "Lord Almighty, George! Look who has moved into the apartment you didn't want. Why did I listen to you?"

And I laughed to myself. These are the wounds that never heal. This is psychological warfare as it should be fought.

Two days later my son Thom came running into my study. "The nest!" he cried. "Look at the nest!"

I bolted for the door. The ospreys, in jealous rage, were dive-bombing my whooping crane. But all they could accomplish was the breaking of their talons on the hard surface of the plaster. Finally they gave up and flew away, followed by my shouts of derision.

The ospreys have not attacked anymore, but we have had other visitors. One morning I looked out the window to see a rather stout lady in khaki trousers and a turtleneck sweater creeping across my lawn on her hands and knees. Field glasses dangled from her neck, and she held a camera in front of her. When I went out to question her, she angrily waved me away.

"Go back," she whispered at me hoarsely. "Do you want her to fly away?"

"But you don't understand—" I began.

"Will you keep your voice down?" she rasped. "Do you know what that is? The club will never believe me. If I don't get a picture of her, I'll kill you."

Yes, we have had bird watchers—lots of them. You see, our whooping crane could be seen from a long way off. After a time they discovered the nature of the thing, but they would not listen to my explanation of the ruse. In fact, they became angry; not at the ospreys—where the blame surely rests—but at me.

No one can say I am unforgiving, though. I have taken my whooping crane down and restored the nest to its old beauty. It is ready and waiting. Let us see whether this year the ospreys are big enough to let bygones be bygones.

Chapter Seven

The Versatile Mammals

The rulers of the earth are mammals: warm-blooded, hairy creatures that bear their young alive and suckle them. They vary from two inches to 100 feet, from a fraction of an ounce to over 150 tons. Their nervous systems are better developed than other animals', and each species is a marvel of special adaptations for its own way of life.

HIS MAGNIFICENCE, THE MOOSE

Jack Denton Scott

Sun fell upon the water, illuminating the incredible scene. Beneath my canoe, at the bottom of a clear lake in northern British Columbia, was an enormous animal. Completely submerged, it looked like a mythical sea monster with its big horse's nose, five-foot spread of shovel-flat antlers and slick brown-black hide.

Suddenly the beast popped to the surface 30 feet away, water bubbling around it, half-chewed pond-weed hanging from its mouth. Glaring and grunting, it tossed its great ax-blade head—and came for me. Easily as an otter, it circled the canoe where I sat, paddle frozen. Then, in a quick surprise maneuver, it turned and swam for shore, taking my fear with it. That was my first meeting with the moose, the largest and most fascinating member of the deer family.

The bull moose looks like a huge, slightly sway-backed mule that has grown strange horns and developed an outsize droopy muzzle. He has a three- or four-inch tail, humped shoulders, a mane and a "goatee" (a hanging, useless hairy strip called a dewlap, or "bell"). His four-foot, stiltlike legs hike him higher than a horse; he often stands seven feet at the shoulder. During the fall he carries 60-pound, palmated antlers, sometimes with a six-foot spread (record, 77 5/8 inches), as easily as a man wears a straw hat.

This magnificent mammal was named in America by the English colonists, who gave him the Algonquian Indian name "moose," meaning "he strips off," because he is a bark- and twig-eater. The moose is a single species (also found in Europe and Asia), but there are four subspecies in North America, differing only in size.

Naturalists believe that the moose came here from Asia during the Pleistocene period, crossing a continent-linking strip of land at Bering Strait. Today it is found in much of wilderness Canada, Maine, parts of New Hampshire and Vermont, Wyoming, Idaho, Utah, Montana and Minnesota, and in Isle Royale National Park in Michigan. But Alaska holds the largest concentration of moose (believed to be well over 100,000), and from there comes the most startling reports of what may be our most unusual animal.

Moose seem completely unafraid of man's mechanical might. Arthur E. Bratlie of the Alaska Department of Fish and Game tells of a bull moose that became annoyed at the noise of a Boeing 720 jet on a runway at Anchorage International Airport. Suddenly he rushed it, smacking it between No. 1 and No. 2 engines. Apparently satisfied that he had proved his superiority, he stepped back, shook his head and strolled off. The jet was delayed a half hour while mechanics checked for damage.

In the winter it is common for moose to trot along snow-cleared highways. Impatience on the part of motorists can cause serious difficulty. The moose consider the highways theirs; and if they are annoyed, they may wreck a car simply by rolling over on the hood, kicking in a windshield or smashing the roof.

The Alaskan Railroad has yet to devise a method to keep moose off the tracks. However, the situation is better than it used to be when the timetable carried the disclaimer, "Not responsible for train delays because of moose." There are still cases of moose attacking diesel engines. Some naturalists claim the whistle is somewhat like the bellow of a mating bull.

For the bull moose, sex is something to be taken seriously. During the mid-September to late October rut, he travels widely, eating little, searching for willing females, fighting, even killing bulls that get in the way. Witnesses call the fight between bulls one of the most awesome combats in nature. "I watched a struggle for twenty minutes," E. B. Bailey of Quebec's Department of Fish and Game told me. "The bulls knocked down trees three and four inches in diame-

ter as they battled. When it was ended, it looked as if a bulldozer had worked over about an acre of ground." In traveling less than 500 miles in Alaska, biologist Frank Dufresne found 14 bulls killed in battle, six with antlers locked in death.

The antlers are a key to moose survival; the hardening of the broad-bladed battle weapons accompanies a heightening of the reproductive urge. Beginning as small buttons on the bull calf, the antlers grow bigger each year until the moose is six, when he grows the remarkable rack that marks the bull in his prime.

This growth begins in April, reaching its amazing size in four months. During this period the spongy antlers are covered in "velvet," a fleshy tissue containing blood vessels that nourish the developing bone. In the later stages of growth the antlers begin to harden, and by August the blood vessels have dried up and the bone is firm. The velvet remains, hanging in tatters as it is rubbed off against trees. By September the antlers are as smooth and shiny as dueling sabers.

Now the nearly two-month rut begins; and the bull, his neck swollen, eyes bloodshot, temper short, becomes a fearsome, belligerent beast with a one-track mind. He bellows, grunts and moos his desires, his voice rising and ending in a sirenlike sound. An interested cow responds in shrill moos and bawlings.

It has often been debated whether the bull moose in rut is a dangerous animal that will attack man, or just a love-smitten boob who doesn't know what he is doing.

The evidence is confusing. Stories of bull moose in rut chasing men up trees are numerous. Yet George Davis, famous New Brunswick guide and taxidermist, who has seen more than 10,000 moose, told me he didn't think they were dangerous—at least not intentionally. "I have never seen a moose charge a human," he said. "They'll charge in the direction of a call, all right; but that's in the belief that it's another moose—either another bull to be fought or a cow to be courted."

Normally, the moose is a wary animal that loses its equilibrium only during the mating season, a period that includes a ten-day courtship. The bull will usually mate with four cows before the fire is gone by the end of October. Gaunt then from lack of food and his strenuous schedule, the moose docilely joins a small group of bulls and cows and behaves himself. The antlers now become a useless weight, discarded in late December, to grow again next spring.

About eight months after the fall fling, usually early in June, a helpless 20- to 25-pound moose calf is born. Sometimes there are twins, rarely triplets. The cow finds an isolated place on an island, deep in a swamp or heavy thicket, where she carefully conceals her offspring for three days until it is able to follow her about. Seven days later the calf can outrun a man. The moose calf may be the fastest growing of wild animals, gaining two pounds every day for the first month and four pounds daily after that time. The calves stay with their parent until the fol-

Massive flattened antlers are characteristic of the bull moose, largest member of the deer family. Inveterate waders, moose are fond of aquatic plants that grow on the bottoms of lakes and streams. They also eat twigs and foliage from maples, willows and other broad-leaved trees. With their long legs and short necks, moose have difficulty grazing on land; they must kneel on their front knees to reach grass and other ground plants.

lowing fall, when, ready to mate again, she drives them away or abandons them.

The cow moose has a strong maternal instinct and does much for her offspring. They learn from her the art of backtracking; of standing motionless in thickets, taking advantage of the natural camouflage; of moving silently and swiftly when they scent danger from afar.

Shortly after they learn to walk she teaches them to swim. Some observers say moose are almost as much at home in the water as beavers, occasionally diving, back-rolling, spending much of their time during the hot summer in rivers and lakes to escape the mosquitoes and other forest pests. Adolph Murie, in his prolonged study of moose on Michigan's Isle Royale, several times saw a moose dive to the bottom of a lake and remain submerged for a minute and a half.

Although the moose calf will grow into the largest antlered animal on earth, his coloring will protect him, almost paint him out of the picture. In spruce, hemlock or any evergreen, the brownish-black back and sides and the yellowish-white legs blend into foliage—and the moose knows it. This camouflage is effective against man, the moose's No. 1 enemy, but something special is needed for protection against keener-eyed predators, such as the wolf and bear. The moose has it in his superb senses of smell and hearing. In an experiment a biologist found that moose were aware of the footfalls of a man two minutes before the scientist could detect the approaching sound.

Speed and stamina are impressive, too. One harness-broken moose drew a sleigh 160 miles on the frozen St. John River in New Brunswick and showed no signs of being tired. Naturalists agree that a moose can outrun a horse, especially on home terrain. And in a race, the wolf, considered by many to be the moose's major enemy next to man, doesn't stand a chance.

A moose's hooves, with tremendous muscle behind them, can break the back or crush the skull of almost any adversary. E. B. Bailey saw a moose kill a large black bear by pounding its head and back with his front hooves.

The hooves, often seven inches long, and aided by additional purchase power of large dewclaws, provide more than defense. More flexible, with a greater division than those of most hooved animals, they enable the moose to spread his toes, improving his footing. He can walk in areas that other large creatures, including man, would find impassable. Arthur Graef, an experienced hunter who has shot 13 prize moose, has seen a 1000-pound bull moose cross a swamp where a hunter would have difficulty walking. He also says that the speed and grace with which a moose negotiates mossy, slippery, rocky terrain and hurdles the tangled hazard of felled trees is almost unbelievable.

Normally the nonmigratory moose isn't much of a mover. In winter, in the company of a few of his fellows, he lives in a "yard"—tramping down the snow, often staying on less than 50 acres. He is a browser, feeding on leaves, twigs, plants, grass, aquatic growth, lily pads, bark. He doesn't need much space to forage for his 35 pounds of daily food. Many naturalists believe that a moose may spend much of his 15- to 18-year life-span in a range whose radius is less than ten miles. His summer domain of woodland and brush, near lake, river or swamp, may encompass a mile or less.

This restricted activity almost brought about his downfall. Indians believed the moose to be an omen of good and also thought that by eating his meat they would gain his strength. In the early days it was thought that the left hind foot of the moose was a certain cure for epilepsy. Bone rings from the antlers banished headache and dizziness; mixed with various herbs, ground antler was an antidote for snakebite. The hooves of the moose were believed to cure more than 600 diseases or afflictions. Sportsmen, Indians and market hunters killed moose of any age or sex during any season, until in Maine, parts of Canada and the West, this mammal dwindled in numbers.

But as science superseded superstition, the moose finally began to prosper. Most states abolished hunting, or, like Canada, had short and stringently controlled seasons. Lumbering and forest fires have meant new vegetation that improves the moose's habitat. Today the moose population in North America is over a quarter of a million and on the rise. The moose now seems to be here to stay.

One of the farsighted men who made the world safe for the moose was Dr. Henry Fairfield Osborn. When he was president of the New York Zoological Society, he said, "Nature has been millions of years in developing that wonderful animal, and man should not ruthlessly destroy him."

To our everlasting credit, we haven't.

PUTTING THE BEAVER BACK TO WORK

Robert Froman

A homeowner in Stony Point, New York, noticed recently that someone had started to dam a brook running through his land. To his delight he discovered that the culprits were a pair of beavers, and for several nights he watched with interest as these engaging creatures went about their engineering project.

Within a couple of weeks, however, the pond backed up by the dam overflowed his lawn and lapped at his driveway. When his basement began to fill with water, the owner lost enthusiasm for his furry guests.

"I couldn't shoot them," he reported, "—they were practically human. So I called the state conservation department."

He had the right idea. A conservation agent captured the beavers, trucked them deep into the Catskill Mountains and released them on the headwaters of a creek. There they could build dams unmolested and

It would be hard to find an animal better outfitted than the beaver for a particular way of life. Its front paws are nearly as nimble as a monkey's; its hind ones are webbed like a duck's; and with its huge front teeth it can fell a sapling with astonishing speed. To keep warm it wears two fur coats: a dense, silky inner coat and a coarse, waterproof outer one. Its flat, scaly tail is a combination propeller, rudder and signaling device.

at the same time help to reduce the area's flood peril.

In the last 20 years there have been thousands of such incidents. Across North America, conservationists are helping the beaver choose sites where his dams will be beneficial to all concerned.

Three hundred years ago there were more beavers than people in North America—an estimated 60 million of them. It was in pursuit of their fur that trappers and traders blazed the first trails into the wilderness. By 1800, however, the beaver had been extermi-

nated in most of New England; by 1928 he had almost disappeared from the United States east of the Mississippi and from parts of southern Canada.

Since then the beaver has staged a remarkable comeback. The big increase in the animal's numbers—fostered in part by conservation efforts, in part by abandonment of marginal farms (which often make ideal beaver habitat), in part by a change in fur styles—has led to new understanding of his place in nature's scheme. In many areas

An industrious beaver drags a sapling along a trail to its home. Young trees are essential to a beaver colony as they provide food and materials the animals can use to build dams and lodges.

For a beaver, happiness is having an aspen limb to gnaw on: The bark is among its favorite foods. A one-acre stand of young trees will sustain a colony of ten beavers for as long as a year.

living beavers are far more valuable than the pelts of dead ones, and, thanks to their building habits, our farmlands are richer.

When a beaver dam is abandoned, it slowly gives way, the swamp drains and vegetation takes over the rich loam left behind. A truck farmer near Poughkeepsie, New York, while digging a drainage ditch across his onion fields, found that the heavy black loam was from 12 to 15 feet deep. At the lower end of his fields he uncovered the explanation—the remains of an ancient beaver dam.

Ecologists believe that this process, repeated endlessly since the last ice age, has been responsible for some of our best farmland. One ecologist, who studied beaver history for the Vermont Fish and Game Commission, attributes the decline of agriculture in Vermont—and the mounting flood toll—to the beaver's century-long absence from that New England state.

Beavers' dam-building skill, their systematic gathering and storing of food for the winter and their affectionate family life long ago moved some Indian tribes to dub them the "little men of the woods." They are not little by rodent standards, however. They grow to a length of three or four feet and a weight of 30 to 60 or more pounds. Their tools are four powerful, chisel-like teeth and two nimble front paws. With their teeth they can fell a tree four inches thick in 15 minutes. With their paws they can manipulate sticks, stones, mud or any building material they want.

In the wrong place, the beaver can be trouble. When he chooses a dam site and sets to work, it takes powerful persuading to convince him that his choice is wrong. A Canadian-railroad section foreman reported to headquarters: "The beaver here are awful.

Every morning we spend hours breaking their dams before we can get to work. If we don't, they flood the tracks. I made a waterwheel and tied tin cans to it to scare the beaver away. They shoved a pole into the wheel and stopped it. I left a lantern burning all night and they covered it. I built a culvert under their dam and they plugged it up. I built a wire fence to keep them away, and they cut down my poles and used the wire on their dams. What do you suggest?"

In the *right* places the dams do an enormous amount of good. Getting beavers to such places is a combined concern of the U.S. Fish and Wildlife Service, U.S. Forest Service and various state agencies. In some remote wilderness areas of the West, when the headwaters of a creek or river are in need of a restraining influence, beavers are dropped by parachute in wooden cages that open automatically upon landing.

To keep silt from washing down into their reservoirs, government agencies and private power companies are placing beavers on dozens of upstream tributaries. This helps stabilize the flow of water into the reservoirs and frequently turns ugly gullies into fertile little valleys.

Many sections of the country have seen underground water tables fall from 25 to 50 feet in the past ten years. Beavers help solve this problem by keeping rainfall on hand until it's needed. For example: In 1954, when drought turned much of the surrounding farmland into a miniature dust bowl, Bear Mountain State Park, New York, remained a green oasis because of water supplies backed up by its 20-odd beaver colonies.

Beaver ponds are a blessing to most other forms of wildlife. Moose feed in them; deer, bear and elk browse around the edges. Muskrats, mink and otter

A beaver swims as well underwater as on the surface because it has transparent eyelids, valves that seal off its ears and nostrils, and lips that close behind the incisor teeth it uses for hauling.

It may look like a hodgepodge of sticks and mud, but a beaver lodge is actually a sturdy and carefully built home that will keep the colony warm and secure from enemies throughout the winter.

share the water, and many fish benefit from the regulation of the flow of the stream.

People who know the beaver respect his intelligence. A Maine naturalist once made a sizable hole in a beaver dam. Three young animals immediately set to work repairing the damage. It proved too big a job for them, however, so after a few minutes one of them swam off and returned with an adult. The old fellow dived to the bottom of the pond, came up with a boulder, shoved it into the break and held it in place there while the young ones plastered it up with mud.

A New York woman tells of making friends with a family of beavers by bringing them presents of alder twigs, apples and candy. One evening she set out sliced apples. They crowded round the plate so greedily that the smallest one couldn't get his share. When his outraged squeals went unheeded, he stamped down to the water and slapped the surface with his tail, the beavers' danger signal meaning, "Dive!" The others instantly splashed into the depths of the pond—while the baby helped himself to the apples.

THE BEAST
WITH THE HIGH I.Q.

Jean George

A trapper I know spent an entire October day setting five traps to take a large red fox he had seen. After brewing the traps in a mixture of wood chips and water to rid them of his telltale scent, he covered them with leaves. Pleased with his artful cunning, he turned to go home. There, not ten feet from him, sat the fox, as E. B. White says, "absorbed in

apple-fall and mirth, and feeling very loud and nirsey." His ears were up, his nose licked wet, the better to "read" the subterfuge on the air. Not only had he followed the trapper to every site; he had doused each trap with his own musk to warn the next fox that danger lay under the leaves.

The more the North American red fox is trapped and chased, the smarter he becomes. Today there are far more foxes—and far smarter ones—than our forefathers ever knew. In trying to outwit the fox, man has forced him to become the canniest animal in the countryside.

One thing early hunters learned about the red fox was that British hounds were no match for him. North America's rough terrain had developed a smaller, more agile beast than had the tended, rolling fields of Great Britain. So hunters began to breed splendid lighter-boned hounds—dubbed such colorful names as Blue Tick, Red Bone, Billy Sunday—that take out after the red fox with a vigor and a voice dear to those who love to get outdoors in the fall and hike across hilly country.

But even these hounds are no match for the fox when he really wants to swing. Slender and long-legged under his dense fur, he is built like a racehorse. Individual foxes have been known to run a pack of hounds for four days, wearing the pads off dogs' feet, leaving their bodies gaunt and skinny. Many dogs have been drowned during a chase—following the crafty and lighter fox over thin ice. Long chases do not faze a fox in good health. He will snack along the way on berries and mice, or spurt far ahead to doze under a bush until the hounds catch up.

A fox named White-Foot, who lived on the Potomac River near my childhood home, showed me why

Skunks are among the small mammals that foxes prey on. But as this red fox pup is about to learn, a skunk—even a small one—is best treated with deference. Though slow to anger, skunks exude a formidable scent when cornered or aroused.

the fox usually wins. One day when the "field" went after White-Foot, he immediately lost hounds and horses by jumping to a rail fence and running it to the end of the meadow. The hounds worked this out after a slight delay and tongued on to a creek, where the trail disappeared again. But even the hounds knew that foxes run along shallow streams to throw dogs off their scent. The master of hounds sent half the field up the creek and half down to find where

the fox stepped ashore. But they never picked up the scent again.

At twilight they gave up and went home. They were met by the wife of the keeper of the hounds, who said she had found the fox, round and full of chicken, sleeping in the henhouse.

Tracking back, the huntsman discovered that White-Foot had crouched in a patch of cattle manure below the stream bank, while momentum carried the hunt over his head and into the stream. Then he had trotted back past the hunt club, losing his own musty scent in the maze of odors on the smelly horse and dog trail, until he found the hennery.

Another intelligent fox kept springing a trapper's sets by yanking the chains with his teeth. But this trapper would not give up. In the mating season he baited a trap with "Persian Love Musk" (vixen scent). The fox, true to his routine, got up at 4 p.m. and trotted down his personal fox-road to the fields. On the way he caught the scent of vixen and swerved to find her. But he stopped short of the set, read the signs on the air and turned off. The trapper, beaten, was going home, when a yap arrested him.

Down the hill came his fox again, followed by another fox, an irate male on whose property he had no doubt trespassed. The first fox led the second right toward the trap. The love scent caught the defender by surprise and he swerved to sniff it clearly. As he did, the trap closed on his paw. No sound came from the captured beast; foxes are silent when hurt. They stoically await death. Immediately, the first fox circled back to the hill, where, the trapper was sure, the home-defender's vixen awaited the victor.

Despite the American farmers' war against the species, foxes number almost one per 50 acres as compared with one per 173 acres a hundred years ago. Besides opening the land—which increases foxes—the farmer has helped with his plow. When digging dens in March in which to whelp their young, foxes refuse to claw anything harder than loose gravel. So the tilled land has helped increase their dens.

One fox in Michigan understood farm practices so well that he would wait at the edge of the woods until the farmer had not only plowed, but disked and harrowed. Each spring the farmer would see him lying on the horizontal trunk of a willow, watching him work. When the harrow finally banged down the lane, the farmer would stop and look back. Sure enough, the fox was always in the field digging into the earth.

Over the years fox dens have become more devious. Usually there are three or more entrances, and

*Although it can look as docile as a house pet, the American red fox, even one as young as this pup, has sharp
eyes and ears, a keen sense of smell and an alert intelligence to use against its principal enemy, man.
While the fox is a nuisance to chicken farmers, it more than redeems itself by destroying mice and other vermin.*

several false tunnels wind downward toward the pantry. Nearby is the nursery where some five to seven pups are born in early April. A smart farmer will dig out the vixen and her pups at this time, for the female does not come out of the den for three days after the pups arrive.

A farmer in Wisconsin, eager to get rid of a den near his henhouse, waited until he did not see the female come or go. Then with dynamite he blew the den wide open—and found nothing there, not even a bone. The hole was merely a false front through which the foxes trotted to throw him off. The real den he discovered later on a nearby hill.

When the pups are a month old, the vixen brings them to the entrance of the den to begin their schooling. Training is rigid. I watched a vixen near my home drop a mouse before her pups and nearly take the hide off the little one that missed it. Pups at the den are warming to behold. Fearless, confident, the tannish-gray youngsters caper and run, fight and wrestle. They chase butterflies and moths and practice their arching pounce on leaves and flowers.

Mortality is high in foxdom during the early months. Diseases like distemper overtake the pups, and farmers and some conservationists eliminate them while they can be caught in numbers. Their reasons are generally sound. Foxes kill not only ducks and chickens, but beneficial game—pheasants, rabbits and quail. Moreover, fox overpopulation the next fall will often result in a rabies outbreak. However, this weeding-out has only improved the fox. The sick and dull-witted are usually caught and killed, leaving the healthy and bright to breed more healthy and bright offspring.

The red fox lives in every state except Florida and Hawaii, and in many parts of Canada. Called the "colored" fox by zoologists, he comes in several tints and shades besides red. The silver fox, the black, the rust and the cross foxes are all the same animal, *Vulpes fulva*.

Foxes make excellent pets. They can be housebroken and are most affectionate. Two traits, however, keep them from becoming popular. They play vigorously all night; and, as a doctor friend in Carlisle, Pennsylvania, discovered, you can't return them to the wild. He kept a pup one summer. It loped and played with his children, and followed them to nearby farms and yards and gardens. While everybody thought the fox was having fun, he was actually making tidy mental notes of all the local delicacies.

That autumn the doctor decided to set the fox free. A week later the countryside was up in arms. Thirty hand-raised pheasants had been purloined, a pond full of exotic ducks ravaged, and a Siamese cat and five kittens were missing! The doctor lured his fox home with beefsteak and penned him up. As far as I know, he is still living with them, demanding fresh hamburger and strawberries every day.

Every hunter I have talked with agrees that the fox enjoys the hunt. A fox in Seneca, Maryland, would call to the hounds from the hill, his weird yap encouraging them to come chase him. One afternoon I saw him run right up to a chained dog. There he flipped and sprawled on his forepaws like a playful terrier. The hound bayed and pulled at his chain. The fox spun into the woods and out again, speaking perfectly clearly in movement, "Come chase me!"

But the fox cunning I enjoy the most was thought up by a monarch of Whitford Woods, Ohio. This fox was old, and at last one day hunters cornered him against a cliff. The fatal bullet was in the chamber. Suddenly, as if the air had wafted to the fox the greatest weakness of man, he stood up, shook himself, trotted up to the gunman and looked him straight in the eye. Dogs howled and swirled in confusion, bedlam reigned—and the fox of Whitford lived on!

THAT CHARMING CHEATER, THE CHIPMUNK

Jean George

A friend of mine, whose flower bulbs are often stolen by chipmunks, had just watched one of these beguiling little thieves make off with several of his finest floral prospects. He refused to set a trap. "I know that chipmunks are just rats in striped clothing," he said, "but I love 'em."

Chipmunks get away with a host of petty crimes. Millions of these three- to five-ounce sprites are spread across the United States and Canada, and each one maintains a hoard of about *half a bushel* of corn, nuts, seeds, flower bulbs. On farms they dig up planted grain and vegetables. They constantly rob bird feeders. Yet few people seem to mind.

The chipmunk *is* a rodent, like the rat, with two gnawing teeth above and two below. Specifically, he is a ground-living squirrel, with a striped face and five dark stripes along his tan body. Because he is fun to watch, he can charm human beings even while he does them in.

I was on the telephone one day when I saw a chipmunk come up the cellar steps, dash around a corner and disappear into the back of the upright piano. I

Pert and sprightly, the eastern chipmunk is a most appealing little mammal. During the warm months,
this furry bundle of energy busily collects and stores seeds, nuts and other plant materials for wintertime use.
The chipmunk is not a strict vegetarian, however; it enjoys insects and sometimes feeds on birds' eggs or baby
mice. Wild chipmunks live from two to four years; captive specimens may attain the ripe old age of eight.

had never seen a chipmunk in a house before. I peered behind the piano to see him stuffing seeds between the strings, his eyes glittering with innocence. Had he been a mouse I would have thrown a book at him. But he was a chippie, big-eyed and bewitching, and I let him stay three days before I realized that a key was now stuck and three felts had been chewed to pieces.

The chipmunk's ability to captivate stems from several things: his bright, clean appearance, his bouncy energy, his amusing habits. One of the latter is the way he stuffs a truly astonishing amount of food into his cheek pockets—a habit that can intrigue

even hardened men like a farmer friend of mine.

When it comes to protecting his granary, this man has no sympathy for rats, mice, crows or squirrels—he shoots them. One day, however, he discovered a chipmunk stuffing his cheek pockets with grain from a wheat bin, and so forgot himself that he started counting the grain-by-grain intake rather than shooting the culprit. When the count got up to 145 grains in the two jowls, the farmer suddenly realized that he was being burglarized while he watched. Still he did not shoot. As he told me later, "I just stood there and enjoyed being taken."

A cousin of mine in Maryland let a chipmunk

steal a quart of shelled pecans because she was so fascinated by his balancing problem. Every time he stuffed his cheeks he would go a few steps, list to one side, then stop and dart back for still another nut or two to balance the load.

Another reason chipmunks are tolerated is that they make their homes away from houses and barns and have tidy habits. Their burrows, in fact, are quite wonderful. Most chipmunks make their dens in a wood or garden. The entrances are not messy, like those of woodchucks and foxes. Generally the front door is a small hole esthetically placed behind a log or under a fern. The entrance goes straight down for a few inches, then slants off for as much as 30 feet, depending on how old the chipmunk is. (Two to four years is the normal life-span for chipmunks, though they have lived up to eight years in captivity.)

Off the main corridor are two or three pantries, sometimes as many as six, each stuffed with food. A few inches beyond the last pantry lies the nursery, a small room neatly lined with roots and leaves. Beyond this, at the end of the main shaft, is the master bedroom. Then, to top off this wonderful plan, beneath the bedroom, and lower than all other rooms, is the toilet!

In these intriguing homes chipmunks divide their time between intense activity—darting down corridors and spewing seeds and nuts into rooms by pressing in their cheeks with their paws—and sleep. Chipmunks hibernate (sleep in winter), but their sleep is not like that of woodchucks and frogs, for chipmunks' respiration and body temperature do not drop so low that they can't awaken.

This lighter sleep of the chipmunk was discovered when naturalists studied his master bedroom. There, under the mattress of leaves and grasses, is cached a special hoard of seeds and nuts. In winter, when half asleep, a chipmunk reaches down from time to time and finds a nut or two to eat.

The courtship of the chipmunk is a twinkling time. Beginning in March the male goes to seek, by scent, the den of a female. When he finds one, he sits up on his haunches and literally "sings" to her. These songs are so clear and bright that they are often mistaken for birdcalls. According to chipmunk protocol, if the female is pleased, she lets Lochinvar enter her den. If he barges in without invitation, however, he is tossed out—with nips on his toes and ears—and his screams are sorrowful to hear. When all goes well, the male visits only long enough to pass on his genetic code, then departs. Chipmunks live separately for the greater part of the year.

The gestation period is 31 days. Three to seven babies are born, each about one ninth of an ounce in weight. Furless and almost transparent, they look like pink glass. In about a week they begin to get their distinctive stripes. Their nursery life is rollicking and playful. Some 31 days after birth, when their eyes open, they box, nip and wrestle. They are weaned at about 40 days, whereupon they go to the den entrance and peer out at the world.

As summer advances, they run farther and farther from home. Finally, about mid-July, they begin burrows of their own. If the going gets tough, however, mother chipmunks permit their young to return home. The children are not forced into the world until they have a secure place to go.

One notable quality of the chipmunk is the ease with which wild ones can be tamed. It takes only a handful of sunflower seeds, patience and an hour a day for two or three days. They can be trained to come to a whistle, which, once learned, they seem never to forget. A woman who spent her summers in Wisconsin had many chipmunks that came to her each June when she called to them, even though she was gone all winter. Once she was gone for an entire year. On her return she was still able, with a whistle, to bring her chipmunks out of the woodlands.

The ability of chipmunks to be readily tamed and yet to live their own wild life led naturalist Kenneth Gordon to investigate their intelligence. He found them amazingly smart in solving maze problems, even opening complicated latches. For one chippie Gordon draped a long string over a horizontal cord, with a peanut tied to one end and the other end hanging low. The chipmunk tried jumping for the nut, unsuccessfully. Then it did something truly astonishing for any animal. It went after the nut *indirectly*, by pulling on the other end of the string. The peanut went up and away from him—an event that would stop most animals. But not this fellow. He kept on pulling until the nut went over the horizontal cord—and down to him! And he seemed to know what he was doing, for he repeated the performance.

Sometimes the little rodents seem almost to satirize human behavior. A California photographer put out kernels of grain to attract chipmunks. For days two male chippies came for the food at different hours. Eventually they arrived simultaneously. Both grew angry, then stood up on their hind legs and strode toward each other, one paw held forward, the other held against the chest, exactly like a boxer. And, like boxers, they teased with the forward paw and socked with the other. When the dispute was settled, the winner ate while the loser sat by.

Chipmunks are heart winners for a final, warm

reason. Who would not enjoy an animal that kisses another of its kind? Chipmunks occasionally do just this. Sometimes when they meet, bouncing over walls and rocks, they press their noses together gently with apparent affection, then leap lightly on their way, tails up. It is a moment that says just about all you need to know about a chipmunk.

RHINO!

David Reed

Standing in the wilds of East Africa, he looks, every inch of him, like a prehistoric monster. He is five feet, six inches high at the shoulder and 12 feet from the tip of the nose to the root of the tail. Two lancelike horns, one much longer than the other, jut from his head. He weighs more than a ton. He looks stolid, but he is a nervous wreck, with a nasty, unpredictable temper. If he senses your presence, often as not he will charge, thundering straight at you like a runaway locomotive.

A half century ago, the black rhinoceros was a common sight in Africa; enormous numbers of these great beasts roamed the lowland plains and mountain forests. Today the rhino is high on the list of African animals that are threatened with extinction. Fewer than 15,000 have survived, and every day their numbers dwindle further.

The rhino is being hunted to death for his horns. There is an ignorant notion, widespread in Asia, that ground-up rhino horn is a powerful aphrodisiac. As a result it has become one of the most valuable animal products in the world. An average-sized horn can be bought for perhaps $70 in Mombasa or some other Indian Ocean port, and resold for several thousand dollars in the Orient. And so an illegal but flourishing business has sprung up.

Although the rhino is not exactly a lovable creature, his extinction would be a great loss, for he is unique. A leftover from prehistoric ages, he has changed little since the time when his ancestors roamed the earth—even Europe and North America —in company with mastodons and saber-toothed tigers. His only living relatives are the horse, the zebra and the tapir.

Nature seems to have goofed in designing the rhino. His legs appear ridiculously short for his great body. His half-inch-thick skin sags loosely, looking like an old rug that has been flung across his frame. He has a keen sense of smell and acute hearing, but his eyesight (like his intelligence) is exceedingly dim.

An elephant or buffalo will spot a man some distance away and move off, but a rhino can't see a man until he is almost upon him. Then trouble starts.

The black rhino is amazingly agile. He can leap from a prone position in the twinkling of an eye, charge at 30 miles an hour, and scramble up steep rocky slopes like a mountain goat. His fury is directed against inanimate objects as often as men. He will charge a car and reduce it to junk. One Kenya game warden found a rhino stuck in a mudhole and pulled him out with his Land Rover. The quarrelsome beast repaid the favor by caving in the side of the vehicle. On another occasion, a rhino was seen battering furiously at a parked tractor. Rhinos sometimes charge passing trains. But this is an uneven match; the train wins.

The black rhino's bad temper is such that he is even conceived in a rage. If a female feels amorous, she charges headlong at a likely suitor and bashes and gores him until he is a bloody mess. If, after this, the male is still willing—and, of course, still alive— mating takes place. The female may then batter the male a few more times for good measure.

After 18 months of gestation, a bouncing 60-pound baby is born. (Twins are unknown.) The calf suckles until he is about two years old. By the time he is five to seven, he is fully grown and goes off to live by himself. Black rhinos lead a solitary existence all their lives. If two bulls meet, they may battle until one or both are dead.

Oddly enough, the rhino is considered the most easily tamable animal in Africa. Once penned, he soon becomes so gentle that he will eat out of his keeper's hand. Captive rhinos will come on call to have their ears rubbed, and some will roll over to have their stomachs scratched. The only problem is the rhino's bulk. If he should lean against you playfully, well, ugh.

Rhinos are amazingly adaptable. They are found in the entire range of African terrain—from scorching deserts to middle-altitude brushlands to the chilly summits of 12,000-foot mountains. They can survive for months in areas lacking surface water, and exist on the moisture acquired from eating succulent plants. But their range is constantly dwindling. The black rhino formerly ranged over much of sub-Saharan Africa; today it is confined mostly to Kenya and neighboring Tanzania. The black rhinoceros has a peaceful larger cousin, the rare white rhinoceros. Once thought to be extinct, the white rhino has made a limited recovery, and efforts are now being made to preserve the species. It is found near the headwaters of the White Nile and in South Africa.

The big event in a rhino's day comes soon after sundown, when he spends several hours at the water hole—almost always the same one, though it may be as much as ten miles from home. This is the only time that he appears even faintly happy; he will romp around playfully, then wallow in the mud and massage himself against trees and rocks. Afterward he returns home, and serious dining begins. Barging through the brush like a bulldozer, he eats like a vacuum cleaner, using his prehensile lip to wrench leaves and buds from trees and shrubs. Even the sharpest thorns are consumed with relish. When morning comes he looks for shade and rests through the day. Usually he lies down, but sometimes he dozes standing up, his head hanging down in a pose of utter woe.

The rhino has only one friend in the world—the little tickbird, who rides on his back and picks ticks from his hide. If something approaches while a rhino is dozing, the birds screech a warning. But the rhino's luck is such that hunters often rely on the presence of tickbirds to lead them to the rhino.

Apart from man the rhino has no natural enemies, but man is enough. Both white and native hunters have littered Africa with the bleached bones of these great beasts. Today licensed hunting has been curtailed sharply, but the rhino's numbers continue to decline at the hands of African poachers. Tribesmen even invade the game parks in quest of the animals. Some kill rhinos with poisoned arrows or spears. But the cruelest method is that of fixing wire snares, attached to heavy logs, along rhino trails. Once snared, the rhino drags the log for miles until he drops from exhaustion. The poachers then chop off the horns and leave the ton of meat to rot. Soon there is only a spiral of vultures to mark the demise of yet one more rhino.

Another problem is that expanding populations of humans and domestic animals have taken over much of the rhino's habitat. But today, with the help of wildlife organizations in the United States and Europe, the East African governments are making efforts to save at least some of the animals. Perhaps the best one can hope for is that it will be possible to concentrate the surviving rhinos in closely guarded sanctuaries. If this can be done, future generations will be able at least to see and to marvel at one of the most irascible, and strange creatures on earth.

Bad temper, poor vision and formidable bulk make the black rhinoceros a highly dangerous animal. It will charge anything that moves and, despite a clumsy appearance, can run as fast as 30 miles an hour.

CAVE OF THE VAMPIRES

Daniel P. Mannix

I met my first vampire bat through Charles E. Mohr, Director of the Delaware Nature Education Center, who is an expert on caves and the creatures that live in them. He had located the most northern colony of vampires ever reported—in the cave of Los Sabinos, Mexico, some 200 miles south of the border—and he promised to take me there.

Our guides, an Indian father and son from the nearby village, discussed the vampires as imperturbably as American farmers would discuss chicken hawks. Yes, the bats came every night to feed on their goats, cows and horses. In the evening the villagers took the more valuable animals into the huts with them. The other animals had to take their chances. After all, the bats didn't take much blood.

"I have seen one drinking a rooster's blood," said the younger man. "The bat was clinging to the leg with his wingclaws and had his hind feet on the ground. When the rooster walked away, the bat walked with him, still holding on to the leg and still feeding."

The guides led the way down a steep slope into a natural amphitheater hung with jungle creepers as big as cables. We climbed through a black slit in the white limestone and found ourselves in a great entrance hall, 70 feet high.

We descended deeper and deeper, in utter darkness except for puddles of light from our head lamps. At intervals the guides left candles stuck to the rocks to mark our path back. Half a mile farther along, we could look back and see the tiny lights twinkling like stars above us.

Then the slope ended in a steep drop, falling away into a vast black hole into which we descended with ropes. I went down first, and while the others were following me I heard a noise that sounded like the chittering call of ordinary bats combined with the whistle of steam from a teakettle. "That's the cry of the vampires," said Charlie, plopping beside me.

We climbed down to the floor of the cave and moved forward into a big room with passages branching off on all sides. Suddenly, on the wall ahead, we saw little shapes running and leaping among the terracelike formations. The long shadows thrown by our lamps added to their height and they looked exactly like little goblins.

Running on hind feet and the elbows of their

wings, the vampires could go as fast as a four-legged animal. As we came closer, several ran to the edge of the ledges and sprang into the air. Others stood their ground, baring their sharp teeth and chattering fiercely. I grabbed one old warrior; he fought savagely in my gloved hand, screaming with rage. Later we found he had sliced out two small pieces of my heavy leather glove with his two long canine teeth. A razor could not have done it as neatly. Charlie tried to catch some of the bats in his collecting net. They seemed to understand perfectly what he was doing and avoided him easily.

Some of the vampires ran up the slippery walls, hooking themselves up with two long fingers growing out of the elbows of their wings. These fingers are amazing instruments. Each one ends in a curved nail, like a squirrel's. Dozens of vampires were hanging head down on the walls above us, their open mouths and grinning teeth pointing downward. At last we were able to catch several good specimens and made our way out of the cave.

The vampire bat is a ghost story come true. Although animals are their usual source of food, vampires occasionally feed on the blood of sleeping men. When a vampire locates a victim, he does not alight upon him and thus wake the sleeper. Instead, the bat lands on the bedcovers, gently rears up on the tips of his wings, and crawls toward the sleeper's face. Every motion is elaborately cautious.

He selects the best spot for his attack, a place with few nerves and lots of blood—the lobe of the ear or the tip of the nose. He nips the flesh gently. If the victim tosses, the vampire leaps back and waits patiently until his quarry has gone back to sleep. Then he tries another spot.

He may try several places before he finds one where the sleeper cannot feel his sharp teeth. Then, stretching his mouth wide open, he makes a single quick slash with his two canine teeth, sideways, as if using a knife.

Vampires do not suck blood from a wound; they lap it up, as a cat laps milk. They seem to know enough to slash open a blood vessel so that the blood keeps flowing out. The bat will feed until its belly is distended and it can hardly fly.

Even so, it is not the amount of blood the bats take that is serious, but the fact that they sometimes carry Chagas' disease and rabies. Some Indians reported an outbreak of rabies, spread by vampires, that killed off 90 percent of the cattle in some districts of southern Mexico. The bats behaved like mad dogs, biting everything they saw. In Trinidad and Panama several deaths of natives from the bites of rabid vampires have been reported.

"Under certain circumstances, vampires can be a real menace," said Dr. Alfredo Téllez Girón, "but trying to exterminate them would be a tremendous undertaking."

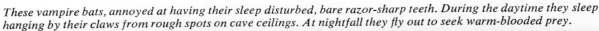

These vampire bats, annoyed at having their sleep disturbed, bare razor-sharp teeth. During the daytime they sleep hanging by their claws from rough spots on cave ceilings. At nightfall they fly out to seek warm-blooded prey.

Chapter Eight

Green Magic

*Green plants are the basis of all earthly existence. They work the magic
that transmutes sunshine, carbon dioxide and water into food and replenishes
the oxygen in the air we breathe. Thus our lives are intimately bound
up with the quiet miracle taking place in the very grass beneath our feet.*

BUDS: NATURE'S PROMISE OF PERPETUITY

Donald Culross Peattie

When pussy willows are out, spring has again captured the old world. Their furry tufts, silvery upon black twigs, are the signs of budding dearest to most of us. And budding is the everlasting reassurance, new each year.

Springtime is crowded with buds filled with leaf or flower or new twig shoots. For each bud holds its own kind of futurity; without buds no leaf would ever burgeon, no sallow send out a withe, nor ever a flowering branch spread tenderly over some old grave. In our zone of winter-naked trees and shrubs you'll find a bud at the axil, or base, of almost every leafstalk. Though purely vegetative, buds are yet embryonic growths. On a great tree they may seem as superficial as your fingernails, but in fact they are deep-set in the twig that bears them, their fibers connected with the very core system of the old wood.

Slowly the buds begin to swell, the woods to wear green again. If you'll walk down by the riverbank to see the cinnamon fern unrolling buds that look like the scrollwork on a fiddle's head, or go up in the drier woods to look at the buds of bracken that open like the slackening of a clenched fist, you will be gazing on what is, perhaps, the oldest type of budding still to be seen among ferns—and ferns may be said to have invented leaves. And when our rattlesnake fern uncoils, you may see within the angle of this year's bud the bud for next spring neatly fitted into a hollowed-out space in the stalk, and in the angle of *that* bud, still another, preparing for spring after next.

So characteristic are the buds of every kind of shrub or tree that the experienced woods walker learns to identify each kind either by the shape of the bud, the color of the bud scales or sometimes by the total absence of scales, as on the sumac and papaw. The beech is notable for the beautiful bronze overlapping scales that bring the bud to a slim, aristocratic point. Flowering dogwood has bulb-shaped buds. Those of the magnolia are covered by big scales as silken as a great cat's ears. The scales on the buds of the cottonwood are gummy.

You might judge by these various coverlets that bud scales are for protection against the cold. The fact is that winter buds *are* cold, cold as ice sometimes, for often ice crystals form inside them, without harm to the sleeping bud. Rather do those gummed envelopes or hard scales protect the tender baby tissue from drying out. For wind, which can evaporate even snow—directly, without its first turning to water—may with its rasping tongue blast the bud tissue. That's what makes an early thaw so dangerous, luring the tissues to unfold, then exposing them to the ravages of the wind.

If, just before spring begins, you slice a winter bud in cross section, you'll scarcely need a hand lens to see how artfully nature has packed next summer's green napery. Never are the leaves telescoped in such a way as to crease and break the midvein, which will be both the water main and the spinal strength of the future leaf. Instead, the folding is all done in the soft tissue between the midrib and other principal veins.

In the plum bud the leaf is simply rolled, lengthwise. Leaves of cherry, peach, apple and elm are folded on each side of the midrib. Sweet gum and sycamore leaves, having numerous big ribs like fan sticks radiating from the base, are folded fanwise between the ribs, ready to be flung out later on in the warm summer breezes.

While the snow is still upon the hills and under the shadows of the conifers, the winter buds' temperatures are already mounting up and up. That is because rapid growth has started, and rapid growth, like running, means quick breathing. Quick breathing signifies intensified oxidation, which gives heat. So certain buds may not have to wait for a balmy spell of spring; they may make it come—the tiny heat they give off

The "fur" of these pussy-willow catkins is made up of tiny male flowers; catkins composed of female flowers are gray-green and more compact.

may melt the snow around them. Thus many alpine flowers bloom beneath a crystal dome of ice.

Why do some buds break into bloom in early spring, some in late spring, some only in summer or even autumn? Length of daylight is the governing factor. Modern experiments have shown that some plants are stimulated to flowering by relatively short days and long nights; these are the early bloomers. As the days lengthen and the nights grow shorter, the late spring flowers appear. Long days and brief nights give us summer flowers.

On a tree, what may count is the position of the bud upon the wood. Buds formed on old wood are ready to open in spring. If a bud is formed on new spring wood, it has no time to complete its embryonic life this spring. At best it will unfold in autumn—like the witch hazel, whose green-gold flowers steal forth after most leaves have fallen and the last white-throated sparrow has lisped a sad farewell.

There are deep-set buds, sometimes under the tree's bark, which may lie dormant as long as "Sleeping Beauty." What gardener, nurseryman or orchardist does not know about their marvelous power to live and wait, sometimes for years? When a tree or shrub begins to run to long, sprawling shoots and barren leafage, the wise husbandman prunes back heroically to dormant buds. That's the way to stimulate flowering and fruiting, to put new life and vigor and shapeliness into a rosebush, an apricot tree, a wine-grape vine. The vineyards of Bordeaux and Burgundy are annually cut back until the stock of the stem looks like an old, gnarled witch—all for the sake of the magic that is in dormant buds, forced into growth by the elimination of the others.

So the silver poplar may be cut back because it has become a beautiful nuisance with its probing roots getting into pipes or under pavement. But even if the stump is leveled to the ground, the buds of those roots send up shoots everywhere. Soon your lawn may be a thicket of poplar saplings—despair of the suburbanite, but proof that a short-lived tree like the poplar may have life nearly eternal.

This gift of perpetuity through the bud is exhibited in my own garden. I have a rosy-green little succulent that, I like to say, was given to me by Catherine the Great of Russia. In the impersonal way of plant life this is truly so. For this neat rosette—a kind of hen-and-chickens—by the process of budding puts forth offsets all around it. Some of these Catherine dispatched from her royal grounds to the most famous botanist of her day, Carolus Linnaeus of Sweden, who planted them in the botanical garden at Uppsala University. There, not long ago, one of the little rosettes was given to me. Transplanted to my California home, it seems quite at ease, continuing by budding to set around it ever-new little rosettes. Truly in a bud lies this year, next year, all the years to come.

THE MARVELS OF CROSS-POLLINATION

Rutherford Platt

As you look across a field on a summer day, you see bees buzzing here and there or butterflies flapping, as seemingly aimless as tossed leaves. Yet this apparently capricious activity is part of a routine of scientific precision—the miracle of nature known as cross-pollination.

To the last detail a flower is designed for one great purpose—reproducing its kind. Color, fragrance, form, the length and shape of each part—all fit with perfection into that purpose. When a flower reaches

Attracted by a daisy's color, this American painted lady butterfly is drinking nectar through its long tube tongue. Highly sensitive taste organs in its feet indicate that nectar is present. The pollen that clings to the insect's body may be dropped on the next daisy it visits, to carry on the process of cross-pollination.

the climax of its size and beauty, little undeveloped seeds called ovules are to be found in a swelling at the base of the pistil. Tiny grains of matter called pollen are held in a little box at the end of the stamen.

By themselves ovule and pollen have no future. Only when the two unite can the cycle be completed and a seed formed. But plants, like animals, must obey the laws of eugenics, the most inexorable of which is that inbreeding weakens a race, while crossbreeding strengthens and perpetuates it. To fulfill its purpose, therefore, the pollen must somehow find its way to another flower of the same species, adhere there to the stigma (the sticky tip of the pistil) and then, after a brief time, travel down and fuse with the ovules.

Consider the problem. A target the size of a pinhead (the stigma) must be hit by a microscopic grain of pollen of the right kind at exactly the right time. The brief life of most kinds of pollen requires that it be launched, transported and at work in the new flower within an hour or two. A fraction of an inch

or several miles may have to be traversed. The way insects and flowers combine to accomplish this almost surpasses belief.

One summer day I focused my camera on two square inches of a yarrow flower cluster. In this tiny sector insects landed at the rate of about one every five seconds—or 5760 visitors in an eight-hour day! They scurried around, dipped in here and there with lightning strokes. Ants came at the rate of perhaps one per minute. A wasp zoomed in, looking like a colossus next to the minute insects. When an ant stepped on his toes he kicked like a mule. All this activity on two square inches of flowers!

Bees are the chief engineers in cross-pollination; if it weren't for them, half of our most beautiful flower species would disappear. The honeybee, which uses pollen as food for the larvae, does the most work and covers the most territory; also, she has better pollen baskets than the bumblebee. These baskets consist of rows of stiff bristles on the hind legs; by packing pollen, moistened with honey, between these

These Anthomyid *flies, related to the common housefly,*
are feeding on the pollen of a blue columbine.
After breaking the sacs on the stamen tips and eating
their fill, the flies will be dusted with pollen
grains, with which they may fertilize other blossoms.

hairs the bee can accumulate a ball of pollen sometimes as much as a quarter inch in diameter and containing 100,000 grains.

Bees work at astonishing speed. On the head of a
thistle a honeybee, thrusting her proboscis into one
flower after another, can pollinate at the rate of about
30 flowers per minute—a theoretical possibility of
about 18,000 per day.

Usually a bee gathers pollen from only one kind of
flower at a time. I have watched when there was
every opportunity for a mistake: Vervain and heal-
all, both dark purple, were growing so close together
that bees working on them almost collided in midair.
Not once did I see a bee touch the pollen of the wrong
flower.

The flowers lure insects with the promise of nectar—a sugar sap irresistibly attractive to them. When
the insect arrives at the flower, nature has made arrangements so that it will tread precisely the right
places to operate the pollinating gears. Many petals

This bumblebee and thistle flower are engaged in
a partnership that is mutually beneficial. The thistle
supplies the bumblebee with pollen and nectar;
the bumblebee, by moving from flower to flower of
the same species, fertilizes the thistle with pollen.

have nectar guides—white or yellow streaks, or bright
dots—that converge at the entrance to the nectary.
Sometimes the nectar guide is a bright circle, like the
red center of certain pinks and mallows, or the little
yellow circle at the center of bluets. The tiger lily has
red glands that not only merge as nectar guides but
also glisten deceptively, as though with nectar drops.
In addition, many flowers have a matting of hairs to
give the insect a good footing.

The insect must impregnate the stigma with pollen
from another plant, and then pick up more pollen.
To do this, his proboscis must slide in at exactly the
right angle, the curve of his belly or back must be
just right to pick up or deposit pollen, or possibly his
legs are to be so planted that they will do the trick.
All this is controlled with amazing accuracy.

The great blue lobelia offers one of the most vivid
demonstrations. Go find a patch in late August or
early September; you won't have to wait five minutes
for a bumblebee's arrival. As the bee pushes in head-

first, the whole flower stiffens and widens, and the top two petals fly apart. Between them a long, curving, cylindrical arm nods up and down at just the right angle to touch the bee's back at the proper spot. From the tip of the arm pollen grains are forced out.

Each successive bee gets a fresh charge of pollen on his back. At length, when all the pollen is gone, the stigma emerges from the end of the cylinder and unfurls two fine, sticky branches to receive pollen from another flower. There is nothing hit or miss about this plan: The stigma in this second stage is in exactly the same spot formerly occupied by the pollen; it touches the bee's back exactly where it will pick up pollen from a previously visited flower.

Red clover uses another system. Its closely packed tubular flowers have nectar concealed at the bottom of each tube. To get his head inside, the bumblebee must push the petals apart. As he does so, the pistil springs up, its stigma brushing his face and picking up the dose of pollen he acquired from his last clover. Then the shorter stamens pop up and dust his face with pollen to be carried to the next flower. The size of the bumblebee's head, his weight and the pressure he exerts are all precisely balanced for this flower. The mechanism does not operate accurately for any other kind of insect.

The lady's slipper has a unique plan. Its gorgeous bulbous sac has no apparent entrance, no stamens or pistil to explore. But on the front of this sac the honeybee sees a network of white veins converging on a vertical slit. She butts her way through it into a translucent chamber where she finds, scattered about the floor, little drops of nectar. The bee takes a few swallows and prepares to be off. But that is not so easy: The edges of the sac closed behind her and she can't get out that way. Only at the upper end of the slipper can she exit—and it is a hole barely large enough for her. To squeeze through, she has to pass under an arching stigma that scrapes pollen off her back. And just above this stigma her way is partially blocked by a mass of pollen. This she squeezes under, bringing down a load of grains to be transported to the next lady's slipper.

These are just a few of the astonishing ways by which flowers achieve cross-pollination through insects. Go to the woods and the fields for the rest of the story. You will find that each kind of flower has its own blueprints and schedules. And as you study them you cannot help feeling that sense of incredulous awe which prompted Jean Henri Fabre, the Homer of insects, to say of cross-pollination: "Before these mysteries of life, reason bows and abandons itself to adoration of the Author of these miracles."

LOOK AT LEAVES

Donald Culross Peattie

It is an old trick of mine to think about leaves when I cannot sleep. I let my mind go to the great oak outside my window, with its half acre or so of leaf surface, all of it doing the tree, and me, a silent good. I listen to faraway foliage I have known, to the high seething of the silken needles of pines above a North-woods cottage, or to the heavy rustle of ranch cottonwoods. And I hear again the stiff rattle of palm leaves in the trade wind of a tropic shore.

Take a leaf—take any leaf—and look at it closely. You will see that the two sides are unlike: The upper surface is darker, often glossy and waxen; the underside paler, sometimes with a protective coating of down. Because it is thus two-faced, a leaf can perform its two separate functions: respiration on the lower surface, work with the sun on the upper.

Trees must breathe good sweet oxygen to keep alive. It's oxygen, entering into a man's blood, that kindles the fires of human energy. So with a leaf. It too must take in oxygen in order to release, from

The veins of this beech leaf supply structural support and carry food that the leaf manufactures to the stem, for transport to the trunk and roots.

the sugars and starches packed away in it as stored food, the energy to expand upon the April air and so to lift, by the power of growth, a sapling into a forest giant.

A leaf breathes through the pores on its sheltered underside—so many and minute that they average about 100 to an area the size of the loop in the let-

With the coming of autumn and fewer daylight hours, the production of chlorophyll slows down, and the cells of this maple leaf form a scarlet pigment.

ter "p" on this page. These pores are usually slit-shaped, like the pupils of a cat's eyes—and just as a cat's pupils expand in darkness or contract in bright light, so the pores of a leaf respond to atmospheric changes. On hot, dry days, lest the leaf wilt by water loss through evaporation, its pores may almost close —but not completely or it would smother. When the pores open their widest, the leaf, and so the whole tree, breathes easier.

The pores of a leaf, even at the top of a tall tree, help to bring water up from the roots deep in earth. Evaporation at the pores causes a partial vacuum within the cells, and this suctionlike effect is communicated from cell to cell back through the leaf-stalks and twigs, along the boughs, down the trunk. Boosted by root pressure from below—the same that causes the sap to rise in sugar maples—thread-fine columns of water are thus sucked up, like soda through a straw. And this goes on, dead against gravity, 100 feet up and more, to the breeze-tossed crown of a great oak or maple.

Meanwhile, on the upper side of the leaf, the side exposed to the sunlight, a primal work of the world is going on. For eons before this atomic age the green leaf has been using solar energy to power the greatest industrial plant on earth. No wheel turns in it, no smoke pollutes the air around it; instead, leaves purify the atmosphere. This foliage factory— which first, of course, serves the tree itself, thus giving us timber, pulp and plastics—uses for machinery the green stuff in the leaf called chlorophyll. And with chlorophyll the leaf is able to capture part of that tremendous cascade of atomic energy that falls upon our planet from the sun.

As each tiny particle of solar energy (called a

"photon") collides with the green in the leaf, the energy leaps to the chlorophyll, setting it aglow. With this energy the chlorophyll smashes open the molecules of the water (H_2O) and of the carbon dioxide (CO_2) that the leaf has taken in through its pores from the air, and silently reassembles these atoms of oxygen, carbon and hydrogen into new patterns constituting sugars and starches, the basic foods in the leaf. Since it is with the energy from photons that the leaf synthesizes its foods, the whole

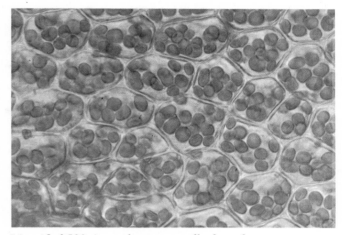

Magnified 500 times, these moss cells show the green ball-like chloroplasts in which nutrients, water and air are converted to living tissue by chlorophyll.

elaborate but speedy process is called "photosynthesis." Throughout the sunlit hours in every part of the world every leaf on every tree is doing this vital work.

No wonder chlorophyll has been called the green blood of the world! It is carried in minute green disks that, like the corpuscles in our own blood, can move about almost as if they led a life of their own. When the sunshine is too strong they can turn edge on, or sink, or flee to the sides of the cells. When the skies grow gray, they may do a half-roll and turn broadside to make the most of the light, or rise to the top of the cell, like fish coming up in cloudy weather to bite.

And leaves help to provide us with the very breath of life. For when the leaf by photosynthesis breaks up those molecules of water and carbon dioxide into their elements, there is a lot of oxygen left over that the leaf itself doesn't use. This it breathes out through its pores, in such quantities that our air is wonderfully freshened. When factory chimneys pour deadly gases into the sky, the oxygen exhaled by leaves helps to purify the polluted air. The winds of the world, forever storming around our spinning globe, thoroughly mix and distribute the leaf-breath. Without that gentle exhalation all animal life on earth would, like a candle lowered into a well full of carbon dioxide, long ago have flickered out.

Thus the man who has a fine old shade tree over his roof lives under a sort of oxygen tent. Moreover, the foliage not only tempers the wind and shuts out the glare, but somewhat air-conditions his house. For the air around leaves is faintly cooled by the evaporation from them, just as a lake or river makes the neighborhood cooler. You feel this sudden, delicious coolness when on a hot day you enter into a wood.

So, summer long, a green, serene benediction is upon us. In autumn every leaf seems to have put on a new color. Not so; the reds and yellows are the natural pigments of certain foods stored by leaves that are merely masked by chlorophyll in the summer. We see orange in fall foliage when red shines through yellow, and mauve when red begins to change chemically. Frost has nothing to do with it. It is the leaves themselves that end their own lives in this blaze of glory. Each leaf produces a growth of callous cells at the base of its stalk; this cuts off the water supply and makes a tear-line, like the perforations on a sheet of stamps, so that any breeze may pull the leaf off, or it may fall of its own weight. In the end, it will turn to mold, enriching earth, or, raked into some bonfire, may rise again in a last blue twirl of pungent smoke.

PLANTS THAT EAT INSECTS

Jean George

One summer my small son Craig brought home from a nearby marsh a strange but oddly familiar plant—a whorl of green antlers trimmed generously with tiny baubles. We put it in a bowl and placed it on the dining-room table. Presently Craig announced that some small water fleas were rowing around in the bowl, apparently brought in on the plant's roots. I rushed to remove them.

As I reached for one sand-colored flea, it flipped away into a bauble. I waited—but it did not come out. I began to wonder. Could this be the marsh plant my father and I had come upon when I was a child—the plant that catches insects and devours them? Carefully I opened the bauble, and behind a tiny hinged door I spotted the entrapped water flea. Then Craig pointed out a mosquito wiggler, caught

by its tail, slowly being sucked into another tiny trap. And thus we began our investigations into the strange behavior of carnivorous plants.

Several days later a plant expert confirmed my guess. "That is a bladderwort," he said, "one of the most amazing plants in the world. It's related to the famous pitcher plants and Venus's-flytraps that live in marshes and swamps."

The botanist explained that carnivorous plants, usually considered rare and hard to find, actually are common throughout the world. "Every section of the earth," he said, "has some kind of pitcher plant growing in bog and swamp areas, where the soil is poor. To survive, these plants catch and digest insects, and so receive essential nitrogen. The array of lures and snares they have evolved is amazing. To me carnivorous plants are even more interesting than animals."

As I studied and lived with these plants I understood what he meant. From a botanical supplier I bought some Venus's-flytraps and planted them in a terrarium in sphagnum moss and sand wet down with distilled water. (They will not grow on a more nutritious diet.)

Within a few weeks I had seven green bear-traps, each about half an inch long, complete with teeth. Slowly the traps opened and revealed vivid beefsteak-red, juicy-looking bait cells. Then three threadlike triggers arose on either side of each open trap, and the traps were set.

We put several houseflies in the terrarium and within four minutes one of them flew down to the bait. Instantly it was caught, for in entering the trap the fly touched the triggers that spring the hinge. In less than half a second the jaws snapped shut. With the fly safely enclosed, the trap slowly continued to tighten on the victim.

Ten days later the trap opened again. The fly had been devoured; only the hard bases of the wings remained. The plant tossed them to the ground and set itself again.

According to Francis Ernest Lloyd, who during his lifetime was an outstanding authority on carnivorous plants, the traps operate about three times before they turn black and die. By then they have done their work of providing food for the development of the plant.

We experimented with our traps. On one we placed a tiny piece of glass. In five hours the trap closed, but instead of opening after ten days (the normal digesting time), the trap reopened, spit out the piece of glass and reset itself within 24 hours.

Each species of carnivorous plant has invented a different kind of trap to catch its prey. But they all have

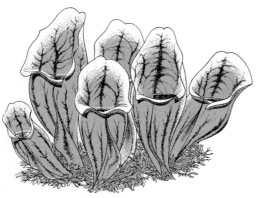

A jumping spider waits to seize any insect that might be attracted to this pitcher plant. A small web spun at the mouth of the pitcher keeps the spider from sliding down its slippery throat and into a pool of fluid so deadly that the plant's victims are not only drowned but dissolved.

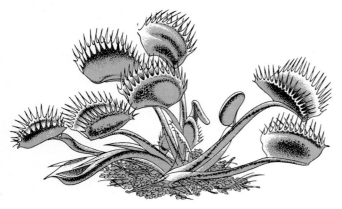

Lured by a compelling fragrance, this honeybee (below) has touched trigger hairs lining the outside of a Venus's-flytrap. With startling suddenness, the flytrap has snapped shut and trapped the bee. Now enzymes and digestive juices the plant secretes will convert the insect into nourishing substances.

This doomed wasp is held fast by a sundew's sticky spines. Like most insect-eating plants, the sundew grows in poor soil and obtains nutrients from insects and other small prey. But, like all green plants, it also manufactures food from nonliving substances and can exist for a while without a "meat" diet.

one eerie thing in common: Their "stomachs" have much the same enzymes and acids as are found in animal stomachs.

The trap most commonly used to get food to these stomachs is the pitfall evolved by the pitcher plants. It is designed to trap flies and moths that usually dine in the attractive corollas of flowers whose heads hang down. Pitcher plants look not unlike lilies or trumpet flowers; some smell like violets or honey.

But the similarity stops there. For where the flower has steps for the insects to climb in and out, the pitcher plant has a one-way staircase that leads to the edge of the pitfall. Once there, the insect cannot return; stiff inward-bent bristles bar his exit. Lured by strong odors, the victim has no choice but to continue until he plunges into the pit. There he is drowned in an acid pool and then digested. Some pitcher plants in Oregon and California add a refinement—a lid that closes on the prey until the insect is devoured.

Ants are a great delicacy, but because they are skilled at walking on all types of surface upside

down, some plants have had to adapt their trapping devices. Brazilian plants have evolved a lobster-pot type of trap. The most beautiful of these is held within a miniature Chianti flask. Winding down toward the trap is a spiral staircase that grows smaller and smaller and is baited with scents irresistible to an ant. The ant follows the seductive trail until it can't turn around. It goes on to the bottom, steps on a treadle, and stiff plant bars close behind it to lock it irrevocably in the plant's prison.

Several carnivorous plants have evolved a quite efficient "flypaper." Among them are the butterworts, found all over the Northern Hemisphere in moist, mossy pockets. Lying flat on the ground, glittering like the points of tasty honey stars, the unobtrusive ovate leaves wait until a moth or bee alights to feast. When the feet touch a leaf, the plant exudes a sticky mucilage to hold the insect. This flow is followed by a dose of acid containing a digestive enzyme that overpowers the insect. Then slowly, neatly, the edges of the leaf roll over and cover the victim. The butterwort takes 24 hours to roll up, three to five days to devour the food, and one day for the leaf to uncurl. Then the "flypaper" is readied once more.

Other flypaper-type plants are the beautiful sundews that look like pincushions and grow in most swamps and bogs. These are sweetly scented—and sticky as household cement. My husband watched a wasp get stuck on one last summer in Maryland. He says that the wasp lighted on four of its six feet, realized the texture was not right and tried to lift up the front two. In doing so, it put down the rear two, and was stuck on all six. It pulled and tipped. A wing went out; it stuck deep among the spines and pins. The wasp bit, and stuck its jaws. Then the glittering heads of the pins began to curl over the wasp. By the end of the day the insect was still, and the plant tentacles, curled daintily over it, were dining.

One of the deadliest plant traps is the fungus that forms nooses to snare eelworms on their way to destroy wheat seedlings. The fungus grows on the damp ground, straight up like a pin, silver in the sunlight. Then a growing branch bends down and fastens itself to its own base, making a tiny noose. There may be many nooses in a group, so that sooner or later an eelworm, writhing over the ground, will get its head in one of them. Immediately the loop tightens. The worm tries to pull back. The noose grows tighter and tighter until the worm is dead. Now the loop sends out tiny runners to cover the worm—and eat it.

Craig and I read in Lloyd's book, *The Carnivorous Plants*, about the bladderwort on our table. We learned that it could regulate water pressure, suck, and close doors. Through a magnifying glass we could see the green bristles that activate the trapping mechanisms. This tiny chlorophyll trapdoor is set by water pressure; the change in pressure inside and outside the bauble sucks the insect into the chamber, the green cells working like a pump as they change the water level and draw the creature in and in. When the prey is within the chamber, the door swings shut and hairs bolt it; it is now leakproof, so that the enzymes that aid in digesting the victim cannot be diluted by outside water.

Charles Darwin wrote one of the first books on the insect-eating plants. He was intrigued by them and asked, with experiments of all kinds, "What kind of intelligence is this?" Gazing at our innocent-looking bladderwort one morning, Craig echoed Darwin's question: "Do you suppose these plants can think?"

"No," I answered, "but the fact that a single green plant *acts* as if it can think is a miracle in itself."

THE WORLD'S MOST EXOTIC NUISANCE

James Poling

Misled by its lovely flower, a romanticist once described the water hyacinth as "a lavender symphony wreathing the world in beauty." But to the army of scientists who are trying to keep it from overrunning the inland waterways of the Gulf Coast states, southern Asia, Africa, South America and Australia, the water hyacinth is more aptly known as the purple curse. For it is not only one of the globe's most widely distributed freshwater weeds; it is

an aquatic plant whose ugly behavior is as striking as its beauty.

The water hyacinth multiplies with unbelievable rapidity. In a single growing season, ten small hyacinths can increase to more than 600,000 closely intertwined plants—a solid acre of exotic, menacing beauty—forming a mat so dense that it weighs 180 tons, so buoyant (because of air-filled bladders the size of golf balls at the base of each plant) that it can support a man's weight. Such a mat can grow and spread until it covers a body of water as a crust covers a pie, sealing it so tight that fish and other aquatic life suffocate from lack of oxygen, clogging it so that boats can't fight their way through. Today millions of acres of lakes, ponds, streams, rivers, canals and swamps throughout the world are encrusted with the devastating weed.

What the hyacinth costs in human misery and economic waste, no one knows. Its mats are ideal incubators for malarial mosquitoes. The fish they kill are sometimes a native population's sole source of protein; they drive wild fowl from their feeding grounds. Wherever water hyacinths are found—be it in the Sudan, Australia, Guyana, Fiji, Louisiana or Thailand—they clog drainage and irrigation ditches, causing heavy agricultural losses. The Rio Light Company, one of Brazil's leading hydroelectricity producers, must constantly fight the hyacinths that invade its turbines.

The weed's malicious activities are almost endless. Along the Gulf Coast, drivers have pulled off highways onto what appeared to be a solid shoulder, only to find themselves, or to be found, at the bottom of a hyacinth-covered drainage ditch. High waters and strong winds have rolled hyacinth mats into great dams, producing floods that have isolated villages along the Congo and the Upper Nile.

Man has only himself to blame for the spread of the water hyacinth. The plant stayed in its native home in South America until 1884, when it was sent to the New Orleans Exposition as part of a horticultural display. Enchanted by its flower, a few gardeners took seedlings home to their ponds and fountains, later tossed surplus plants into nearby streams. A visitor from Florida carried back a pailful to beautify the St. Johns River. Floods, hurricanes and currents did the rest. Within six years, the hyacinth had spread from Florida to Texas; later, it moved as far north as Virginia, as far west as California.

The plant reached Australia in 1895, again probably transported by someone infatuated with its beauty. It was present in India by 1902. The invasion of Africa began about 1950. The plant was first seen in the Congo River near Brazzaville, introduced, it is said, by a missionary. It took only six years for the weed to spread along a thousand-mile sweep of the Congo and its tributaries, as well as into the Sudan, Uganda, Ethiopia, Rhodesia and Malawi.

The U.S. Army Corps of Engineers has been waging war on the hyacinth since 1899 when Congress first ordered an attack on the plant, which even then was threatening navigation on the inland waterways of the Gulf states. The first weapon the Engineers employed was the pitchfork—but the flowers grew faster than men could fork them up on the land. Then came dynamite. It failed, too. The Corps tried arsenic, but the poison killed cattle, crops and hyacinths with equal ease. One scientist even tried a flamethrower. The next growing season the burned plants were not only the first to sprout; they also grew nine inches taller than adjoining plants!

In 1951 the Marine Growth Control Section of the New Orleans District Corps of Engineers put into service a contraption resembling a seagoing lawnmower. The rotating saw blades on its prow cut a 40-foot swath through a mat. Unfortunately many of the mangled plants floated off to grow two or three new stalks, where previously there had been only one. But the mowing machine at least opened channels to shipping—for a season.

The postwar development of chemical herbicides finally produced an effective anti-hyacinth weapon—2,4-D. Spraying this chemical on the pest by hand, boat, plane and marsh buggy—at a cost of $25 to $50 per acre—hyacinth fighters have at last brought the weed under control in the two most badly infested states, Florida and Louisiana. In Louisiana, 87 men and a small flotilla of spray boats have reduced half a million water-acres of hyacinths to 110,000. And whereas the Corps of Engineers once had to struggle to clear 300 miles of the state's 10,000 miles of clogged waterways, it can now keep 3000 miles open with comparative ease. Of the 63,000 acres in Florida that were critically infested before 2,4-D, 55,000 have now been sprayed, and the state's previously clogged waterways are almost always passable.

Even so, the two states have no hope of *eradicating* the hyacinth with the herbicide. As one of Florida's leading experts, John Woods, says, "We spray, yes, but the plant keeps growing in regions that are practically inaccessible to us." In Louisiana's Atchafalaya River basin alone, for instance, there are 75,000 acres of hyacinth-infested swamps, virtually impenetrable because of their dense stands of cedar, cypress and moss-hung oak. During every growing season these swamps discharge a steady stream of new plants into open water, where they are free to float off and reinfest the cleared waterways.

Meanwhile no one is quite sure what the cumulative effect of 2,4-D will be on fish, wildlife and crops. Hoping to overcome such problems, scientists are trying other experiments in hyacinth control. One entomologist, citing an imported Australian beetle that cleared 500,000 acres of West Coast rangeland of Klamath weed, thinks it possible that the hyacinth can be wiped out by its natural enemies, and the search is on. In Uruguay scientists have found a beetle that eats hyacinth leaves and two moths that bore into its roots and facilitate rot. In India Dr. V. P. Rao is experimenting with a grasshopper and two species of caterpillars known to subsist on hyacinth.

Even if man should finally rid the world of the water hyacinth, our rejoicing might be short-lived. For the natural law of plant succession decrees that when one species of plant dies or is destroyed, another shall immediately rise to take its place—with no guarantee that the new plant won't be equally troublesome.

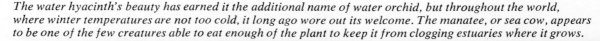

The water hyacinth's beauty has earned it the additional name of water orchid, but throughout the world, where winter temperatures are not too cold, it long ago wore out its welcome. The manatee, or sea cow, appears to be one of the few creatures able to eat enough of the plant to keep it from clogging estuaries where it grows.

Chapter Nine

A Treasury of Trees

*Among the trees are to be found the tallest, the heaviest, the oldest and,
for mankind, perhaps the most bountiful of living things. From the
substance of trees we derive food, fuel and shelter; from their grace and
enduring beauty we draw inspiration and a sense of spiritual renewal.*

THE WONDER OF WOOD

Donald Culross Peattie

Wood is man's best friend. Most versatile of all living substances, it held him in his cradle; was the frame of the bed he came to, rejoicing, the log upon his hearth; and will make his last home. It was the murmuring tree above his childhood play, and the roof over the first house he called his own. It is even the page he is reading at this moment.

Living, a tree sweetens the air where it breathes. It lays the dust and tempers the wind. When it is felled, sawed and seasoned, it lays bare the hidden beauty of its heart, in figures and grains more lovely than the most premeditated design.

Touch any object made of wood—the tabletop of bright maple, the chopping bowl of yellow birch, a paneled wall of knotty pine, the lean strength of an ash rake handle, a basket of woven willow splits or a tobacco pipe of brier. Pass your fingers sensitively over this wood, then press your full palm upon its firmness. Compared with metal or clay or stone, it seems warm still, still living out its useful days.

With its 1000-odd native species of trees, the United States started out with the greatest forest heritage that ever fell to the lot of a lucky people. So wood has gone into the very fiber of the nation. The first exports back to England from the Jamestown colony came from the forest—mighty pines for masts, pitch, turpentine, black walnut. By the time George Washington had inherited Mount Vernon (a wooden house, like millions of American homes) and planted around it now-mighty elms and tulip poplars, the country's wood-wise pioneer ways were already 150 years old.

When British shot fell back from the live-oak sides of the frigate *Constitution,* she got her name *Old Ironsides.* When the backwoods boys fought beside Robert E. Lee in their homespuns dyed with butternut, they were known as Butternuts, and that tree became a synonym for tattered valor. The cabin where Lincoln was born was made of the logs of that grand old tree, the American white oak. The rails that he split were black walnut.

Wood fired the racing steamboats on the Mississippi and fed the first railroads. The treeless plains were spanned on ties cut from eastern forests. On rims of hickory and spokes of oak, pioneers rolled west to the Pacific. There new woods came to hand —redwoods and Douglas fir 300 feet high, tremendous sugar and ponderosa pines, and gigantic western cedars, timbers such as European man had never seen before.

And every kind of tree has its own virtues. Some are perfect in their capacity to absorb sudden shock, like the ash so carefully selected for baseball bats, or the persimmon of golf-club heads. For airplane construction no wood in the world equals the light Sitka spruce. Most cabinet woods are chosen because they shrink little in seasoning. On the other hand, early settlers learned to fit seasoned hickory dowels into chair seats of green sugar maple: When the maple shrinks it clasps the hickory leg in a grip that nothing can loosen.

The same species of wood may have uses ranging from the trivial to the sublime. The little box that holds berries in the market is made of deal. But when you camped beneath its fragrant boughs you called it spruce. Once a year it becomes your Christmas tree. The newspaper publisher calls it pulp and on its macerated fiber he flings at your door each morning the news of the world. When the violinist's bow drops on the strings, the note thrums down through the bridge to the violin's rich, soft belly— made of spruce.

The wood that holds the graphite in your pencil is probably eastern red cedar; its dark pyramidal outline may be seen along the stone fence of any New England pasture. For sharpening with equal ease in all directions no other wood can quite take its place. Birch is too hard, spruce too splitty. Only eastern red cedar is perfect.

The shingles on your house are probably made of another kind of cedar, the western red—the same kind of tree that the Northwest Indians used for their giant canoes, single logs hollowed out by fire to hold 40 people. The Indians used this wood for their totem poles, too, not only because it endures so well the sun and rain but because the tree grows so high. Western red cedar is one of the most gigantic growths on the planet—a king of the forest yesterday, today a roof above your head.

But of all American woods none has been more significant than white pine. Nowhere else is there a wood so light that grows so tall. Within 30 years of their arrival, the Pilgrims were exporting white pine all the way to Madagascar. A single tree made a mast tall as a ship could carry, yet so light it was never top-heavy. When the English Navy sailed to some of its greatest victories in the 18th century, it spread its sails on masts and yards of New England white pine. No wonder that the tallest pines on the Crown lands of America were blazed with "the king's broad arrow," to warn the colonists that these were reserved for the Royal Navy. It was an offense punishable with fines and floggings to cut such a tree. You can imagine how much attention the New England patriots paid to *that!*

White pine built New England's loveliest colonial mansions and churches. A favorite of the carpenter, it works smoothly under the plane, and shrinks or swells little when properly seasoned. I use a match made of it to light my pipe; it burns readily but not with a flare-up like pitch pine. When you blow it out it goes out, not lingering as a dangerous coal, like hickory. Fleets were launched to export white pine, railroads were bent to great stands of it, mushroom cities rose in its clearings and it founded great fortunes. Under its boughs evolved the American lumberjack.

For toughness the pioneers turned to hickory. Not steel itself is as shock-resistant. And the handles of most hammers, axes, hatchets, picks and sledges are still made of hickory. As a fuel a cord of hickory almost equals in thermal units a ton of anthracite, and epicures will have no smoked hams but those cured over green hickory coals, so subtle is their aroma.

Every American soldier, from Washington's armies to Westmoreland's, has known the feel of a native black-walnut rifle stock under his palm. Under hard usage, walnut does not splinter; instead of growing rougher with handling, it becomes smoother. In their increasing scramble for walnut, hardwood buyers now make a farm-to-farm quest. Once the log is at the sawmill it is carefully watched for sign of figured grain. If any turns up, the saws are stopped, and the flitch of wood moved up to the veneer knives. These will pare off sheets less than 1/32 of an inch thick. It is said that one single black-walnut log, one showing a uniquely beautiful figure, sold in the veneer trade for $20,000 wholesale.

You and I can get to know the commoner kinds of woods as we learn the faces of our neighbors. I asked a cabinetmaker one day if I might have any scraps left over from his work. We went over a basketful of them together, till I could recognize Douglas fir by its heavy growth layers of orange wood on a yellow background, and redwood by its lightness, its warm hue and the glossy sheen. He taught me rosewood with its sunset streaks of color, chocolate-brown walnut, ruddy applewood, magnolia of a driftwood gray, and fooled me with a heavy block of pink wood that proved to be mahogany before it is given the deep cherry-colored stain. I have added to my collection of wood blocks until I know many a wood even under stains and paints. My nose is curious, too, about the smell of a burning log. Every section of America has its particular hearth perfume—piñon smoke in Santa Fe, fat pine in Carolina, mesquite floating out of desert chimneys in the Southwest.

For the final gift of wood to us is its sacrifice on our home altars. The companionable whisper of a burning log is the teakettle song of the moisture in it; its aroma rises from the rich oils and gases stored up through its living years. Sometimes as the flames penetrate to a hidden storehouse of the wood, the essences ignite in a sudden blue tongue of hissing flame. Gums and resins are driven seething through the cracks in the bark. Slowly into flame go the cellulose, wood oils and gases. The mineral constituents such as potash and calcium remain as ash.

Form and plan are in the very structure of wood from the moment it begins to grow. The tree has the power of reproduction and the power to repair injuries and go on with a stout heart. It can overcome obstacles, split rocks apart, travel far in thirsty search for water. It can adjust to circumstances. It can endure, with an immortality all its own: Wooden piles under the streets of Venice have been found intact after 1000 years; white cedar in the swamps of eastern Virginia has lain buried an estimated 3000 years, yet it is being dug up today and sawed into boards that may last another thousand.

Each tree, too, is an individual; no two are alike, nor two boards from the same tree. Each piece of wood, with its grain and rings, is as different as your fingerprints are from those of anyone else in the world. Wood reminds us, in its pliancy and resilience, of human flesh and, yes, even human spirit.

Say if you like wood has no thoughts, and no tongue to speak them. But let him who says this look in his own heart and produce for us a thought that will warm the hearth or endure 1000 years.

BRIDE OF SPRING—
THE DOGWOOD

Donald Culross Peattie

Loveliest event of spring is the blossoming of America's favorite little tree. Like brides and bridesmaids the dogwoods line the roadsides, upholding on slim arms their sprays of starry bloom. No wonder that, in all the land, only the remote and lofty redwoods have as many organized friends.

Both in the wild and planted, the dogwood is rooted deep in America's past. Virginia has made its blossom her state flower, and you see it everywhere in the Old Dominion, from Jamestown Island, where the first white settlers landed, to the Blue Ridge. There is dogwood on the battlefield of Fredericksburg, and in the woods about Appomattox Court House.

Jefferson planted it at Monticello, and Washington at Mount Vernon. The approach to that hallowed home has been in recent years lined with a thousand flowering dogwoods, all the way from Alexandria to the gates—a spectacle as fair as the blossoming of the famous cherry trees in the capital city. Indeed, as a thank-you to Japan for the cherries, Uncle Sam sent dogwoods, and the Japanese—connoisseurs of gardening for 20 centuries—flock to the parks of Tokyo when these come into bloom.

The flowers appear on the tree before the leaves, blooming on the winter-naked wood. They are borne in long flat sprays along the branches, turning their faces candidly toward the sky. It is no simple flower; only at the heart bloom what the botanist considers the true flowerlets—tiny and greenish-yellow. Around this modest cluster gleam the great petals (bracts to the botanist), four to six of them, snowy white or softly pink.

But its very perfection has cost the dogwood dear. Who hasn't seen the Sunday motorist with pathetic branches of dogwood, the petals already drooping

The delicate blossoms of the eastern dogwood appear in spring just as the first green leaves unfold. Eastern dogwood differs from its western cousin by having notched instead of smoothly rounded bracts.

and discolored? After hours in the drying wind and sun on the highway, all that is left is the corpse of stolen beauty. Such field-picked dogwood is stolen not only from the owner of the land but from all the passersby who might have enjoyed the bright loveliness of it, this year and in the years to come.

It was to halt this plunder that the Wild Flower Preservation Society, with headquarters in Washington, set out in 1924 to capture public opinion. Newspaper and magazine articles and editorials, motion-picture films and posters urged the public to leave the dogwood for others to enjoy. So enlightened, people became ashamed to despoil the roadsides.

Not for its beauty only has dogwood a price on its head. Its resistance to sudden shock is one of the highest of all woods. Therefore 90 percent of all the dogwood cut goes into the textile industry, where it becomes those shuttles that are hurled at top speed to carry the weft through the warp. A wood used thus must not crack under continuous impact, and it must wear smoother, not rougher, lest it fret the warp. These qualifications dogwood perfectly meets.

Only in the virgin forests can be found trees suitable for shuttles—long, straight and knot-free. And so intense has been the cut that few big stands remain; today the largest are beyond the Mississippi, in Arkansas and Texas. Dogwood falls to the ax now chiefly in pinelands destined to be cut over; the lumberman first goes through the woods and takes out all of these precious little trees. But when the land is cleared, unless it is given to the plow the dogwood has a way of venturing back.

It is helped in its progress by the birds, which scatter the seed after they have feasted on its cheerful red berries. The berries are relished by 90 species, among them the beloved bobwhite. This is as good a reason as any for planting dogwood, and another is its loveliness in autumn, when the leaves turn crimson on the upper surface and frosty white underneath, with the berries gleaming a cheerful scarlet in clusters like jewels.

As a tree companion the dogwood is faultless; its roots do not wander where they should not, its boughs do not drop litter. It will not darken a room, yet needs no pruning. Hardly free of pest and disease, it may begin flowering when it is only four feet high. Little wonder that communities are forming dogwood associations, to plant, protect and publicize this beloved tree.

A dogwood tree that was very possibly planted by Washington's own hand still stands at Mount Vernon near the northwest corner of the flower garden. Measured a few years ago, it was found to be 25 feet high and to have a trunk one foot in diameter. In Washington's diary for 1785 we find that he celebrated his birthday by moving several young dogwoods from the forest to "the shrubbery on the north side of the grass plat." And on March 1 he planted, "close to the old cherry tree near the south garden-house," a circle of dogwoods with a redbud in the center for contrast of the rosy blossoms with the white.

Two kinds of flowering dogwood trees grow in the United States, one in the eastern states and one on the Pacific Coast; together they are native to 38 out of the 50 states. Flowering dogwoods grow naturally nowhere else save along the southern coastline of British Columbia and in Ontario just above Lake Erie.

Pink-flowering dogwood became known to commercial horticulture about 85 years ago. Thomas Meehan, a great grower of his day, discovered a branch with lovely rose-blushed petals on a white-flowering tree growing on the hills above Wissahickon Creek (now part of Fairmount Park in Philadelphia). When he saw that it kept on "coming pink" for several years, he propagated it by grafting.

In one of the most magnificent displays of dogwood in the world—at Valley Forge—white drifts of blossom lie each spring upon the hills. Where those ragged, starving heroes trod the snows with bleeding feet, the pink boughs mingle with the white. And every Maytime thousands of Americans make a pilgrimage to this national shrine to see how immortal glory can be made visible.

THE "BIG TREE" FOREST KING

Donald Culross Peattie

The mightiest of living things is the giant sequoia, or Sierra "big tree." After 30 centuries of growth, *Sequoia gigantea* is practically a geological phenomenon. Only its closest kin, the redwood of the California coast ranges, approaches it in girth.

The home of the giant sequoia lies between 4000 and 8500 feet altitude on the western slopes of the Sierra Nevada. There, snow drifts among the titans up to 30 feet deep—a mere white anklet to such trees. The summers are dry; if rain does fall it is likely to come with violent thunderstorms and lightning bolts that have been seen to rive a sequoia from crown to roots. Those who know the species best maintain that the tree never dies of disease or senility. If it survives predators in its infancy and the hazard of fire in youth, only a bolt from heaven will end its centuries of life.

The province of the giant sequoias extends for 260 miles. You will not happen upon any single "big tree"; giant sequoias grow only in groves of five to 1000. The Giant Forest, the Mariposa, Calaveras and General Grant groves are perhaps the most famous and accessible. It is all too likely that nature will never spontaneously create any more groves.

To see the "big trees" you must travel far and climb high. It is a day's run by car from San Francisco or Los Angeles. Your car engine will be boiling by the time you see the red firs and white of the upper forests. Then come the Jeffrey pines, clad in great orange plates of bark like the leathern shields of Homeric soldiers. Somber Douglas firs darken the late afternoon as with oncoming night. At last the sugar pines with rugged purple trunks, the mightiest pines in all the world, close about you.

It will be dusk, no doubt, when you reach the giant groves. And the forest will be still, yet watchfully alive. A deer may put an inquisitive black muzzle in

your out-held hand. It will be a long moment before you realize that the vast shadow behind the little doe is not shade but a tree trunk so gigantic that you cannot comprehend at first that this is a living thing. Were a cross section of that great bole put down in a city street, it would block it from curb to curb. That mighty bough, the lowest one, is still so high above the ground that it would stretch out over the top of a 12-story building. If it were cut off and stood in the ground, that bough would appear as a tree 70 feet high and seven feet in diameter at the base.

Yet the trees conceal their true gigantism by the very perfection of proportion. Each part—breadth at base, spread of boughs, thickness of trunk, shape of crown—is in calm Doric harmony with the rest.

On second view, by morning light, the impression of the giant sequoias is not so much of outsize as of color. The ruddy trunks are richly bright. The metallic green of the foliage is the gayest of all Sierra conifers. Unlike the misty dimness of the redwood groves with their overarching canopy, the sunlight here reaches right to the floor. Instead of the hush of the redwoods, you hear among the "big trees" the lordly racket of the pileated woodpeckers at their irreverent carpentry.

The General Sherman is usually considered the all-round exemplary giant sequoia. It is 272 feet high, has a basal circumference of 102 feet; at 16 feet above the ground it is better than 24 feet in diameter, and raises a clean shaft clear of any boughs for a height of 130 feet. In the North Calaveras Grove lies prone the tree called Father of the Forest; inside its hollow trunk a man once rode horseback without having to bend his head. Though the crown of this tree is gone, the taper of the trunk indicates that the Father of the Forest stood 400 feet high—which would have made it the tallest tree in the world.

The "big trees" of North Calaveras Grove were discovered one spring day in 1852 by a miner, A. T. Dowd, who pursued a grizzly bear far up into tall timber. When he encountered the "big trees," his astonishment was so great that he allowed the bear to get away. His fellow miners came, incredulous, and beheld 50 acres of what was later called the North Calaveras Grove, covered with trees as tall as 330 feet.

In 1853 John Lindley, an English botanist, in a formal botanical publication named the mighty conifer *Wellingtonia gigantea* after the Duke of Wellington,

Dwarfing the man standing near its base, the General Grant sequoia soars 267 feet and measures 40 feet in diameter. This snow-capped titan may be 35 centuries old—and it is still growing.

victor of Waterloo, who had died the previous fall. Loud was the patriotic anguish of American botanists. But fortunately the generic name of *Sequoia* for the coast redwoods had been published in Germany six years before *Wellingtonia*, and when it was realized that the "big trees" too are sequoias, Americans were satisfied. For the name had been bestowed in honor of Sequoyah, the great Cherokee chief who devoted his life to developing an Indian alphabet and teaching others to read it.

In the early 1850's a disappointed gold-seeker, G. H. Woodruff of New York, collected seeds from the "big tree" cones in an empty snuffbox and paid $25 to send them east to the nursery firm of Ellwanger & Barry in Rochester, New York. From these seeds sprang 4000 tiny trees. They did not sell very well in the eastern states, but in England where they were retailed as Wellingtonias they sold rapidly. Botanical gardens in England, France and Germany wanted specimens. Cities planted avenues of them. Soon every man of wealth or title thought he must have a specimen for his grounds. "The great event of the year 1864," wrote Tennyson's son, "was the visit of Garibaldi to the Tennysons, an incident of which was the planting of a Wellingtonia by the great Italian." Eventually Ellwanger & Barry paid Woodruff $1036 as his share in the profits on a snuffboxful of seeds.

Californians, even then unabashed in the claims they made for their state, asserted that the "big trees"

Incongruously, the cones of the giant sequoia are only two or three inches long. Beneath each scale of the cone is a pinhead-sized seed that may someday grow to a 300-foot tree.

were old when the pyramids were abuilding. John Muir counted the annual rings on the biggest stump he ever saw and claimed he had found over 4000. But accurate ring counts in recent times have not put the age of any logged tree at more than 3100 years.

Yet 30 centuries of life are awe-inspiring. There is something comforting about handling a section of sequoia wood that seems scarcely less living now than when it grew before the time of Christ. Somewhere about two inches inside the bark of a tree recently cut will be the rings laid down more than a century ago— in 1849, year of the gold fever. And it is humbling to note that those particular rings may be 15 feet from the center of the tree, the starting point of its growth.

Why, out of a world of trees, do these live so long? If there is any one answer, it lies in the very sap of life itself. The sap of the "big trees" is nonresinous, hence only slightly inflammable. Though fire is a deadly peril to the thin-barked young sequoias, when bark has formed on the old specimens it may be a foot or more thick and practically as fire-resistant as asbestos. The only way that fire can penetrate is when some more inflammable tree falls as a brand against a giant sequoia and, fanned to a blowtorch by the mountain wind, sears its way through to the wood. Even then fire seems never to consume a great old specimen. The repair of fire damage begins at once, even if the wound is so wide that it would take a thousand years to cover it. The high tannin content of the sap has the same healing action that tannic acid has on our flesh when we apply it to a burn. It is highly antiseptic, deadly to the spores of infecting fungus growth.

A giant sequoia waits 175 or 200 years before it first flowers, perhaps the most delayed sexual maturity in all nature. When it comes, the trees are loaded with millions of male and female conelets from November to late in February. The greeny-gold pollen showers all over the giant's body and drifts in swirls upon the snow. A single tree will bear hundreds of thousands of cones when in the full vigor of its life.

The flaky seed which produces all these tons of vegetation is so small that it takes 3000 of them to make one ounce. There are from 96 to 304 seeds to a cone, and the cones themselves are almost ridiculously small —hardly larger than big leather buttons. They do not mature until the end of the second season; and not till the end of the third, at the earliest, do they open their scales in dry weather and loose the seeds which drift but a little way from the parent tree. Perhaps only 15 percent of the seeds have the vitality to sprout. And long before they do they are attacked by squirrels and jays. Many are lost in the duff of the forest floor. Of a million seeds on a tree in autumn, perhaps only one is destined to sprout when the snow water and the sun of the late mountain spring touch it with quickening fingers.

The tiny seedlings are attacked from below by cutworms, above by armies of black wood ants. Ground squirrels and chipmunks, finches and sparrows cock a bright eye at them and pull them up for a toothsome salad. Deer browse them by the thousands. If a seedling survives its first year, it may face the centuries with some confidence.

All the properties of sequoia wood save one are inferior to those of nearly every other timber tree. It is so brittle that when a "big tree" falls to earth the green timber often cracks both lengthwise and across, into fragments fit only for lead pencils. Its single virtue is that it lasts forever. In consequence, it was early sought by lumbermen for shingles, flumes, fence stakes and poles.

The giant groves promised ready fortunes, by the look of them. So logging railroads were hurried up the mountains, mills were set up, and the Lilliputian lumberjacks fell to work among these woody Gullivers. In this wise was accomplished the destruction of the Converse Basin grove, probably finer than any now standing, and the slaughter went on till there remained here but a single great specimen. This the superintendent spared in order that it might be named after himself, the Boole Tree. Today in the Converse Basin there is not one seedling sequoia to give hope that this species will ever grow there again. Instead there are thousands of logs that were never utilized, because they proved too big or too costly to handle, millions of board feet gone to waste because the wood smashed to bits in its fall. The whole ghastly enterprise ended in financial failure.

The long battle to save the "big trees" was begun by Colonel George Stewart, a newspaperman of Visalia, California. He was joined by public-spirited citizens, by newspapers and magazines in California and finally in the eastern states. When fraudulent surveys and applications for possession of the sequoia groves were made under the old Timber and Stone Law, Colonel Stewart brought about suspensions of the applications. When a Secretary of the Interior lifted the suspensions, 40 men of Visalia marched into the nearby groves to file private claims and so save the trees for the nation. Victory came in 1890 when Sequoia and General Grant national parks were created. In 1940 General Grant Park was absorbed by Kings Canyon National Park. With other fine sequoia groves in Yosemite National Park, Sequoia National Park and Tahoe National Forest, the future of the king of trees seems assured.

GAZE IN WONDER AT A TREE

Donald Culross Peattie

The greatest force in the natural world is growth. And the noblest example of that force is a tree. Springing from a trifling seed, it can split rock and soar skyward a hundred feet and more. It draws up water against gravity, and spreads at last in an architecture of boughs and twigs splendid as a Gothic vault, but living to the outermost leaf.

If a plant had a brain, said Darwin, it would lie in its roots. Deep in the earth they seek and find, they dodge and pry. Their delicate tips, wearing a sort of helmet called a root cap, penetrate the soil with a spiral motion like that of a corkscrew. Meeting an obstacle such as a rock, they may circumvent it, or heave it aside, or even crack it open by dissolving it with acids that they can secrete.

If (as has been calculated) a single tuft of bluegrass may in one growing season produce 84,500 root branches and a million root hairs, what then must be the root system of a grand old bur oak? Like a mirror image of the tree above, the underground growth has first a taproot corresponding to the trunk, then huge primary branches, then more slender secondaries and slimmer tertiaries. From these slant off thousands of "obliques," and *these* send out millions of capillaries, hair-fine. Clustering near the tips of the capillaries are even finer root hairs by the billion.

It is only through the root hairs that the tree can "drink." All the rest of it is practically waterproof. So, in a drought, don't water your tree friend at the base of the trunk. Carry your hose out under the outermost branches, for it is down there that the root hairs are thickest.

Even in a drought a grand old tree will find drink enough to keep alive in the film of moisture that clings to every grain of soil. As each soil particle is stripped of moisture, adjacent grains of soil are forced, by the law of capillarity (the blotting-paper principle), to yield up their moisture and send it toward the thirsty roots. Thus a big tree can tap an astonishingly large area.

How does the water mount up the tree? Using tracer dyes, botanists have followed its course. Through the sapwood of the tree runs a sort of plumbing system consisting of very narrow cellulose tubes. These pipes run from the bottommost root out into the veins of the leaves. And up these pipes goes the water taken from the soil by the root hairs.

The force that pulls the water up is the evaporation (botanists call it transpiration) through the leaves and their pores. The pull that is felt in the tiniest veinlets of the leaf is communicated back through the sapwood of the trunk all the way down to the root hairs. A 100-year-old beech with a quarter-million leaves gives off by transpiration some 50 quarts of water daily. This creates a force strong enough to pump up, in six months, ten tons of water from the soil, sending it all forth again into the air in quiet, freshening breath.

Far longer than our own is the life of a tree, and far stronger. We animals burn ourselves up with our living; trees hoard their power, calmly increasing it year by year. A tree has no set limit to its size or age. In the Sierra Nevada Mountains of California there once stood a bristlecone pine that the U.S. Department of Agriculture estimated to be 4600 years old.

Trees have a blessed power to repair injuries, and grow over what they cannot thrust aside. A balm-of-Gilead poplar tree near Waterloo, New York, was young when farmer James Wyburn Johnson hung up his scythe on a bough of it. "Don't touch that until I return," said he, for he was off to war. That was in 1861. He fell in battle, and slowly the bough grew around the steel blade. Now on Memorial Day services are held beneath the "Scythe Tree."

Many a cannonball, a plowshare, the antlers of a deer have been found thus deep imbedded in the living wood. And how did a Bible get into the pine on a ranch in Mariposa County, California? A university student noticed a scar in the trunk, probed it with his knife and discovered within a leather-covered book of Holy Writ, around which the wood had grown.

All this power of growth in a tree resides in just one layer of cells, the cambium, which sheathes every part of the tree. If you scratch a bit of twig with your fingernail, you will notice just under the bark a thin band of green denoting the presence of the cambium. This paper-thin, fragile layer is forever dividing its cells lengthwise. And the two halves of the cell have each a different destiny. For toward the center of the tree the cambium lays down rings of wood, but toward the outside it builds new bark.

The whole tale of a tree's growing can be seen in the end of a freshly cut trunk. Outermost lie the layers of bark, then the cambium with its telltale ribbon of green, then the pale sapwood with its life-giving water; and, at the center of the trunk, the dark and ponderous heartwood, stained and clogged by resins and oils and solidified by the tremendous weight and pressure of the cells above and around it. Once, in the tree's youth, that dense heartwood was clear sapwood, but the pressures of living turned it into this pillar of strength at the tree's core. For the dead cells of a living tree still serve to hold up the whole marvelous structure, and to brace it against the wind.

In California's great earthquake of 1906 along the San Andreas fault line, buildings of stone and steel dumped their upper stories into the streets; strong walls kicked out and roofs fell in. But botanists found that, though some trees were uprooted, not one healthy tree had been snapped off in the trunk. For a tree is not only stronghearted but amazingly supple. We have all seen how "the wind, it plies the saplings double." That same "give" lies in the mightiest oak or beech, because of the structure of its wood.

Most of the cells in that wood are like hollow tile blocks. They are made of cellulose, in double walls, and cellulose is flexible. This gives wood its flexibility and enables the tree to "roll with the punches."

The pores with which the tree breathes are mostly on the underside of the leaf. Closing somewhat on dry, bright days, they cut down on the escape of moisture from the tree; or, opening in the cool darkness, they let the tree breathe freely. The oxygen in that calm respiration has been released during the complex work done by the upper side of the leaf.

This work, called photosynthesis, is performed in partnership with the sunlight. The chlorophyll, the green stuff of the leaf, has the rare ability to use solar energy. With this it breaks up the molecules of water in the leaf, and of the carbon dioxide taken in through the leaf's pores. By rearranging these atoms of oxygen, carbon and hydrogen into other chemical forms, the leaf is provided with the sugars and starches it needs for food. Not the mightiest factory on earth can compare in production with this silent industry.

The waters in the earth are to its trees not only drink. In them lie, in solution, elements that the tree needs: nitrogen, calcium, phosphorus, potassium, iron, copper, zinc, magnesium and many more. Swept up by the transpiration stream to the living protoplasm, the growing cellulose, the functioning leaves, this nourishment goes to the making of a noble tree. Only in water can the chemistry of its life take place—the making of its food, the building and growth of its cells, the greening and the glory, year by year, of its foliage. So every great tree is an invisible fountain, a verdant monument to life itself.

The California redwood, the world's tallest tree, may exceed 350 feet. Its wood is so resistant to decay that 500-year-old logs have been used for lumber.

Part Two

The Life of the Sea

Chapter One

Three Quarters of the Earth

Fish with built-in headlights, microscopic plants that feed whales, a 40,000-mile mountain range—the oceanographers' discoveries have surpassed the sailors' yarns. Yet we still know less about the depths of the ocean that blankets almost three quarters of the earth than we do about the surface of the moon.

UNEARTHLY WORLD AT THE BOTTOM OF THE SEA

Rutherford Platt

Today strange lands more inaccessible than the planets are being discovered at the bottom of the sea. Down there in a hidden world are plains vaster than our Great Plains, mountain ranges more massive than the Alps. The bottomland is utterly dark. But it is not silent, nor is it motionless: Muffled shock waves from earthquakes travel through the deeps; horizontal wrenchings and vertical shiftings result from stresses and strains in the earth's crust and the elastic mantle that underlies it. Incredible forms of life have been found in this dark region where it is "impossible" for life to exist.

But explorers will never walk around down there, for no "space suit" could protect a man from being squashed to death under a weight of water that can reach a pressure of seven *tons* per square inch. The Piccard bathyscaph can descend to the bottom of the ocean, but men in it can make only a spot-check of what they encounter in the little circle of their electric lights. They cannot go outside.

This world of incredible grandeur is now being revealed by remote control. Ingenious deep-sea equipment is being invented to explore and map undersea regions. Electronic, mechanical and sonar sensors are helping scientists find clues to some of the great mysteries of the Earth, such as how the oceans and continents were created, and whether the continents are drifting.

This dark realm lies far beyond and below what people on beaches think of as deep ocean, where dolphins play and seaweed jungles teem with life. These are actually just the waters upon the continental shelf. The famous experiments in underwater living conducted by Jacques-Yves Cousteau and by the U.S. Navy's Sealabs take place on this shelf, which is the shoulder of a continent upon which the ocean has trespassed. It slopes outward very gradually to a maximum depth of 600 feet, and ends suddenly at the true rim of the continent, known as the shelf break. Beyond lies the continental slope, which rapidly descends to the appalling depths that are just now beginning to be explored.

Among the extraordinary devices developed for this exploration are specially designed cameras mounted with strobe lamps and encased in heavy aluminum-alloy cylinders to withstand the extreme pressures. Lowered miles into the depths to within 6 to 20 feet of the bottom, the cameras provide superb pictures of the ocean's floor.

Dr. Maurice Ewing, director of the Lamont Geological Observatory of Columbia University, has put a 1600-pound weight at the top of a hollow steel shaft. Triggered to plunge into the ocean bottom, it can penetrate as far as 60 feet and bring up a core of bottom sediment for study under microscopes.

Oceanographic ships are being outfitted with new kinds of deep-ocean exploring instruments capable of extraordinary precision. They are floating laboratories designed for work in the open sea. One result: As this is written, increasingly detailed maps of our under-ocean lands are coming off the presses.

A surprising revelation is the ruggedness of the terrain: The vertical distances (depths of valleys, heights of mountains) are much greater than on the continents; when averaged out, the depths on the bottom are five times greater than the heights reached on continents above the sea.

Seen from the perspective of the ocean bottom, the continents are tremendous blocks of granitic rock thrusting abruptly upward. In some places the walls of the continents are cut by underwater canyons bigger than Arizona's Grand Canyon. Such a one is the Hudson Canyon, which cleaves the continental shelf off New York. The canyon slopes gradually downward, starting from under the Verrazano-Narrows Bridge in New York harbor. Sixty miles off-

Dwelling in waters so deep that no light penetrates, this female anglerfish attracts prey with her "fishing rod,"
a jointed spine of her dorsal fin that has a luminous, wriggling lure at its tip. Some anglerfish have no
luminous organs, making it difficult for the sexes to find each other and mate. When a young male and female
meet, the male attaches himself permanently to the female's side; the female grows to maturity, while
the male becomes nothing but a small parasitic machine whose only function is to fertilize the female's eggs.

shore, the Upper Gorge cuts through the shelf break, plunging to a depth of 8000 feet. From there the Lower Gorge cleaves the gently sloping hillside formed by centuries of deposits until it reaches the Sohm Abyssal Plain, 16,500 feet under the waves. There towers Caryn Peak, a weird volcanic pinnacle five times higher than the Empire State Building.

The puzzle of what helped gouge the canyons was solved in a surprising way. One day in 1929, 12 telegraph cables between the United States and Europe, running parallel but spaced miles apart, were mysteriously broken, one after the other, over a period of 13 hours. The breaks took place in deep water beyond the rim of the continent off Newfoundland and began approximately one hour after a local earth tremor.

Twenty-three years later oceanographers finally were able to clear up the mystery. A great event had occurred in the mysterious deep. A mass of stones, sand and mud, which had been torn from the coast by waves and deposited on the shelf of the Grand Banks, was shaken up and toppled off the shelf by an earthquake. Traveling as fast as 50 miles an hour, this turbid mixture tumbled down the continental slope to the floor of the ocean, cutting one cable after another. The phenomenon is known as a turbidity current. Heretofore, no one had realized its magnitude or the power of which it is capable. Composed of water mixed with heavy rock and sediment, it moves like quicksilver—and attains great velocity and gouging power. This process, repeated over the millennia, may help cut the big canyons in the deeps.

The Sohm Abyssal Plain extends northeast from Caryn Peak. The Hatteras Abyssal Plain stretches southeast of Caryn. These two flat bands, about three miles deep and 200 miles wide, curve until they almost encircle a comparatively rough terrain named the Bermuda Rise. This area is about 12,000 feet below sea level, except at its center where a steep, sharp mountain stabs up through the ocean—Bermuda!

Abyssal plains are the deep-sea floor of the ocean. Here are no swaying seaweeds, no cycle of day and night, no apparent tides or waves. All is dark. Most abyssal plains are studded with volcanoes, called "seamounts." Some, especially in the Pacific, are beheaded and are called "guyots." In ancient ages these volcanoes repeatedly erupted through the ocean floor belching fiery lava that built up until it emerged above the sea. Later the volcanoes became extinct and the tops, eroded by wind and waves, flattened to sea level. But the crust of the Earth is thin and elastic under the ocean depths; in time it sagged, drowning the volcanoes. Today we discover the guyots with their flat tops as much as a mile under the surface.

Queer chasms called trenches are sometimes found at the edges of the abyssal plains near the continental margins. Their origin is still unknown. Averaging 20 miles wide at the top and hundreds of miles long, a trench has steep sides and a flat floor, and is usually about 25,000 feet deep. The Challenger Deep in the Marianas Trench east of Guam is the deepest spot in the ocean thus far discovered—almost seven miles under the blue water.

In the Atlantic, beyond the abyssal plains, under mid-ocean, lies a huge highland region called the Mid-Atlantic Ridge, whose mountain peaks break through into the sunshine at the Azores, Iceland, Ascension and other islands. It was detected in 1873 by the famous expedition of the British ship *Challenger,* which sounded the depths with a lead weight.

Today the new ocean-exploring devices have revealed that the Mid-Atlantic Ridge is a segment of the longest mountain range on earth. It runs from the Arctic Ocean basin the full length of both the North and South Atlantic oceans. Continuing in the deep water between Africa and Antarctica, it bends east and then branches northward under the Indian Ocean, loops south of Australia, through the South Pacific, then north up the eastern side of the Pacific, where it runs ashore at Baja California. These globe-circling mountains are labeled Mid-Ocean Ridge—a colossal geologic mystery, 40,000 miles long, that emerges from the sea in only a few isolated places.

The most exciting discovery about the Ridge is that it is sliced down the middle. This slicing has been carefully studied in the North Atlantic, where it is called the Rift Valley of the Mid-Atlantic Ridge. There the astonishing crack averages more than 6000 feet in depth; the severed sides stand 8 to 30 miles apart, suggesting a hellish tearing asunder.

In the Atlantic the line of the Rift follows the turns of the opposite coastlines. If the American continents and Europe-Africa were pushed together, they would fit at the Rift like a jigsaw puzzle—a dramatic hint that these continents may have been formerly one landmass that split apart at the Rift.

The key question is: What force is great enough to displace continents? One exciting suggestion comes from the discovery of unusual amounts of heat in the Mid-Atlantic Ridge and Rift, leaking out from the mantle through the crust at the bottom of the ocean. Is this kind of heat merely the result of volcanic eruptions, or is it being brought up slowly from the hot interior of the Earth by convection currents? According to the convection-current theory, hot materials deep within the Earth's mantle become excessively heated, perhaps by radioactivity, expand and rise toward the ocean floor. Just below the crust the ascending mantle slowly divides and spreads horizontally, dissipating heat as it does so. As it cools, the mantle grows denser and sinks back toward the deep interior where it heats up again. Thus, a kind of wheel, revolving with infinite slowness, is formed within the mantle, and the moving mantle carries the crust along with it. Many geologists think that the slow spreading apart of the mantle creates a stretching force sufficient to cause the Rift Valley. This force, they say,

When in danger from predators, these crimson deep-sea prawns secrete a thick fluid that becomes a cloud of flashing sparks on contact with the water. The predators are stopped—and baffled—long enough for the prawns to escape.

tore the continents asunder, inched them apart through geologic time, and is even now continuing to separate them.

Why, in the course of millennia, is there so astonishingly little sediment on the ocean's floor? And what happens to the eight cubic miles of land sediments that are washed by rivers into the oceans each year? Part of the answer is that some sediments dissolve as they run into the sea, and more disintegrate on the long slow trip to the bottom. Only the nearly insoluble materials in the sediments survive the journey. Nothing is left on the floor of the ocean except fine clay particles that come from the land, and a peculiar ocean deposit called ooze, composed mainly of the skeletal remains of microscopic marine animals.

The clay particles and ooze are deposited by a perpetual "phantom snow" with flakes so tiny that they are beyond the range of most microscopes and so nearly weightless that one may take years to sink from the upper layers five miles down to the floor. The sediment accumulates at an estimated rate of 1/25 inch every thousand years. Even at that rate it should have reached a thickness of 10,000 feet after three billion years—about the time the deep oceans have existed.

Yet the carpet of ooze is much thinner than this. Moreover, photographs with deep-sea cameras show that large areas of the ocean bottom are bare rock! Where have the sediments gone?

Some explain this by a theory about a grand cycle that scientists suspect may be occurring in the deeps, especially under the trenches. According to this theory, developed by Dr. Robert S. Dietz of the U.S. Environmental Science Services Administration, the ocean floor on which the sediments are falling is also slowly moving, being nudged by the convection currents. It could be, Dietz reasons, that the sediments are gradually being carried back toward the continental margins as if they were riding a conveyor belt.

Why don't they pile up against the continental margins? Perhaps they are pulled into the trenches. According to Dr. Dietz, the trenches occur where the convection currents in the mantle are starting to descend. They drag a bit of the Earth's crust with them and thrust it, with its veneer of ocean sediments, under the continents. At such depths, the Earth's interior heat is intense enough to melt the sediments, which, because of their granitic origin, slowly crystallize into fresh granitic rock. Since these sediments are deposited so slowly, it is possible they are carried under the continents and turned into new granite as fast as they collect. Thus the continents of the Earth may be constantly and forever renewing the materials

that wash out of them, by reabsorbing them via the action of convection currents.

The utmost penetration of light into mid-ocean is about 3000 feet. Most sea life is far above that depth, at no more than 300 to 600 feet, where there is enough sunlight energy for marine plants to manufacture food through photosynthesis. In the 1870's U.S. and British ships discovered, in the blackness below the light line, a mid-depth band of life, where sizable fish swim happily under water pressure of two tons. These strange fish have evolved internal adaptations that enable them to survive the tremendous pressure of the water where they live. Many are luminous and have big mouths with long, sharp teeth. Some lure their prey with their eerie glow to within striking distance of their huge jaws. Others are scavengers that feed upon carcasses of dead fish and other debris descending from above the light line.

But can life exist on the very floor of the abyssal wilderness? The answer is a surprising "Yes." Ocean-bottom cameras have shown living things on the firm ooze of abyssal plains and trench floors—mostly small, burrowing creatures: worms, sea cucumbers, mollusks. By rare luck the camera caught a vivid picture of an acorn worm, 40 inches long. It was devouring ooze and defecating modernistic coils and spirals as it went on its way.

These inhabitants of the ocean's floor, marvelous as they are, have cells similar to those of all other living things on Earth. Because of the miracle we call evolution, they survive by adapting their internal pressure to the surrounding water. Their existence is one more testimony to the hardiness of life.

INEXHAUSTIBLE RICHES FROM THE SEA

George A. W. Boehm

Men of vision have long recognized that a great storehouse of natural wealth lies in and beneath the waters covering 70 percent of the Earth. But only recently has a concerted effort begun to exploit these resources. There is a worldwide surge of scientific interest in understanding the oceans and finding new ways to recover from them a vast abundance of food and minerals.

Much has been accomplished within the last decade. Marine fishermen have doubled their annual catch. Oil, gas and sulfur have been pumped in steadily swelling torrents from the sea floor. Engineers have been devising equipment to mine an inexhaustible

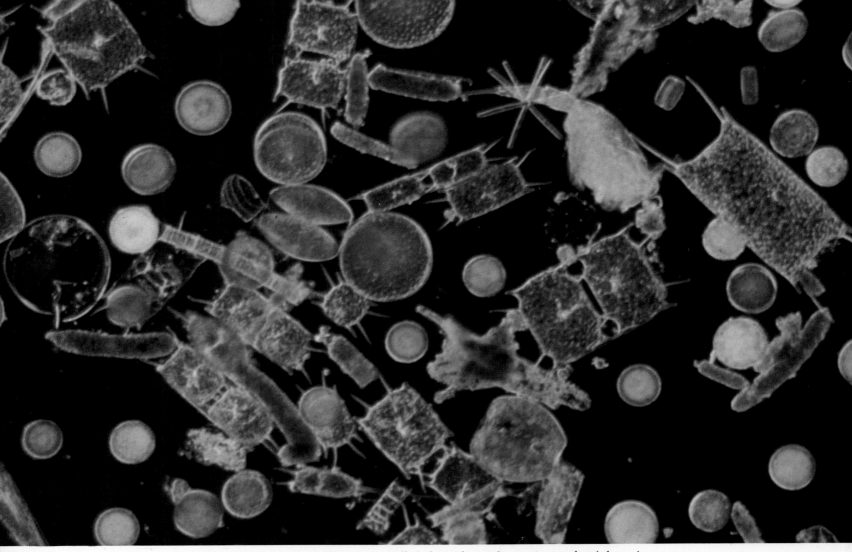

Diatoms (shown here 125 times actual size) are one-celled plants that make up nine tenths of the sea's floating plankton. Alive, they are at the base of the food chain, serving as the main source of nourishment for plants and animals that live by filtering plankton from the water. When they die, their shells sink to the bottom, forming layers of diatomaceous earth, which is mined and used in industrial filters and metal polishes.

supply of important metals from vast deposits on the bottom of the ocean.

The science of oceanography is still relatively young. The bottom of the oceans is in most areas no better mapped than was the North American continent before the Lewis and Clark expedition. A few years ago, for example, a U.S. Coast and Geodetic Survey ship, on her way from the Panama Canal to Key West, discovered a 6000-foot mountain rising from the bottom of the sea to within 90 feet of the surface—its existence had never before been suspected. Biologists still know little about the breeding and migratory habits of most fish.

But if the current burst of interest is any indication, many gaps in knowledge and technique are sure to be filled within the next few decades. Virtually all the leading maritime nations—notably the U.S.S.R., Japan, Great Britain, Germany and the United States—are expanding their research programs. The United States has outlined a program that would involve spending 2.3 billion dollars on oceanography over a ten-year period. It is a coordinated effort involving the U.S. Navy and 14 federal agencies, with contracts going to various private research centers. Significantly, the growing store of knowledge will be brought fully to bear years hence when the world's population will have doubled and many mineral resources on land will have been depleted by a voracious technology.

A deeper understanding of marine resources will basically alter man's attitude toward the ocean. Up to now man has used it as a nomad uses the grassland or a primitive hunter the forest. The new attitude, labeled "aquiculture," implies cultivating and managing the resources of the sea the way modern farmers and foresters husband the resources of the land. Rather than simply gathering the fruits of the water, man will involve himself in the natural processes that create resources and will do his best to regulate them to his advantage.

The aquicultural approach has led scientists to speculate about ways to herd fish, increase the stock, build up the productivity of the water. The most promising places for aquiculture are bays and estuaries, where the waters are easily accessible from land. One of the most impressively productive of such enterprises is mussel culturing in the Gulf of Taranto, Italy, where

the annual yield averages 11,000 pounds of meat per acre of ocean bottom.

There are also opportunities for aquiculture in the shallow water on the continental shelves, which, added together, have an area equal to that of all Asia. Scientists will have to understand this environment as intimately as an Eskimo understands his world of ice and snow. One pioneer is already at work: The French oceanographer Jacques-Yves Cousteau has been colonizing the ocean floor. In 1963 seven of his associates lived in cylindrical steel huts resting on the bottom of the Red Sea. Five of them spent a month at a depth of 50 feet; two spent more than a week at 80 feet. Supplied with a flow of air from the surface, all worked a six-hour day that included hard physical labor. Cousteau believes that men can live in such colonies at the limits of the continental shelf, as far down as 600 feet. The U.S. Navy's Sealab II provided living quarters for three 10-man teams who successively spent 15-day periods at a depth of 205 feet in an experiment off the coast of California in 1965.

The ocean is an inexhaustible, self-replenishing storehouse of most of the basic materials that a modern economy needs. Dissolved or suspended in the water or lying on the ocean floor are countless tons of all the natural chemical elements; the production of plant matter equals the growth on all the croplands, meadows and forests, and the community of animals easily outweighs all the creatures who live on the land.

The basis of life in the ocean is a thin soup of tiny plants and animals, collectively known as plankton, which inhabit the sunlit upper layers of water. They are the foundation of a living pyramid. That is to say, they are the staple food of small fish which, in turn, are eaten by larger fish.

It might be possible to stimulate the growth of plankton in certain locations—a procedure somewhat analogous to fertilizing a pasture. Oceanographers are investigating schemes for stirring up parts of the ocean to bring to the surface nutrients that make plankton flourish. One approach, favored by scientists at Woods Hole, Massachusetts, is to install a vertical pipe to raise water from lower levels through a physical process that depends on slight temperature and salinity differences. A National Academy of Sciences committee has suggested setting a large heat source—perhaps an atomic pile—on the bottom to start vertical convection currents. Such ideas, not economically feasible at present, may someday prove important.

The fact that seawater itself is rich in minerals has inspired proposals to "mine" it by chemical processing. Common salt has been produced by evaporation for centuries, and in recent times potash has also been

Common among the floating plankton are larvae of animals that reside on the ocean floor when they mature. Arachnactis (top) is the larva of a sea anemone which, as an adult, burrows into sand or mud. Having a larval stage that swims enables this species to spread itself over a wide area before settling down. The late larval stage of Polydora (bottom) matures as a bottom-dwelling sea worm.

recovered. Since 1924 the Ethyl Corporation has been extracting bromine, and since 1941 the Dow Chemical Company has supplied the nation with magnesium made from seawater. Someday it may pay to get rubidium, cesium, sulfur, boron, strontium and fluorine from the ocean.

Oceanographers have long been aware that the bottom of the sea contains ore deposits comparable to those on land. In the early 1870's the British oceanographic vessel *Challenger* dredged up from the bottom of the ocean lumps of a strange mineral that looked like fire-blackened potatoes. These nodules were found to be exceptionally rich in manganese and contained substantial amounts of other metals—chiefly iron, copper, cobalt and nickel.

During the International Geophysical Year (1957-58), dredging in deep waters revealed that much of the ocean floor is literally cobbled with nodules. Individual nodules grow in layers like onions and at an incredibly slow rate, generally no faster than one millimeter in a thousand years. Yet, as worldwide surveys have shown, there are so many nodules forming all the time that they could supply all man's needs for their major metallic constituents, and still the total growth would easily exceed the rate of depletion.

Several companies have been investigating ways of dredging and refining these nodules. Engineer John Mero, consultant to Newport News Shipbuilding & Dry Dock Company, has stated that the best way to mine nodules is to suck them off the bottom with a sort of hydraulic vacuum cleaner. According to Mero, a single dredge with a capacity of 5000 tons per day could supply the United States with 50 percent of the manganese, all the cobalt and 10 percent of the nickel it needs.

An entirely different kind of nodule, rich in phosphate rather than metals, also promises to be worth mining. Phosphorite nodules on Forty Mile Bank, west of San Diego, are very nearly comparable to high-grade phosphates mined on land. Surveys indicate that this reserve may be about a billion tons— plenty to provide California agriculture with phosphate fertilizer for decades to come.

Most nodules are found in deep water, but submarine prospectors have discovered other mineral deposits in extremely shallow water. Rich tin ores lie off the coasts of Thailand and Indonesia. Gold occurs in sands and gravels near Nome, Alaska. Sam Collins, a 55-year-old oil-drilling and pipeline contractor from Texas, has struck it rich in a brand-new mining business: scooping diamonds from the floor of the ocean. With financial backing from the de Beers organization and other mining houses, Collins has averaged almost a million dollars' worth of diamonds per month dredging gravel in shallow water off the coast of South West Africa.

Some species of today's commercially valuable fish are in danger of depletion, while worthless fish threaten to take over the ocean. Because of this danger, a number of the world's fisheries are coming under management spearheaded by some 200 experts: marine scientists from universities and government, representatives of industry and "fishery diplomats." They circulate among a number of international agencies that keep track of the population of certain fish in specified areas and then recommend regulations as to the quantity of fish the participating countries should catch.

The key concept in fishery management is "maximum sustained yield"—the rate of exploitation that the resource can tolerate without diminishing. This kind of conservation calls for carefully regulated harvesting, rather than hoarding. Foresters know now that periodic thinning out improves a stand of trees; similarly, a fish population may be all the healthier if it is reduced so survivors have plenty of food.

Biologists have already had considerable success in predicting fish populations. The U.S. Bureau of Commercial Fisheries, for example, makes reliable forecasts of the abundance of haddock and other ground fish so that fishermen and processors can plan their operations a year in advance. The bureau has also been able to correlate the appearance of skipjack in mid-Pacific with water temperatures measured off Hawaii.

The peculiar habit shared by salmon and a few other marine fish of returning to spawn in the very streams where they were hatched suggests that it may be possible to improve fish genetically, like any domestic animal. Prof. Lauren R. Donaldson of the University of Washington is doing just that with Chinook salmon. Since 1949 he has been selecting his breeding stock with an eye toward several factors that make for desirable fish. His goal is a fish that matures early, lays a lot of eggs, has healthy offspring, resists disease and has a hefty, meaty body.

Although farsighted oceanographers continue to seek ways to locate and exploit new resources beneath the waters, many scientists feel that not enough emphasis has been given to the programs already under way. They deplore the fact that in a recent fiscal year Congress appropriated a meager $123,800,000 for oceanography, against more than five billion dollars for space. They feel that it is far more urgent for man to become familiar with a major portion of his own planet than it is to explore the Moon.

WIND
AND WATER

Rachel L. Carson

As long as there has been an ocean, its waters have stirred to the passage of the winds. It is a confused pattern that the waves make in the open sea— overtaking, passing or sometimes engulfing one another; each group differing from the others in origin, speed and direction; some doomed never to reach any shore, others destined to roll across half an ocean before they dissolve in thunder on a distant beach.

The water that composes a wave does not advance with it across the sea; each water particle describes a circular orbit with the passage of the wave-form, but returns very nearly to its original position. And this is fortunate, for if the huge masses of water that compose a wave actually moved across the sea, navigation would be impossible. In the lore of waves one frequently hears the picturesque expression, the "length of fetch"—that is, the distance that the waves have run, under the drive of a wind blowing in a constant direction, without obstruction. The greater the fetch, the higher the waves. Really large waves cannot be generated within a bay or a small sea. A fetch of perhaps 600 to 800 miles, with winds of gale velocity, is required to get up the largest ocean waves.

Forces within the sea itself may affect a wave most profoundly. Some of the most terrible furies of the ocean are unleashed when tidal currents cross the path of the waves or move in direct opposition to them. This is the cause of the famous "roosts" of Scotland, like the one at the southernmost tip of the Shetland Islands. During northeasterly winds the roost is quiescent, but when the wind-borne waves roll in from any other quarter they encounter the tidal currents, either streaming shoreward in flood or seaward on the ebb. It is like the meeting of two wild beasts. The battle of the waves and tides is fought over an area that may be three miles wide when the tides are running at full strength. "In this confused, tumbling and bursting sea, vessels often become entirely unmanageable and sometimes founder," says the *British Islands Pilot,* "while others have been tossed about for days together."

Waves higher than 25 feet from trough to crest are rare anywhere, but storm waves may grow to more than twice that. The greatest possible height of storm waves at sea is a much debated question, with most textbooks citing a conservative 60 feet, and mariners stubbornly describing much higher waves. Yet there is one record of a giant wave which, because of the method of measurement, seems to be accepted as reliable.

In February 1933 the USS *Ramapo,* proceeding from Manila to San Diego, encountered seven days of stormy weather. When the gale reached its fiercest intensity, winds of 68 knots came in gusts and the seas reached mountainous heights. While standing watch, one of the *Ramapo's* officers saw a great sea rising astern at a level above an iron strap on the crow's nest of the mainmast. Since the *Ramapo* was on an even keel with her stern in the trough of the sea, he had an exact line of sight from the bridge to the crest of the wave. The dimensions of the ship thus gave the height of the wave. It was 112 feet.

But whatever their height at sea, it is around the shorelines of the world that storm waves are most destructive. The upward-leaping water masses from thundering breakers may engulf lighthouses, shatter buildings and make the most massive shore installations appear fragile as a child's toys. In winter gales the force of a wave may be as great as 6000 pounds to the square foot. During the height of a winter gale in 1872 at Wick, Scotland, while the resident engineer watched incredulously from a cliff above, the whole mass of a concrete breakwater was slewed around until it was finally broken away from its attachments, lifted and deposited inside the pier. After the storm, divers investigating the wreckage found that the waves had torn loose and bodily moved a mass weighing not less than 1350 tons, or 2,700,000 pounds. Five years later it became clear that this feat had been a mere dress rehearsal, for the new pier, weighing about 2600 tons, was carried away.

Keepers of lights on lonely ledges at sea, or on rocky headlands exposed to the full strength of storm surf, have experienced happenings that seem almost supernatural. In 1840, during a night of heavy seas, the strongly bolted entrance door of the Eddystone Light was broken open *from within,* and all its iron bolts and hinges were torn loose. Engineers ascribe such phenomena to pneumatic action—the sudden back-draft created by the recession of a heavy wave combined with an abrupt release of pressure on the outside of the door. At the Bell Rock Light on the coast of Scotland one November a ladder was torn from the tower 86 feet above the sea. At the Bishop Rock Light during a winter gale a bell was torn from its attachment 100 feet above high water.

On the Atlantic Coast of the United States, the 97-foot tower on Minot's Ledge is often completely enveloped by masses of water from breaking surf, and a light on this ledge was swept away in 1851. And as the keeper of Trinidad Head Light on the coast of Oregon watched during a December storm, a wave seemed to rise in a solid wall of water to the level of the lantern, 196 feet above high water, and hurled its spray completely over the tower. The shock of the blow stopped the revolving of the light.

Along a rocky coast, the waves of a severe storm are likely to be armed with stones and rock frag-ments. Once a rock weighing 135 pounds was hurled high above the lightkeeper's house on Tillamook Rock, 100 feet above sea level. In falling, it tore a 20-foot hole through the roof. At the lighthouse at Dunnet Head, built on the summit of a *300-foot* cliff at Pentland Firth in Scotland, the windows have been broken repeatedly by stones swept from the cliff and tossed aloft by waves.

Thus the sea's waves forever batter the coastlines of the world, here cutting back a cliff, there stripping

away tons of sand from a beach and yet again building up a bar or a small island. The high clay cliff of Cape Cod is wearing back so fast that half of the ten acres which the Government acquired as a site for the Highland Light has disappeared, and the cliffs are said to be receding about three feet a year. At the present rate of erosion, the disappearance of the outer cape may occur in another 5000 years.

The cliffs on the south shore of Nantucket Island, off Cape Cod, are retreating as much as six feet a

year under the grinding attack of rock-laden waves. As the fragments of rock are chiseled out and wrenched away, they in turn are ground in the surf to contribute more weapons for the attack. On a rocky shore, this grinding and polishing of rocks goes on incessantly and audibly. The breakers on such a coast have a different sound from those that work only with sand—a deep-toned mutter and rumble not easily forgotten, even by one who strolls casually along such a beach.

This "powerful marine gnawing" is also eating away many parts of the British coast. Old records show astonishing annual rates of cliff erosion—up to 19 feet between Cromer and Mundesley, and 15 to 45 feet at Southwold. And a map dated 1786 gives a long list of lost villages on the Holderness Coast, marked "washed away by the sea."

Yet we owe some of the most beautiful shoreline scenery to the sculpturing effect of moving water. Sea caves are almost literally blasted out of the cliffs by waves which pour into crevices in the rocks and force them apart by hydraulic pressure. The roofs of such caves (and of overhanging cliffs) are subjected to blows like those from a battering ram as the water from a breaking wave is hurled upward. Eventually a hole may be torn through the roof of the cave, to form a spouting horn.

The sea waves that have fixed themselves most firmly in the human imagination are the so-called tidal waves. The term is popularly applied to two very different kinds of waves, neither of which has any relation to the tide. One is a *seismic* sea wave produced by undersea earthquakes; the other is a *storm* wave—an immense mass of water driven by winds of hurricane force far above the normal high-water line.

An ominous withdrawal of the sea is often the first warning of the approach of seismic sea waves. In 1868 the western coast of South America was shaken by earthquakes. Shortly after the most violent shocks, the sea receded from the shore, leaving ships that had been anchored in 40 feet of water stranded in mud; then the water returned in a great wave, and boats were carried a quarter of a mile inland.

Natives on the beaches of Hawaii on April 1, 1946, were alarmed when the voice of the breakers was suddenly stilled, leaving a strange quiet. They

The cliffs of Cape Kiwanda, Oregon, show the sculpturing effect of the sea. With the passage of time, the restless Pacific surf has gradually eaten away the porous sandstone, carving it into inlets, caves and castlelike turrets.

could not know that this recession of the waves was the sea's response to an earthquake in the Aleutian chain, 2300 miles away; or that in a matter of moments the ocean waters would return with great turbulence at 25 feet or more above normal tide levels, sweeping people and houses out to sea. In the open ocean the waves produced by the Aleutian quake were only a foot or two high; it took them less than five hours to reach Hawaii, so they must have moved at an average speed of about 470 miles per hour.

Storm waves claim about three fourths of the lives lost by tropical hurricanes. They were responsible for the disaster at Galveston, Texas, on September 8, 1900, and for that on the lower Florida Keys on September 2–3, 1935. The most fearful destruction by hurricane waves within historic time occurred in the Bay of Bengal on October 7, 1737, when 20,000 boats were destroyed and 300,000 people drowned.

But the largest and most awe-inspiring waves of the ocean are invisible; they move on their mysterious courses far down in the hidden depths of the sea, where they may toss submarines about, just as surface waves set ships to rolling. They seem to break against the Gulf Stream and other strong currents in a deep-sea version of the dramatic meeting of surface waves and tidal currents. But the water masses involved are unthinkably great, some of the waves being as high as 300 feet.

Of their effect on fish and other life of the deep sea we have only the faintest conception. We can only sense that in the deep and turbulent recesses of the sea are hidden mysteries far greater than any we have solved.

SEAWEEDS—
HARVEST OF THE OCEAN

Donald Culross Peattie

In the doldrums of the North Atlantic—so goes the legend of the Sargasso Sea—lies a vast morass of seaweed, deadly in its sluggish power. Twisting in the currents, it winds itself about any craft unwary enough to venture there. Their ship held helpless, the crew become gaunt skeletons, the sails but wavering shrouds of mildew, until the rotted hull sinks through the suffocating mass.

Oceanographers long ago exploded this delightfully horrid fantasy, only to be themselves mystified by the seaweed's behavior. For there *is* a Sargasso Sea, bounded roughly by the Azores in the eastern Atlantic and the Bahamas and Antilles in the west.

And there *is* a plant called sargassum, or gulfweed, a twiggy little thing looking something like holly, and kept afloat by air sacs. The first European sailors to see it were the crew of Columbus, sailing west in 1492, and when they encountered seaweed in masses they feared they must be driving on hidden reefs. So the Admiral took a sounding with a cannonball—and got no bottom at 200 fathoms!

While most other seaweeds grow on rocks, this one is wholly rootless, floating free in mid-ocean. But now you see it, now you don't. Some scientists in search of it have crisscrossed the Sargasso without finding any. Others a few months later have reported it abundant. When you do see it, it looks like an ocean meadow, the "hay" rolled into long, yellowish windrows. When you don't, it is probably because the old plants, dying, have sunk, and the new ones have not yet developed air sacs to buoy them up into sight.

Seaweed needs neither fiction nor a vanishing act, however, to make it marvelous. Right offshore, on this California coast where I live, grow the largest giant kelps in the world, the sequoias of the ocean. Forty and sixty feet down they are rooted by suckering holdfasts; their stems, flaccid but tough, may attain 150 feet; their foliage is ample and heavy as the leaves of a rubber tree. They are buoyed up by double rows of bladders or, sometimes, by a single float the size of a grapefruit. Some, like the trees of earth, are perennials; in others, which are annuals, this leviathan growth is the work of a single season.

Of the smaller seaweeds that grow there, as many as wild flowers in the fields, some are brilliant in color and exquisite in design. The most beautiful of all, looking like corals, are found in the Great Sound of Bermuda, in the Bay of Naples, and in the waters around Key West. Some indeed, like corals, have helped to build the land we walk on. Their surfaces encrusted with lime, they have, by their endless living and dying, created reefs, atolls, isles and peninsulas. Animal corals get all the credit but the coralline seaweeds have probably done fully half the work.

I can see the top of one submarine forest as I look from shore near my house. It is a brown band, 50 to 150 yards wide, lying heavily on the brilliant Pacific and following the coastline as far as eye can see. Stretching intermittently from Alaska to Mexico, this mass of seaweed aggregates hundreds of square

Kelp, such as these beached Pacific varieties, grows in a thick, tangled mass in low-tide zones. Fish swim through the dense jungle of stalks; sea otters float on the surface; and mussels anchor themselves to the holdfasts at the base of the plants.

miles and weighs uncalculated millions of tons. So thickly is it matted that I can see two white egrets and a great blue heron standing out there in open salt water—perching on the topmost boughs of this undersea wilderness.

There goes the only sort of boat that seeks out the seaweed beds, a plodding kelp barge, working back and forth like a reaper combine in a field of wheat. A ten-foot bar up forward cuts the kelp under water; the valuable weed is then carried by an endless conveyor belt onto the boat, which holds 300 tons.

The giant kelps of the Pacific are the only ones that can be harvested mechanically at present. If properly cut, harvesting makes them grow better: Old shoots are removed and vigorous young growth is given a chance to sprout.

In World War I, when supplies of potash from Germany were cut off, the giant kelps saved the day, so rich are they in this important mineral. Kelp also yields acetone and calcium acetate, necessary in the manufacture of gunpowder.

In the laboratory, seaweed, in the form of agar, helps to push out the frontiers of science and save many a life. About 85 years ago the great Dr. Robert Koch, discoverer of the tuberculosis germ, was seeking a satisfactory medium in which to cultivate bacteria. The wife of his associate, Dr. Richard Hesse, suggested he try an ingredient she used in making preserves. The recipe had come from Dutch friends in Java, where *agar-agar* is the Malay word for a seaweed gelatin widely eaten in the Orient. Agar was just what science needed, for it keeps firm at the temperatures used for incubating bacteria and resists their liquefying action. Laboratories take only a small percentage of the agarweed harvested today. It is used in widely separate enterprises—cake icing, artificial limbs, orchid growing, dental plates.

World War II curtailed U.S. supplies of Japanese agar, but a reddish-purple agarweed was found to be abundant enough on the Pacific Coast to meet the crisis. Harvesting this agarweed is a hard and hazardous business. It grows like a low shrub under the great trees of giant kelp, in 15 to 30 feet of water, just deep enough to call for diving operations with helmet and oxygen, yet so shallow that the water is turbulent. A crew of three goes out—a boatman, a line tender and a diver. Clambering over the steep rocks, the diver gropes through the dim light and roiled water, searching for the slim-fingered, reddish-purple seaweed. Clinging sometimes to the stems of the giant kelps for support, he cuts the weed and piles it in a wire basket, which, at his signal, is drawn up. Two hours of such labor tire the strongest, and only on some 100 days

in a year are the waters calm enough for the work.

On the New England coast, "mossers" go out in boats and grapple with rakes for the seaweed called Irish moss, which old-fashioned cooks know as the substance that stiffens blancmange. Like agar, Irish moss slips into innumerable places in our daily lives; its smoothing, binding and stabilizing properties give much of the goodness to your ice cream and chocolate milk. Because workers in Irish moss never have chapped hands despite the wetness of their job, chemists perceived in it a valuable base for lotions. New England imported Irish moss by the hundreds of tons from the Old Country, until about a century ago a Boston mayor noticed it growing in abundance right on that rockbound coast.

In the oddest ways, in things you handle or consume daily, you'll find seaweed extracts turning up. One of them helped to make the electric-light bulb, as a lubricant in the hot wiredrawing of the tungsten filament. In a detergent another made washing dishes easy. Your wife may use seaweed in her hair in one of the new wave-set lotions. You had it on your face in your shaving cream this morning. It was a granulating agent in the aspirin pill you took lately. It's used in the sizing of cloth—some fabrics it makes waterproof, some fire-resistant. It can even be spun into "seaweed rayon."

Long ago people discovered that seaweed would give back to their hungry fields much that had been lost to the sea: the precious nitrates, phosphates, potash and manganese needed by crops. These rich fertilizers are forever being swept into the sea, but the seaweeds take up great quantities into their wavering stems and fronds. So seaweed makes excellent manure. It makes good fodder, too, and in Europe is fed by shore-dwelling people to their stock. Denmark, a country of fine seashores and fat cattle, produces a seaweed meal for cows. In the United States a dairy herd given supplementary feedings of dried seaweed a few years ago won the world's record for milk production.

Some people are wise enough to make seaweed a staple of their diet. The Japanese, the Chinese, the South Sea Islanders and the Greenland Eskimos prize it as their principal vegetable. Certain seaweeds are rich in vitamins A, B and C and in iodine. Yet it is not because it's good for me that a clear seaweed soup appears on my own table. I like the delicate taste of it, as I like the very names of the seaweeds I gather on the shore—sea silk and mermaid's-hair, laver and daber locks, wrack and tangle. Harvest of ocean, fresh with its salt and cleanly beauty, the seaweeds offer mankind a bounty yet to be fully explored.

The Seashore's Many Worlds

Wherever land and sea meet—along a sandy beach, against a rocky
shore, across a mud flat or at the edge of a coral reef—a weird and wondrous
array of plants and animals exists in a turbulent world that can
be breathtakingly beautiful and at the same time unyieldingly harsh.

THE MYSTERY OF LIFE AT THE SEASHORE

Rachel L. Carson

The edge of the sea is a strange and beautiful place. All through the long history of Earth it has been an area of unrest where waves have broken heavily against the land, where the tides have pressed forward over the continents, receded and then returned. For no two successive days is the shoreline precisely the same. Today a little more land may belong to the sea, tomorrow a little less. Always the edge of the sea remains an elusive, indefinable boundary.

Only the most hardy and adaptable creatures can survive in a region so mutable, yet the area between the tide lines is crowded with plants and animals. In this difficult world, life displays its enormous toughness and vitality by occupying almost every conceivable niche. It carpets intertidal rocks, descends into fissures and crevices, hides under boulders, lurks in the wet gloom of sea caves. Where the casual observer would say there is no life, it lies deep in the sand, in burrows and tubes and passageways. It tunnels into solid rock and bores into peat and clay. It encrusts weeds or drifting spars or the hard chitinous shell of a lobster. It exists minutely, as the film of bacteria that spreads over a rock surface, and as Lilliputian beings swimming through dark pools that lie between the grains of sand.

Each grain of sand holds a film of water about itself by capillary attraction, and even the blows of heavy surf cannot cause one sand grain to rub against another. In this minuscule world, inconceivably minute beings swim through the liquid film around a grain of sand as fish would swim through the ocean covering the sphere of the earth. Among the fauna of the capillary water are single-celled animals, water mites, shrimplike crustacea, insects and the larvae of certain infinitely small worms—all living, dying, swimming,

feeding, breathing and reproducing in a world so small that our human senses cannot grasp its scale.

Many larger forms of life also inhabit the sand. Walking across the flats of a Georgia beach, I was always aware that I was treading on the thin rooftops of an underground city. Of the inhabitants themselves little or nothing was visible. There were chimneys and stacks and ventilating pipes of underground dwellings and various passages and runways leading down into darkness. There were little heaps of refuse as though in an attempt at some sort of civic sanitation. But the inhabitants remained hidden, dwelling silently in their dark, incomprehensible world.

The most numerous inhabitants of this city of burrowers were the ghost shrimps. A curiously formed creature with a long slender body, the ghost shrimp seldom goes abroad and so has no need of a hard protective skeleton; it is covered, instead, with a flexible cuticle suited to the narrow tunnel in which it must be able to dig and turn about. On the underside of its body are several pairs of flattened appendages that beat continually to force a current of water through the burrow, for in the deep sand layers the oxygen supply is poor, and aerated water must be drawn down from above. When the tide comes in, the ghost shrimps go up to the mouths of their burrows and begin their work of sifting the sand grains for bacteria, diatoms and perhaps larger particles of organic detritus.

Their holes were everywhere over the tidal flat; in diameter the entrances were considerably smaller than a lead pencil, and surrounded by a little pile of fecal pellets. The pellets accumulate in great quantity because of the shrimp's way of life; it must eat an enormous amount of sand and mud to obtain the food that is mixed with this indigestible material. The holes are the visible entrances to burrows that extend down several feet into the sand—long, nearly vertical passageways from which other tunnels lead off, some continuing down into the dark, damp basement of this shrimp city, others leading up to the surface as though to provide emergency exit doors. The owners of the burrows did not show themselves unless I tricked them into it by dropping sand grains, a few at a time, into their entrance halls.

On the muddier parts of these same Georgia flats the lugworm lives, its presence marked by round black domes, like low volcanic cones. Wherever the lugworms occur, on shores of America and Europe, their prodigious toil leavens and renews the beaches and keeps the amount of decaying organic matter in proper balance. Where they are abundant, they may work over in a year nearly 2000 tons of soil per acre. Vast plains of sand are thus continually drilled by

A mole crab emerges from hiding, its long feeding antennae bent as they strain plankton from receding waves. Behind the shorter, breathing antennae are two jointed eyestalks the crab uses to reconnoiter while still buried safely in the sand.

these and other marine worms. One—the trumpet worm—uses the very sand that contains its food to make a cone-shaped tube for the protection of its soft body in tunneling. The living trumpet worm may sometimes be seen at work, but it is much more common to find the empty tubes in the tidal debris. Despite their fragile appearance they remain intact long after their architects are dead—natural mosaics of sand, one grain thick, the building stones fitted and

cemented together with the most meticulous care.

Another successful exploiter of the shoreline is the mole crab, a surf-fisher who uses nets so efficient that they catch even microorganisms adrift in the water. In preparing to feed, the crab backs down into the wet sand until only the mouth parts and the long, curling, feathery antennae are exposed. It makes no attempt to take food from the incoming surf, but waits until a wave has spent its force on the beach and the backwash is draining seaward. When the spent wave has thinned to a depth of an inch or two, the mole crab extends its antennae into the streaming current. After "fishing" for a moment, it draws the antennae through the appendages surrounding its mouth, picking off the captured food.

Whole cities of mole crabs live where the waves are breaking, following the flood tide shoreward, retreating toward the sea on the ebb. Several times during the rising of a tide, a whole bed of them will shift position, digging in again farther up the beach.

It is an extraordinary thing to watch the sand "come to life" if one happens to be wading where there is a large colony of mole crabs. One moment it may seem completely uninhabited. Then, in that fleeting instant when the water of a receding wave flows seaward like a thin stream of liquid glass, there are suddenly hundreds of little gnomelike faces peering through the sandy floor—beady-eyed, long-whiskered faces set in bodies so nearly the color of their background that they can barely be seen. And when, almost instantly, the faces fade back into invisibility, the illusion is strong that one has seen nothing except in imagination—that there was merely an apparition induced by the magical quality of this world of shifting sand and foaming water.

On any beach inhabited by ghost crabs, their burrows appear and disappear in a daily and seasonal rhythm related to the habits of the owners. During the night the mouths of the burrows stand open while the crabs are out foraging on the beach. About dawn the crabs return. Whether each goes, as a rule, to the burrow it formerly occupied or merely to any convenient one is uncertain.

Most of the tunnels are simple shafts running down into the sand at an angle of about 45 degrees, ending in an enlarged den. Some few have an accessory shaft leading up from the chamber to the surface. This provides an emergency exit to be used if an enemy—perhaps a larger and hostile crab—enters the main shaft.

The early morning hours are spent repairing, enlarging or improving the burrow selected for the day. A crab hauling up sand from its tunnel always emerges sideways, its load of sand carried like a package under the legs of the functional rear end of the body. Sometimes, immediately on reaching the burrow mouth, it will hurl the sand violently away and flash back into the hole; sometimes it will carry it a little distance away before depositing it. Often the crabs stock their burrows with food and then retire into them; nearly all crabs close the tunnel entrances about midday.

All through the summer the occurrence of holes on the beach follows this diurnal pattern. By autumn most of the crabs have moved up to the dry beach beyond the tide; their holes reach deeper into the sand as though their owners were feeling the chill of October. Then, apparently, the doors of sand are pulled shut, not to be opened again until spring.

The winter beaches show no sign either of the crabs or of their holes—from dime-sized youngsters to full-grown adults, all have disappeared, presumably into the long sleep of hibernation. But, walking the beach on a sunny day in April, one will see here and there

The ghost crab is a model of natural camouflage and defense. When it stands still, its sandy color makes it invisible against the beach; when fleeing from an enemy, it scuttles for cover at a speed over five feet per second; when another ghost crab approaches its burrow, it makes a rubbing noise to warn the intruder off; and when it retires to its burrow, it can close the opening to remove all signs of its presence.

an open burrow. And presently a ghost crab in an obviously new and shiny spring coat may appear at its door and very tentatively lean on its elbows in the spring sunshine. If there is a lingering chill in the air, it will soon retire and close its door. But the season has turned and, under all this expanse of upper beach, crabs are awakening from their sleep.

WONDERLAND OF THE GREAT BARRIER REEF

Francis and Katharine Drake

One of the world's greatest natural wonders has only recently begun attracting hordes of international visitors, unveiling before their fascinated eyes scenes of grandeur that have remained virtually unchanged since time began. This is Australia's Great Barrier Reef, the vast coral rampart that wraps itself like a protective arm around Queensland's seaward shoulder, fingers outthrust toward New Guinea. Once synonymous with the "ends of the earth," this many-splendored realm, where every cay is treasure-laden and where, amid paroxysms of spray, rock and ocean wage their age-old battle for supremacy, is now only 15 flying hours from San Francisco.

Far and away the largest structure ever created by man or beast, the Reef, lying 20 to some 200 miles offshore, covers no less than 80,000 square miles. Its length is 1250 miles; it is hundreds, sometimes thousands, of feet thick, and in its intricate complex of pools, caverns, crevices, chasms and grottoes it harbors virtually every known (and some still unknown) swimming, crawling, floating, boring member of marine society. In a single hour, a visitor may encounter almost anything from the dazzling little fire-fish, flaunting diaphanous fins like Salome's veils, to the giant "man-eating" clam, more than four feet across and weighing a quarter of a ton.

An immense lagoon lies between reef and mainland, and the flight over it is breathtaking. We peer in disbelief at a surface of incomparable colors—peacock blue shot with turquoise, exuberant purples daubed with gold, violet, jade. Scattered like emeralds over the lagoon are hundreds upon hundreds of fairy-tale islands, sides zooming sheer from polished water, skirts hemmed with golden beaches, crests agleam with mint-green vegetation.

The expanse of water lying between the islands and the glittering knife-edge of the Outer Reef looks guileless, yet it is actually the villain behind countless shipwrecks. Beneath that smiling surface lurk innumerable reefs, some paralleling each other like accordion pleats, some overlapping to form labyrinthine traps, still others looped around like trip wires. Capt. James Cook, who in 1770 pioneered this perilous obstacle course, came close to forfeiting all hands together with his bark, H.M.S. *Endeavour*, when submerged coral gouged through oak beams like paper.

It is hard to believe that the architects of this vast realm of guile and beauty are creatures hardly bigger than a pinhead, unable to see, hear or even move about. Yet, over the eons, these insignificant organisms have built up the Great Barrier, inch by inch, mile by square mile. The reef-building polyp is little more than a gelatinous blob with only three "working parts"—mouth, tentacles, inside cavity—yet it is full of surprises. In its tissues dwell thousands of invisible plant organisms (algae) that, in exchange for board and lodging, multiply the polyp's oxygen supply.

The all-purpose mouth absorbs food, expels waste. The tentacles, which in some species are exposed at night when surface seas swarm with nutrition, conceal secret weapons in the form of numerous coiled whips of stinging cells. When edible organisms (tiny crustaceans and newly hatched fish) brush against the tentacles, the whips lash out, paralyzing the victims, which are then drawn into the mouth.

Inside its cavity the polyp transforms limy secretions extracted from the sea into a skeleton. As successive generations of coral colonies die, their innumerable trillions of skeletons gradually pile higher and higher. Cemented by the accumulation of reef debris, they form the basic material of which the whole gigantic structure is composed. In life, the aggregated corals achieve hundreds of extravagant colors and shapes; only dead coral is chalk-white.

Coral polyps can live only in depths penetrated by sunlight, which automatically restricts building areas to shallow water, generally between 50 and 70 feet; below 180 feet all polyps perish. Considering such stringent house rules, here is a curious paradox: Barrier Reef coral extends sometimes thousands of feet *below* the 180-foot limit at which survival is possible. How, then, did this come about?

The most generally accepted explanation is still the one offered by a young naturalist named Charles Darwin back in 1842: the gradual subsidence of the coastline. Darwin figured that eons ago the Austra-

A three-inch saber-toothed blenny lurks among the coral, ready to dart at a larger fish and bite holes in its flesh. Blennies can leave the water and crawl from pool to pool on ventral fins.

lian mainland must have extended to the present Outer Reef; the present islands were peaks of a towering coastal range. By freak coincidence the shore sank at the precise rate at which corals normally grow upward; with neither side gaining on the other, the lagoon has remained perpetually shallow. Geologists believe that this process may have been going on for 50 million years, providing successive generations of polyps with ideal reef-building conditions.

The myriad strange and wonderful inhabitants of the Reef are best seen via "fossicking," an Australian pastime usually defined as "rummaging around." This thrilling adventure costs nothing but a few stiff muscles and perhaps a fall into one of the pools that emerge at low tide. Our fossicking outfit is simple—blue jeans, the cuffs tucked into high, thick-soled sneakers, socks, a stick, old leather gloves. The rule for the gloveless is *"Don't touch"*—coral scratches infect quickly in the tropics; some reef-dwellers sting, nip, spike, poison. The sea wasp, a few square inches of jelly, can kill a man in two minutes with one side-swiping tentacle. Wisest plan is to go with a veteran fossicker; he spots far more than a rookie does.

At ebb tide we cross our reef to the sea edge from which the submerged coral gardens may be seen. Two turtles are paddling by, only a few yards off, eyes at half-slit, backs big enough for a bridge game, ancient faces expressionless as stone.

The water is so clear it seems not to exist; coral gardens show up with the richness of an Oriental rug, and depth perception is sheer guesswork. That weird-looking coral sculpture, seemingly only an arm's length away, is actually 50 feet down. So Mad Hatter-ish is the underwater scenery that in no time we begin "seeing things." We discover a navy-blue cauliflower, a rainbow-hued hedgerow made of staghorns and a fine crop of heliotrope mushrooms growing upside down on pink grass. There are dozens of "flowers," perfect in texture and outline, but bewildering in color—blue chrysanthemums, pea-green poppies, lavender apple blossoms, clumps of jade lilac embowered in shocking-pink ferns. Soon buildings begin to show up: a miniature Tower of Pisa painted magenta; the facade of the Parthenon. And there are enough instruments scattered about—flutes, lutes, organ pipes, spooky green bagpipes—to strike up a band.

But a sea edge is no place for woolgathering. The tide can sneak up and cut off retreat in a matter of minutes. Marooned fossickers, attempting to swim back, have run into all sorts of potential killers—tiger sharks, hammerheads, barracuda, devil rays, sea snakes, octopuses, moray eels.

Most feared by Reef waders is the foot-long stonefish, which lies sluggishly on the bottom of a pool. This vampire-shaped, almost invisible ghoul is plastered with scabs, warts, slime and bristles. Down its back runs a line of razor-sharp spines, each em-

In a crevice of a coral reef a hungry moray eel waits to ambush any passing octopus, crustacean or fish.

This stonefish is well protected: It looks like a rock and its spines hold a powerful venom.

bedded in twin poison sacs. Few who have unwarily trod on a stonefish have recovered from the prickings; those who have tell of pain so excruciating that death seemed preferable.

No need to fear the enormous dugong, though. This beast was once, because of its half-human face and sorrowful sighing, believed to be a mermaid. Like a mermaid, it is harmless.

The fish cavorting in the pools look so unreal they might be staging a Mardi Gras in ribbon-counter colors and jazz patterns—tiger stripes, spots, spirals, checks, even asterisks. Their shapes are equally bizarre—wafer-thin, triangular, rectangular. Some look like dragonflies, others like beer bottles and fountain pens. We discover an 18-inch porcupine-toady that actually has two shapes. Except for the teeth, which can snap barbed wire in two, it seems as sedate as a sole; then we toss in a shell, and *presto!* it turns into a dark-green balloon, abristle with venom-tipped cactus spikes.

We see an orange-red goatfish, harrowing sand with a pronged beard; a walking fish, which spends most of its time out of water, one eye on the sky, the other revolving. Most bemusing of all is a preoccupied little anglerfish peeking over a ledge. It is actually *casting*, dangling in front of its mouth a miniature fishpole that sprouts from its brow. Nature even baited its "line" with a blob to resemble raw meat.

We squelch across to where some giant clams, world's largest bivalve, wait, hinge-side down, rigid as tombstones. The shell of one, agape by ten inches, exposes a seaweed-colored mantle flecked with iridescent green algae. Despite its man-eating reputation, it feeds only on microscopic organisms that the tide washes into its maw. We cannot resist touching that great fleshy mantle with our stick. Instantly the monster squirts like a fire hose, shell edges move— but they do not slam shut. The clam cannot close without first siphoning off water; occlusion takes six or seven seconds, ample time to withdraw hand or foot. The adductor muscle is quite powerful enough to fetter a human being inescapably but, horror tales notwithstanding, generations of swimmers and pearl divers have no proof that this has actually happened.

Wherever we turn, we encounter the grotesque, 18-inch bêche-de-mer, gorging on coral grit, heaving along its obese, inner-tube-like body on tiny retractable feet. A delicacy to Asians, it looks dingy and uninteresting until lifted, when a singular capability comes to light: The bêche-de-mer promptly eviscerates itself. Out fly intestines, a snarl of sticky white filaments, followed by other internal organs. Far from dropping dead after this macabre exhibition,

the creature simply creates for itself a complete set of replacements.

Crab armies are all over the place, racing for bomb shelters, vanishing into commandeered shell-homes. One handsome fellow with blazing red eyes and a china-blue back is the size of a soup plate; another, a species of spider crab, is so hirsute that it suggests motorized seaweed. There are also blue-uniformed soldier crabs, all of them defying Crab Law No. 1— they move forward, not sideways.

More wonderful shell varieties show up here than anywhere else in the world. These include the prized pearl shell (the Barrier supplies 85 percent of the world's mother-of-pearl market); the huge (18-inch) reddish-gold bailer, still used in Australia to bail rowboats; the perfidious textile and marbled cones, so exquisite they fairly beg to be picked up, yet so venomous that one touch can be fatal.

It is time to depart. Already small ripples encircle our ankles, the life-giving tide is returning to feed and refresh all that wait on its measureless bounty. The Great Barrier orchestra begins to tune up—a medley of weird little sounds: *suck-cluck* from the thirsty clams; *scrape-scrape* from the crabs; and, from countless toy waterfalls, a decorous murmur.

The sound is as old as creation, as new as the surf pouring life into yet one more generation. It is the pulse of eternity, that mystical throb from which all living things take their beat.

A giant clam displays its blue-green mantle and one of two siphons through which it circulates water.

Colorful Creatures of the Coral Reef

In the underwater fairyland of the coral reef live fish and other sea animals whose colors are even more vivid than those of the coral itself. The layman, struck by the beauty of these animals, is usually content to admire them. The scientist, aware that nature has a purpose for almost everything, wants to know what these colors are for. "The loud colors of coral fish," writes the naturalist Konrad Lorenz in his book *On Aggression,* "call loudly for explanation." Observing several kinds of what he terms "poster-colored" coral fish, Lorenz noticed that most of them establish territories which they defend vigorously against other members of their own species. His conclusion, which is widely accepted, is that the coral fish have evolved these sharply contrasting patterns to warn or frighten potential intruders away from their territories. Most of the less brightly colored coral fish do not establish territories and are not hostile to their own kind. But when two poster-colored fish of the same species meet, there is almost always a fight, the result of which is that the intruder is either driven off or killed. In only two circumstances do these fish strike their colors: Some fish become so angry at the sight of another fish carrying the same pattern that the two sexes must fade to a duller shade in order to approach each other and spawn. And some of them change their patterns before sleeping, assuming a different "night dress."

Poster-colored, with tusklike teeth to open shellfish, the ten-inch harlequin tusk wrasse (below, left) *swims and hunts alone. Less striking are fairy bass* (below, right), *which congregate and feed on plankton.*

Beautiful but deadly, the lion-fish (above) *has spines with venom potent enough to kill a man.
The equally beautiful clown angelfish* (below) *is not venomous but can sometimes be poisonous to eat.*

The clown fish gets food and protection by living with the sea anemone. Immune to tentacles that poison most other creatures, the clown fish picks food particles from the corners of the anemone's mouth.

The blue-spotted stingray (below, left) has poisonous spines near the base of its tail. The feather star (below, right) is a free-swimming animal that catches plankton in delicate pinnules of its arms.

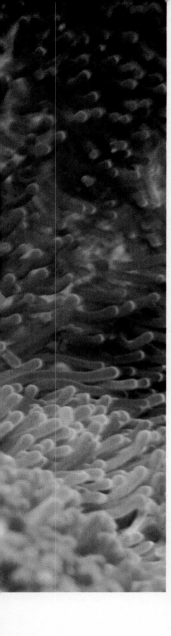

The bright colors of the blue hamlet (left) and the bigeye (right) vie with the coral's subdued pastels. Bigeyes hunt at night and spend the day in the reef's nooks and crannies.

The fire urchin, the size of a small grapefruit, scrapes food from the ocean floor with a mouth located on its underside. Hundreds of poisonous spines protect it from enemies.

THROUGH A
SKIN-DIVER'S MASK

Virginia Bennett Moore

Nothing in the world can really prepare you for what lies beneath the tropical sea. The moment my skin-diver's mask first broke through that cerulean surface in the West Indies, I was Columbus finding a new world of clear blue water, white bottom sand and painted coral. As if the seascape were not enough, along came a paletteful of those bright citizens of the deep, the fish, silent, self-possessed, lively, even a little curious about the great finned Cyclops that swam among them.

I had seen fish before, but never like this. They were shape, pattern, movement—and, above all, color. They staged their pageant in a bath of living blue, itself a stunning visual experience. It was a whole family of colors, really: cobalt, azure, ultramarine, peacock, brilliant turquoise, sapphire and lapis lazuli.

As I eased into the water and lowered my faceplate, that first day in the U.S. Virgin Islands National Park at St. John, things began to happen in a series of images. There was the sand, a pale silken carpet. Lacy towers of colored stone: the coral. Bare trees, outstretched: more coral. Suddenly there appeared a welcoming committee of fish trailing angel robes. Snowy eight-inch disks edged in black, they kept their calm gaze on me—alert, poised, darkly serene of eye. What were they? Palometas, or long-finned pompanos, explained a park ranger.

Reassured by the palometas, I kicked along. My mask was a window that framed the underwater world, while my body rested comfortably half sunk into the lovely liquid cushion that was the sea. Suddenly something moved at the top of the window. Looking up, I thought someone had spread a coat of quicksilver on the surface, now seen from below as wrinkled and bubbled by the caprices of each crossing wave. Hung just this side of the pulsating silver surface like ornaments on the ceiling were half a dozen unmoving shapes watching me intently. They were thin, two-foot torpedoes of transparent green,

*Swimming above a Florida reef, a skin diver surveys
this forest of brain and elkhorn coral—species
that can withstand the wave action in coastal shallows.
More delicate corals require deeper, calmer waters.*

were suddenly fired with life. One turned out to be a smooth purple ray, about two feet across its diamond-shaped back, the other a large flounder. The ray flew as smoothly as a sample of magic carpet toward the safety of deeper water. The flounder shot in the opposite direction. It had lain sprinkled with sand to deceive passing fish.

Just then the big reef came into full view. It was a castled and battlemented undersea island, full of lively grottoes and tangled forests, making one think of a pageant, a carnival, a busy medieval town. Here kings and queens, nobles, soldiers, pages, children and clowns all parade in incredible finery.

Among the first fish I saw were damselfish, a family of square-cut little town dwellers with diminutive faces. As with many reef fishes, their sides are flat as a pumpkin seed. A platoon of sergeant majors swam by, clad in white uniforms topped with vivid yellow, smart black bars down their sides. A solitary beau gregory looked as if it had been dipped into two different pots of Easter-egg dye—its bottom half golden yellow, its top royal blue. A jewel fish was dotted every half inch with single blue dots like sapphires on a black velvet cloak.

Then there were parrot fish. Thick-bodied, thick-tailed, stodgy in demeanor, these otherwise dignified citizens look in their color schemes like a wild bunch of do-it-yourself projects. They come in red or blue, multiple tones of green, spotted, striped or streaked, their tails and fins ·yet another color. The island name of one species, the black knight, evokes an image, but one still less splendid than the fish—a deep, stained-glass blue, with black streakings along the forehead and nape. Another wears black chain mail on a white ground and has a blood-red belly. Anyone who designed his own parrot fish might well see the matching reality swim by.

As I watched, enthralled, it came to me that fish have personalities and even temperaments. Damselfish are among the most pugnacious homeowners on the reef. A four-inch fish will not hesitate to chase one four times its length. A three-inch beau gregory tried to rout a six-foot man by butting his faceplate. A blue parrot fish took a personal dislike to a particular black-and-white one, and flashed to the attack every time it appeared.

Once I had seen the reefs, I was simply hooked on

with alligator jaws, and fins set so far to the rear it looked as if the fish had tried to swim out of them. Barracuda? Needlefish, said the ranger.

What were those tracks on the bottom? To my surprise the small cowrie, on the beach a pretty shell, had become a living creature. Creeping under its shiny tan globe, it had cut a distinct furrow. Over here, the sand looked as if a pincushion had been rolled along. That bunch of eggplant-colored knitting needles, the spiny sea urchin, came this way, stiffly using its bottommost spikes as legs. The long spines break off in your flesh if you jab them. Since sea urchins cling to coral everywhere in the shallows, they are a constant reminder that you are touring an alien world and owe its inhabitants respect.

Down there by a sponge called "dead-man's-fingers" was a shape so still I could make it out only now. It was a foot-long "Tiparillo" with a cigar-holder snout and some fins at the tail like the fletching on an arrow—the trumpet fish. Only its bright, round eyes were moving: It seemed touchingly eager to pass for a frond. As I held my breath and swam down for a closer look, two shadows on the sand fish. Each day brought something new to look at. The sea, where life itself began, is still the mother of more kinds of living things than any other place on Earth. Though the tropical Indo-Pacific is blessed with the greatest variety of fish, the Caribbean runs it a close second. One incomplete count lists 340 species around Puerto Rico and the Virgin Islands. It isn't hard for a vacationing fish watcher to get to know 50 to 75 of them.

Many species have colorful habits. Filefish, a foot and a half long and thin enough to be cut of sheet metal, feed standing on their heads. Wrasses often bury themselves in the sand at night to sleep. Many kinds of parrot fish sleep surrounded with a mucous balloon that may take them half an hour to blow up at night and another half hour to get out of in the morning. The Silent World is often quite noisy. Certain fish chatter, while others make so much noise grinding their teeth or strumming their swim bladders with special muscles that they play a symphony on ship sonars.

Each fish seems to be designed in some way for its locality or its life. The translucent green needlefish is invisibly hung against a green surface; the mirror-barred white palometa might look like shimmering coral to a predator from the deep. The outline of the spadefish—a spectacular white disk with black bars —could fade against waving fronds and sea fans as a zebra's image would be broken on the hot plain. And the Nassau grouper has eight different changes of dress to fool the shark as well as its victims.

Questions about color in the reef kingdom are still only partly answered. It is not always camouflage. Some fish even use it to express their feelings. A surgeonfish, chasing an irritating schoolmate, was seen to turn pale with wrath on the front half and very dark on the rear. Fish may also blanch with fear. I watched a brilliant yellow fish thickly covered with black polka dots swim into a clump of coral and, startled, come out clad in a blackish hood, his belly blanched light cream.

As you paddle around the populous reef, you find the waters filled with great schools of tiny visitors. They are the fry, the plentiful young of sea fishes of every description, almost too small and numberless to have a name. At times you can pass among the fry until they fill your vision. They are a gleaming mist of life whose droplets are sorted by sizes. They are pale, quick, hunted—and forever on the move.

Any day, but especially on days when storms kick up the water until it begins to look like milk, you also share the water with great patrols. Here a school of amberjacks, there of cavallas, yonder of Spanish mackerel, appears. All swim in a kind of easy blue-white glory, full of muscle, moving in unison, casting a wary eye on everything. These fish are predators. Unlike the calm, almost trusting reef dwellers, seeing you they prefer to be gone. But on these murky days the dim visibility brings them closer.

One day as I dipped into St. John's Caneel Bay, mask on, I found myself among fry fleeing some unseen terror. Oblivious to my threatening bulk, they skittered all around me like flakes of snow on the wind, shining silver leaves relentlessly driven, a storm of fish. Then I saw two mackerel about a foot and a half long. They were swimming up and down, almost cynically holding the fry at bay or driving them back and forth with a gesture while waiting to take the first bite at their leisure—perhaps when I had gone. For the school, though too large to be entirely consumed, can never entirely escape, any more than mice can outrun a whippet.

Not all little things in the sea feel hunted. One day not far from shore I acquired a small school of white fish just the size and shape of 50-cent pieces, with yellow borders, a sharp yellow fin jutting out of their backs, and almost no tail—probably baby yellow jacks. They were cheerfully swimming their hardest to keep up with me, dipping as I dived, rising and turning as I did, their little bodies shimmering with exertion. When I rested they peered in through my faceplate bold as chickadees, with big eyes black as buttons. When I put my hand under one, it did not mind. And when at last I climbed out of the water, it was with a pang that I saw them run, hesitate, scan the sea, gather themselves and swim away.

Theirs is a world that, having seen, I cannot put aside. Through the snorkeler's faceplate I keep looking again and again.

SHELLS OF THE SEVEN SEAS

Donald and Louise Peattie

With every tide the seas cast up on the beaches of the world new treasure for those who come seeking it. Shells, prized by man from prehistoric times, are now a global hobby. On all the shores of ocean, collectors by the tens of thousands are searching the strand or dredging the tidal mud and diving into tropical waters for the living animals that offer in most perfect state these jewels of the sea. There are some 100,000 species to be found, not only in the seven seas but in ponds, rivers and meadows. They pass from hand

The chambered nautilus uses its pearly shell (shown in cross section) to alter its level in the water. Through a tube connected to its body, the nautilus fills the shell's chambers with gases so it will rise in the water and reabsorbs the gases to sink.

to hand, from one country to another and among scientists, hobbyists and museums.

Their variety, in shape and tint and size, is dazzling. A shell may look like a petal frozen in stone or like an ear, an egg, a screw, a butterfly, a turban, the paw of a lion, the comb of Venus or the wing of an angel. Every one once housed a living creature—a mollusk, to which clan belong the succulent oyster and the tedious garden snail.

The mollusks, one of nature's oldest and most successful experiments in animal structure, are spineless. But whereas the *internal* skeleton of an animal with a backbone is grim and unsightly when at last exposed, these *external* skeletons—the shells of mollusks—keep their color and luster after death, each a little monument to the passing beauty of life.

Just as our fingernails are products of our flesh, the shell is a limestonelike deposit of the animal living inside, secreted by the mollusk's mantle, the ruffly fold you see on a snail as it "comes out of its house." The glands of the mantle regulate the rate of growth, the form and color and pattern of the shell.

The outermost layer of a shell is a horny skin. The middle layer is the thickest—so thick in some of the giant clams of Zamboanga in the Philippines that each clam may weigh 100 pounds or more. The innermost layer is thin and has a porcelain sheen. This heart of the shell may gleam with a pearly luster, glow with a delicate earlobe pink, or shimmer with peacock greens and blues, as in the abalone, pride of the California coast. From this layer comes the mother-of-pearl used in buttons, jewelry or inlay. Here the true pearl is formed when some irritating substance gets into the shell and is sealed off by the animal.

At a glance you can usually classify a shell as one-valve or two-valve. Bivalves, such as oysters, clams, mussels and scallops, consist of two halves connected by a hinge of ligament. The univalves tend to form a continuous spiral; these are the sea and land snails. The spiral may be drawn out into a spindle in the distaff shells, flattened in the cone shells, hidden within the cowries—yet it is always present. Nowhere is this spiral more lovely than in the chambered nautilus, where it grows into a flawless logarithmic curve where the width of the turns increases at a fixed ratio to their length.

The mollusk is not a simple or unfeeling creature. Within its armor the soft body has heart, stomach of sorts, liver, kidneys. Sea mollusks breathe through gills, and if they live deep in the mud they send up a long siphon to reach clean water. Mollusks often have delicate senses. Some have compound eyes, like those of an insect; they may have a keener sense of smell than ours. The sense of touch, as with us, is distributed all over the flesh but is especially strong in the soft mouth parts, the folds of the mantle, and in the "foot."

This foot is the basic part of the snail that you see when it is well extended from the shell. Using the muscles of the foot, the snail undulates along in a sort of thumb-and-fist progress. Scallops, by opening and shutting their bivalves rapidly, bite their way forward, discharging water behind them through their siphons in a sort of jet propulsion. And the fighting conch of Florida jumps, lumbers, topples and rolls. If you capture one, it may escape by using gravity to help propel its top-heavy house down the slope of the beach back to the sea.

As the lover of shells wanders along the shore, salt wind in his face and his eyes conning the sand, he will learn that the sea-ripened loot tossed at his feet by the breakers is different every day. Finds will be richest at low tide or after a storm that has wrenched up the wrack of the bottoms and washed it high. And at the waterline are living creatures like the razor clams, so sensitive to your step that they will bury themselves out of sight at your coming, or the exquisite little coquina clams of Florida beaches, whose tiny, rainbow-colored halves you can open into butterfly shapes.

Without dissecting these living creatures, you will not know "the he-shell from the she-shell." Yet mollusks have a sex life, and it is easiest to understand its oddities if we think of flowers, for flowers, too, are commonly male and female at the same time. Some flowers are wind-pollinated in chancy, extravagant fertility; others are economically self-fertilized. Again, flowers may be at one stage all male, or all female, or double-sexed. Mollusks may use any of these curious arrangements. Thus oysters never meet their mates, and many a snail is hermaphroditic, or two-sexed.

The small fry get all varieties of maternal care or neglect, from being set adrift in the waters, helpless as frogs' eggs, to being carried in a pouch, kangaroo-fashion. Some come neatly packaged in egg cases, from which they may emerge either complete, as tiny replicas of their parents, or in a free-swimming larval stage, like tadpoles.

You may think that you have found a living mollusk when you see a shell moving rapidly across the sand, only to turn it over and discover that a hermit crab has taken up residence there. If it is indeed a live mollusk newly tossed up by the tide, or if by dredging you have found one that you wish to keep, you will want to clean it. This is best done by boiling it and delicately withdrawing the fleshy parts within. Tiny shells become clean enough by drying in the hot sun.

Cast-up shells of clams, mussels, scallops, sea snails and sand dollars carpet the shore of Padre Island off the Texas coast. Other beaches on the island are composed entirely of lighter, smaller shells that have been pulverized by the surf.

Some people wash or lightly oil their specimens to make them glossy.

Shells have had value since our earliest knowledge of humanity. As a medium of exchange, even in prehistoric times, they traveled far across the world. In the graves of Cro-Magnon man, who lived some 10,000 to 37,000 years ago in western Europe, have been found red helmet shells native to the tropic seas of the Orient. In wilderness America, too, shells were currency. On the coasts the Indians had "mints" where shells were sorted, cleaned and polished, and then strung on thongs of hide. With this wampum they traded far and wide. The little yellow money cowrie spread from its tropical home waters over many lands as a sort of coinage, through hundreds of years.

Certain shells are so beautiful and rare that they are used like jewels for adornment; thus the golden cowrie of the Fiji Islands is worn only by the chieftains. Other shells are so coarse and common we crush them up to surface roads or make mortar. On one little shell was built the wealth of the ancient city of Tyre, in Phoenicia. For the snail that lives within it exudes a fluid from which the Tyrians produced a dye ranging from rose to deep violet. So prized was this dye that it created a mighty commerce, and became a mark of distinction. Only senators of Rome were permitted to wear togas with this purple border.

The western Pacific is the richest of all sources of shell treasure, from southern Japan in the north to Australia's Great Barrier Reef, from the Marquesas to the Malay Peninsula. In a fine collection there will be shells from the Caribbean, too, and Iceland, the Red Sea, Panama, Tasmania and the Indian Ocean. But it is not necessary to travel the world over to amass a handsome collection. One of the best I ever saw belonged to a man who specialized in the shells of the Gulf of California, and bartered for other kinds.

The best shelling grounds in the United States are on the beaches of two islands off the west coast of Florida—Sanibel and Captiva. There you may gather moon shells, cone shells, jingle shells, olive shells, the Chinese alphabet shell scrawled with inscrutable ciphers, the delicate angel's wing, the rare junonia, the left-handed whelk called *perversa* (most snail shells spiral to the right as you hold them) and dozens more. As daily you grow richer in your finds and your knowledge, no one is the poorer for it. The tides, indeed, have always more to give. And in this interest, shared by countless numbers over the world, you enter a happy fraternity. You come to understand that any shell, having held life, holds wonder—as a child knows, hearing against his ear that whisper like the sound of far-off surf.

Chapter Three

Denizens of the Deep

*Seals cavorting with obvious zest, men-of-war sailing before the wind,
sharks shaped like submarines—these are but a few of the innumerable creatures
that make their homes in the sea. From the restless, wind-lashed
surface to the eternally black abyssal plains, the sea abounds with life.*

THE SQUID: NATURE'S NIGHTMARE

Ronald N. Rood

They have reached out and torn sailors from life rafts. They have reduced huge tuna to bones before the hooked fish could be boated. Large members of the clan even dare to battle with the sperm whale. Yet most people who know anything about the squid —one of the sea's most bizarre and terrifying creatures—assume it's some sort of octopus, because it has snaky arms at the end of a bullet-shaped body. This is like comparing a tiger with an alley cat.

A 50-pound octopus with a ten-foot arm spread is a giant; the biggest squid are ten times as large. Octopuses retreat singly into scattered holes on the ocean bottom; though one may occasionally maul a diver who surprises it in its den, most leave the scene when man appears. Squid, on the other hand, may attack anything—even anchors, boat hooks or the hull of a ship. They work in ravenous mobs in open water. An attack by one may be the signal for a frenzied rush by others.

Like the octopus, the squid has eight arms with rows of suckers—but with the added touch of tooth-like horny rings around the edge of each sucker. And there are two more arms, called tentacles, which have no equal in all nature. Like long rubber cables, they can stretch far beyond the reach of the other arms or snap back until they are nearly hidden. Armed at the tip with suckers (some 20-foot specimens even have retractile claws), the tentacles shoot out toward a victim, clamp fast and pull the prey back to that writhing nest of arms with the parrot beak in the center.

Unlike the baggy octopus, a squid is long and thin, with two horizontal fins at one end. It travels by jet propulsion. Taking in water by opening the muscular mantle that surrounds its body like a loose overcoat, the squid squirts it out through a powerful siphon near the head. This shoots the squid backward, slender rear section first. Rocketing through the water, it can overtake nearly anything that swims. By reversing the flexible siphon, it shuttles back and forth through a school of fish. Those two tentacles whip out like living lassos, catching fish after fish—killing far beyond its needs. Just a bite out of each one, and it's dropped for a new victim.

When I saw my first living squid in a tank at Woods Hole, Massachusetts, I had the uncanny feeling that I was being watched. The eyes are intelligent, alert, arrestingly human. Each eye has a movable lens to focus on objects at any distance, a refinement possessed by no other invertebrates outside the class. It has an iris and pupil, just as we have. Sometimes there are even eyelids.

This wouldn't be so surprising if the squid were close to us on the family tree. But squid are mollusks, with a history that stretches back 400 million years, far beyond man's. As the ages passed, their ancestors —some with dozens of arms—developed shells like ice-cream cones, sometimes 12 feet long. Later types had coiled shells, like a ram's horn. Today they have no outer shells but are built around a cartilaginous internal rod called the "pen." It is the internal support of cuttlefish—a member of the same class as the squid, and closely resembling it—which provides the cuttlebone for your pet parakeet.

The numbers of squid are fantastic. Ships occasionally get false bottom readings from echo sounders due, some scientists say, to millions of squid suspended halfway to the bottom, feeding on plankton. Sometimes this layer is found on the surface. One ship sailed for two hours through a solid sea of squid stretching to the horizon in all directions.

The squid is a living kaleidoscope. Rob it of its prey, and it flashes an angry red. Frighten it, and it turns a pale, watery color. It can be mottled like the sand, rippled like the surface. It has thousands of tiny color cells, opening and closing like drawstring bags. One instant they're open, showing their colored lin-

ing. A fifth of a second later they snap shut. Deepwater forms may have hundreds of light-producing areas, sparkling like fireflies.

If camouflage doesn't work against a predatory enemy, the squid has an emergency measure—it shoots out a blob of black, gooey "ink" through the siphon to form a smoke screen. Squid from the depths even have luminous ink to make a flare in the water while the darkened owner sneaks away.

Only rarely does the real giant squid come up from the depths to be seen by man. An occasional specimen is vomited up by a dying sperm whale. Fishermen sometimes see an injured one lying on the surface.

On March 25, 1941, the English troopship *Britannia* was sunk in the central Atlantic. A dozen men clung to a tiny raft. Only one or two could sit on it at a time, while the rest waited their turn in the water. Suddenly one of them cried out. Horrified, the others saw a great squid throw a tentacle around his body. Then the other tentacle clamped fast. Before their eyes, the unspeakable creature broke the sailor's hold on the raft and pulled him to his death.

Soon afterward, another man felt a tentacle grasp his leg. For some reason, it let go again. But where the suckers had fastened on, they left raw, bleeding sores. The scars, like prints of bottle caps, were still visible two years later.

On October 26, 1873, near Portugal Cove, Newfoundland, two men and a boy were out fishing when one of them spotted a floating mass in the water. It hung limp, like a piece of wreckage. But, prodded with a gaff, it came to life, reared up and lunged at their little boat. Its arms spread out, exposing a beak in the center twice as big as a man's head.

It slipped one tentacle across the gunwale like a python, pulling the little craft toward that horrendous mouth. It gouged at the planking, staring at the men with dinner-plate eyes. Then it threw an arm over the boat to secure its hold and sank beneath the water. Spellbound, the men watched their boat tip until water rushed in over the side.

Twelve-year-old Tom Piccot saved them all. He grabbed a hatchet and began to chop at the grisly creature. Not until he had hacked it free did it drop away. Then it lay alongside the boat and glared at them, its great cylindrical body pulsating and throwing out clouds of ink.

Squid come in many sizes and have a wide array of adaptations. This squid is shown about six times life size; the luminescent organs around its eyes and on its tentacles could be searchlights or lures for attracting plankton.

They raced for shore. Their countrymen wouldn't believe their tale until they showed the evidence—a 19-foot tentacle like a heavy rope in the bottom of their boat. Beside it was another chunk as big as a man's arm.

The longest squid actually measured was 57 feet, found on a New Zealand beach in 1888. One measured in 1959 at the Marine Laboratory, University of Miami, was 47 feet long.

No one knows how large squid may grow. Several authorities think they may reach 70 feet, including 50-foot tentacles. Such a creature would weigh well over a ton. There's an interesting point for further speculation, too. The suckers of a 50-foot squid leave circular rings on the skin of the sperm whale about four inches across. Yet whales have been found with round scars 18 inches across—more than four times greater than scars made by the largest squid known!

Compared with such giants, most squid are tiny— less than eight inches long. These constitute one of the most important food items in the ocean. Schools of fish cut great swaths through their millions. (It is this fact, plus their own cannibalism, which keeps them from overrunning the ocean completely.) Porpoises and killer whales often gorge on them. Man has long enjoyed them, too—consuming half a million tons a year. Fried squid is delicious, but you must first pound it to a pulp or you will be chewing on it all afternoon.

The mating procedure of the squid is extraordinary. Sometimes the male "courts" the female, or fights with other males for her favor. At other times he merely seizes her abruptly in a many-armed embrace. Then, since he's a cannibal, he may forget himself. Many a squid romance ends as abruptly as it starts— with a squid dinner.

The sex organs of both male and female are hidden deep within the cavity of the mantle. The male squid's sperm are wrapped in small packets called spermatophores. With one of his arms he reaches into his mantle cavity, takes a few packets from the genital organ and places them in the mantle cavity of the female. The wrapping unravels, releasing the sperm. Later, as the eggs pass along their way to the outside, they are fertilized by the waiting sperm.

The female gently blows the fertilized eggs out through the siphon and catches them in her arms. The eggs—from a few hundred to 30,000, depending on the species—are about the size of cooked tapioca. She presses them against underwater objects in footlong, sticky strings, then swims away. The babies hatch in about a month. They are fierce little beauties with rainbow colors, looking like exquisite rice-grain editions of their parents. They spread quickly, but not before fish scoop them up in great numbers. So the chain of life continues.

Today, the squid has taken on scientific importance in the study of nerves and mental health. Biologists have discovered a giant nerve in several species that is 40 times thicker than the largest nerve worked on previously. Instead of working with fibers thinner than a human hair, scientists can now use one that approaches the diameter of a wooden match. Since nerve tissue is much the same no matter what animal it comes from, this should facilitate research in nerve action, vital body activities, hormones.

And so we probe into 20th-century health and disease, aided by an appalling creature whose beginnings trace back almost as far as any living animal on earth today.

BEWARE THE DEADLY MAN-OF-WAR!

Fred Warshofsky

One sweltering August Sunday 19-year-old Stephen Koenig joined millions of other New Yorkers in a lemminglike run to the cooling sea. At Rockaway Beach, a slender ribbon of sand that stretches into the Atlantic Ocean, he splashed happily into the water. A moment later he was screaming in agony. Arms flailing, he began thrashing to shore. "Help me!" he cried. "Get it off me!"

Another bather reached out and tore at the strange bluish strings that garlanded Koenig's neck and shoulders. Suddenly that man, too, cried out in pain as the stringy "weeds" stung his hands. Within minutes, several other victims were stumbling with pain-filled cries from the suddenly deadly ocean.

Coughing and choking, Koenig reached the boardwalk, then passed out. He was rushed to Peninsula General Hospital, where the emergency room was already jammed with bathers clamoring for treatment of mysterious, painful stings.

An intern placed an oxygen mask over Koenig's face and urged him to breathe deeply. Koenig gagged and passed out a second time. He awoke in bed, an anxious circle of doctors around him. Only then did he notice the puffy, angry red welts that laced his neck, chest and arms. It was three days before he could leave the hospital.

Stephen Koenig's harrowing experience had been with a purple-blue blob of jelly called the Portuguese man-of-war. That same hot week in August

more than 100 other swimmers were stung at New York beaches as shifting winds sailed hordes of the deadly men-of-war into shallow coastal waters.

Physalia physalis (from the Greek word for bladder) is among the most fascinating and least-understood creatures in the sea. Cruising the Gulf Stream, it ranges from the Caribbean north to Nova Scotia, whence it is swirled into the North Atlantic and drifts eastward to the English Channel, the Irish Sea and even the Mediterranean. In the Pacific, a smaller version of *Physalia* ranges from the California coast to Australia.

Seen from shore or shipboard, a fleet of *Physalia* is an impressive sight: graceful ballooning floats shimmer like iridescent blue-and-purple Christmas-tree ornaments atop the white-crested ocean. Three centuries ago, so the story goes, one such fleet was sighted by English ships off the Portuguese coast. To sailors on deck, the *Physalia* looked like miniatures of the Portuguese galleons that once ruled the seas, so they named them "Portuguese men-of-war."

Like an iceberg, there is far more mass and menace to the man-of-war than meets the eye at the surface. Trailing away beneath each float like streamers of confetti is an array of murderous fishing tentacles that slowly writhe and reach as much as 60 feet below for prey. These deadly fishing lines are studded with thousands of stinging cells that contain a poison almost as powerful as a cobra's venom.

Unfortunately it is impossible to keep *Physalia* in aquariums or other captivity for any length of time, so much of its life cycle remains a mystery. The most intensive studies have been made at the University of Miami's Institute of Marine Science, where scientists have identified the *Physalia* poison as a neurotoxin—a protein substance that deranges the nervous system. To the small fish (up to six inches long) and the larger planktonic animals that compose the man-of-war's main diet, the sting means instant death.

So powerful is the poison that even a beached *Physalia* is dangerous—a false step onto one of the dried blue strings will cause an excruciating hotfoot. In the Miami laboratory, *Physalia* venom has been frozen and stored for as long as six years without losing its potency.

In the water, the venom acts with incredible swiftness. "Within minutes," explained Dr. Charles E. Lane, marine-biology professor, "as the neurotoxin goes to work, blood pressure drops alarmingly. Breathing becomes difficult, the pulse rapid and feeble."

These symptoms were vividly demonstrated when

A wary snorkeler surfaces a safe distance from the bladderlike float of a man-of-war. By angling its rayed crest in the breeze, this dangerous jellyfish relative can drift along like a sailboat.

As shown in this underwater view, a man-of-war trails its tentacles below it while floating on the surface. Any small creature unlucky enough to swim too close to them is quickly immobilized by their poison.

a scientist associated with the University of Miami ran afoul of a *Physalia* while skin diving off Miami's Crandon Park Beach. Writhing in pain, the scientist was rushed to a hospital where he lapsed into shock. His breathing grew labored; to save his life, doctors placed him in an iron lung. For two months he bore graphic evidence of the encounter—a trail of fiery red welts across his chest.

Joseph C. Goodman, a retired businessman from Stamford, Connecticut, was not so lucky. Hit by a man-of-war while swimming off Miami Beach in 1964, he staggered out of the water and fell unconscious on the sand. A lifeguard tried mouth-to-mouth resuscitation while a vacationing doctor applied chest massage. It was in vain. Goodman died.

There is no antidote for *Physalia* stings, but common rubbing alcohol seems to neutralize the poison and is used as a standard treatment. Natives on the Bimini Islands in the Bahamas have developed their own treatment—they wash the infected area with a strong detergent. If none is handy they use urine.

Just under the *Physalia*'s iridescent float is its remarkable digestive apparatus—consisting of hundreds of stubby, vividly colored red, orange and pink gastrozooids or feeding polyps. When the tentacles reaching down into the sea have captured food, they contract and, like fishermen hauling in a net, raise the paralyzed prey to the gastrozooids. Eventually the dead fish is studded with these polyps, which act like a communal stomach. Each gastrozooid secretes a potent enzyme that swiftly breaks down the proteins of the victim's body.

The *Physalia*'s floatlike bladder, which ranges from 8 to 12 inches across, is topped by a graceful, rayed crest of flexible membrane. To keep the float above the surface where it can catch the breeze, it is filled with a gas (mostly carbon monoxide) supplied by a gland.

Like the lion in the jungle, the man-of-war has its own jackal seeking scraps from the king's table. As the *Physalia* fishes through the heaving, plankton-rich meadows of the high seas, a bright, blue-and-silver-banded fish darts in and out among the tentacles, tearing shreds of fish and crustacea from the deadly lines. This is the *Nomeus*, or man-of-war fish. Often the small *Nomeus* will leave the *Physalia* and swim in ever-widening circles. Larger fish, looking for a meal, will arrow after the *Nomeus*, which swiftly darts into what appears to be a forest of seaweed. Its unwary pursuer follows and is immediately overwhelmed by the lethal tentacles. And even as the fish is being hauled up toward the gastrozooids, the *Nomeus* is snapping at the tentacles for its reward.

For some years it was thought that the *Nomeus* was as vulnerable to *Physalia* venom as other fish, but was agile enough to avoid the writhing tentacles. Dr. Lane's Miami laboratory recently disproved this theory. He reports: "We took a group of fish the same size as the *Nomeus* and determined the amount of toxin needed to kill them. We then gave the *Nomeus* ten times that amount, and the little scavengers swam away as if nothing had happened."

With its awesome weaponry and consorts of the food-luring *Nomeus*, it would seem that only violent storms or perverse winds could drive the man-of-war to destruction. But *Physalia* does have a natural enemy—the huge, lumbering loggerhead turtle. These giant sea turtles weigh up to 500 pounds and are armored with a horny, brownish-red shell from which an immense beaked head rears out.

One observer tells of seeing an enormous loggerhead plowing through a fleet of men-of-war with its eyes swollen shut from a thousand stings, its mouth trailing broken strings of tentacles like blue streamers from a Maypole. With great snapping gulps, the loggerhead tore through the fleet, in its wake a clear strip of water, on either side the bobbing blue floats, now quite defenseless.

We don't know by what strange chemistry nature has rendered the great loggerhead and little *Nomeus* partially immune to the lethal poison. In time the answers will come and with them possibly a medical use as an antidote for the toxic venom. Until then, the man-of-war will remain a deadly mystery, ghosting before the wind and spreading its tentacles to paralyze and devour any prey unfortunate enough to cross its course.

THE LOBSTER: ODDBALL OF THE OCEAN

David MacDonald

Fossils dredged up from Long Island Sound prove that 100 million years ago the North American lobster looked just as he does today—like Rube Goldberg's weirdest whatsit. With horny armor plating, spindly legs and menacing pincers, *Homarus americanus* might have resulted from the mating of a giant roach with a Stillson wrench. Yet his bizarre design has enabled him not only to survive for eons in a hostile underworld but also to remain uniquely himself—ugly, ornery and very, very odd.

To begin with, the lobster is both inside out and upside down. Besides crawling around in his bones, he carries most of his nervous system along his belly instead of his back. His brain consists of two parts, pinhead-size, above and below his throat. He listens with his legs, tastes with his feet, has molars in his stomach. His kidneys are behind his pointed little forehead.

Except for a comparative few in northern Europe, true lobsters are peculiar to the cool West Atlantic, and peculiar is just the word. "The lobster is a real case," said Dr. D. G. Wilder, a biologist at the Canadian government fisheries research station in St. Andrews, New Brunswick.

Scientists know him as an arthropod, a hardtop "bug" with multijointed legs: a king-size submarine cousin of the spider. His body is made up of a fused head and thorax, rigidly encased in a lifeless cuticle called chitin, and a flexible segmented tail. He has two pairs of whiplike antennae, sharp at detecting food or danger, but so insensitive to pain that they can be snipped off without his seeming to notice it. His stalked eyes contain thousands of facets, yet he's sadly myopic.

This scavenger has six pairs of mouth parts, one pair, the mandibles, being food grinders, which chew sideways. Behind these come the heavy crusher claw and a slightly smaller sawtooth cutter, both used mainly for self-defense. The male's claws, larger than the female's, can grow out of all proportion to his body. One huge 35-pounder landed in Massachusetts had claws weighing 24 pounds—too heavy for him to lift when out of water.

Equally unusual are the lobster's eight slender walking legs, bristling with tiny sensory hairs that pick up underwater sounds and smells. For lack of a better place, some of his 20 pairs of gills are located at the bases of his legs. Then there's the long meaty tail, equipped with four pairs of swimmerets. His streamlining is, typically, all backwards. Though *Homarus* nimbly walks forward on his delicate legs, his heavy body buoyed up by the water, he flips his tail when frightened and scoots away in reverse.

The shell is usually a mottled greenish-black, which blends with his surroundings on the rocky ocean floor. But differences in diet and environment produce such striking exceptions as yellow, scarlet and gaily spotted "calico" lobsters. Whatever the color, all turn red when they get into hot water.

Beneath that crusty exterior is an even crustier personality. Wary, cranky and distinctly antisocial, *Homarus* spends most of his days in hiding, burrowed under rocks or in clumps of seaweed, with his big claws held at the ready. Yet he is game to tackle anything that moves. Recently a Toronto man was unpacking a crate of live lobsters when one reached up and wrenched a pipe from his mouth—and with it a tooth!

At moments of fear or shock, and sometimes for no apparent reason, lobsters may dismember themselves. Scuba-diving in Northumberland Strait, Dr. Dick Wilder once grabbed a lobster by the claws. It simply shucked off both—along a perforated breakaway seam near its body—and ducked under a rock. Luckily, the lobster can grow new claws, legs or other spare parts.

In summer, *Homarus* gorges so ravenously that his shell finally splits a seam across the back, between the body and tail. He then lies on one side, jackknifes into a V shape and gradually squirms out through the crack. This incredible molting process may take about 15 minutes. The blood recedes from his big claws, and

they shrink enough to be pulled through joints only a ninth of their normal size. As the lobster backs out, his entire shell falls away in one piece. This includes the grinding teeth of his stomach, the film over his eyeballs, his antennae—even the tiny crust on microscopic sensory hairs.

Completely defenseless and covered only by a jelly-soft skin, the freshly molted lobster stays holed up in his burrow. Within a few hours, by absorbing seawater, he swells to his new size—15 percent longer and 50 percent heavier than before. (If he's replacing a lost part, the rest of the body's growth slows to let it catch up.) It takes several weeks for the new suit to harden.

After the female of the species has shed her tight corset, every second year she's in the mood for love. She

Homarus americanus is the clawed lobster found along most of North America's Atlantic Coast. All lobsters are essentially scavengers—scouring the ocean floor for algae, eelgrass or bits of animal food. When they have molted, or are growing new parts, lobsters crave shell-building calcium carbonate. They satisfy this need by eating crusty sand dollars, the shells of snails and, occasionally, even members of their own species.

plays up to a courtly male with come-hither sweeps of her antennae across his head, then, with claws clicking like castanets, they join in an ungainly courtship dance. They embrace and he deposits sperm in a sac between her last two pairs of walking legs.

The female retains the live sperm for months. Then, with her tail curled into a pocket, she lays her eggs there and releases the sperm cells. The fertilized eggs, resembling dark-green caviar, remain cemented to her undercarriage for almost a year. When they begin to hatch, she stands on tiptoe and shakes off perhaps 75,000 beady-eyed larvae, about the size of mosquitoes, which float to the sea's surface.

Thenceforth the lobster's life is a constant fight against all but impossible odds: He has about one hope in 10,000 of growing up, one in a million of lasting to middle age—good reason for his snappish disposition. At the very outset, when baby lobsters swim and eat plankton on top of the water, 99 percent fall victim to fish or bigger lobsters. The few that survive, after molting three times in as little as four weeks, sink to the ocean bottom and run for cover.

With luck a lobster can live for 50 years or more. Trouble is, by the time he's about eight years old, ten inches long and a pound or so in weight, *Homarus americanus* has become fair game for his deadliest foe, *Homo sapiens.*

When white settlers first came to this continent, the North Atlantic coast was literally crawling with the crustaceans. Storms washed waves of lobsters ashore at Plymouth Colony, where they were used for fertilizer or food for the poor. In time, however, the lowly lobster became such popular fare that he was fished much too intensively. In Canada's Maritime Provinces, for example, the catch rose to a record 100 million pounds in 1885, then steadily slumped to only 27 million pounds in 1918. *Homarus americanus* seemed headed the way of the dinosaur and the dodo.

Since then, strict conservation measures have rescued him from extinction: Fishermen are now obliged by law to release the smaller lobsters as well as all egg-bearing, or "berried," matrons. Even so, with 8000 U.S. fishermen and 25,000 Canadians tending four million traps, up to 90 percent of all lobsters that reach legal size are being caught each year.

Numerous attempts to start lobster colonies on the Pacific Coast, both in the United States and Canada, have failed. Two years ago, however, a hundred prime New Brunswick lobsters were flown out to carefully chosen waters off Vancouver Island, where most appear to be doing fine. Additional shipments have been made. If this transplant works, as one in Russia's coastal waters already has, another thriving commer-

cial lobster fishery could eventually be established.

Recently vast lobster colonies have been discovered from 75 to 150 miles off the New England coast, on the edge of the continental shelf. Last year U.S. trawlers netted an estimated 2000 tons of these deepwater monsters. While inshore lobsters run only about one pound, because they've been fished so much for so long, the average offshore weight is five to six pounds; some weigh 25 pounds.

Thanks to modern packing and shipping methods, the market for live lobsters today is virtually worldwide. Now more and more people are sitting down, tucking napkins into their collars, and asking themselves, "How can something that looks so kooky taste so good?"

SEALS FOR TEXAS

N. J. Berrill

I have always liked seals. The first seals I ever saw were in a circus, throwing balls from nose to nose with amazing skill and obvious enjoyment. Later on I found them, in the zoo of a great city, almost as interested in their human spectators as we were in them. A coin in a slot machine sent a herring shooting through the air to drop into the pool, and the seals on the high ledge dove after it. Seals swim with a lithe sense of satisfaction, and a seal pool in a city park is the center of attraction.

Where we live in Maine a seal comes into the cove regularly during May and June, just behind the herring shoals, perhaps to see who has arrived among the summer people. And a year or so ago the zoos of Dallas, Galveston, St. Louis and Boston sent a call out to the Boothbay Harbor hatchery to send some baby seals, so out we went to find some.

The time had to be right, for the state of the tide was important, and we set out at noon. It took us an hour or more to thread out of the harbor past the bell buoys and channel beacons, through Fisherman's Passage inside the islands, and up the ten miles of saltwater Damariscotta River to the narrows, where the ledges cut far across and the tide runs fast.

Suddenly the river turned and widened, and the wind was gone. The boat slowed, circled and cautiously moved close to shore inside the point. Ledges from the point cut the river almost in two here, though most of them were under water with the high tide. The main ledge extended from a green knoll out about a hundred feet, with white gulls crowded

Harbor seals are sometimes incorrectly called leopard seals because of their spots. This baby, still in its white infant fur, can already swim well, but will rest on its mother's back when it is tired.

on its bare rock. A few boulders also stood above water . . . and then one of the boulders began to move. Three or four large seals, almost the color of the brown rock itself, had been basking out of the water and had been alerted by the passing of the boat. As we approached closer they slid into the water and disappeared, and in a few moments the gulls left too, taking to the air in sudden clamor as the panic of a few went through the crowd.

The engineer took the boat back through the narrows and the anchor was dropped a few hundred feet below the seaward ledge. This ledge, like the first, ran straight out from the point, and the two together with the shoreline constituted three sides of a box. We cast off in the dory, and the wind blew us rapidly up toward the ledges. The seine net was put over, one end with a weighted rope anchoring it near the tip of the shorter ledge, the other end halfway toward the tip of the long ledge. Half of the fourth side of the box was now closed, and the trap was set. Seals might already be within and others could get there, either through the half-open side or through the narrow gap in the middle of the long ledge.

It was a stiff pull to bring the dory back against the wind, and the tide had still another hour of flood. But before the boat could be tied up to wait there was a cry, "There's one in it now!" and a sudden turmoil was visible in the middle of the line of corks holding up the net. The dory dropped back, part of the net with an entangled seal was brought inboard, and the net released. It was a baby not two months old, and no sooner was it hauled into the larger boat than a great brown seal jumped clear over the net, turned about and attacked the net violently.

This was the mother, showing her age by the warm color of her coat, and not so much outraged at what had happened as frenzied by the danger to her other baby that had drifted unwarily toward the net. We rowed back and got this youngster too, though there was no thought of catching the grown seals, especially the mothers. With their intelligence, experience and powerful bodies, our net would have been lost.

The first baby aboard was a bull pup, and its male disposition was only too obvious. In spite of its recent experience of entanglement and capture, the youngster snapped viciously at every foot that came anywhere near. The second pup was female and gentle from the beginning, although after ten or fifteen minutes the bull's display of masculine emotion had quieted down, and it was hard to tell the two apart. They were brother and sister, which is rare, for the harbor seal commonly has but one offspring a year. I reached down and tickled the soles of their flippers, and the male pup curled them up and squirmed every time. His sister again showed more equanimity.

These babies, like all those in the river, were born elsewhere. Earlier in the spring all the seals were offshore, around the outer treeless islands in family groups, all the way from southern New Jersey to the Arctic Ocean and on to Alaska. In the West the harbor seal extends from Baja California to the Bering strait and into the Arctic Ocean; only there it is called the hair seal. There is a subtle distinction between hair and fur, a matter of coarseness and curliness that makes it attractive or otherwise to the shorn and shivering human race. Fur is good, but hair other than our own is undesirable, and the harbor seal has for the most part escaped from the terrible slaughter inflicted on its cousins. Only the most vigorous and concerted international action has saved the western fur seal, and this for the sake of an industry rather than an innate love of the animal itself.

This does not mean that the harbor seal is let alone. Seals eat fish, though not exclusively, for clams and crabs are by no means despised. They will eat any fish that is available, with no particular preference for the commercial food fishes, and squid and octopus are taken as readily as fish. But whether it be fish, crabs or squid, any animals suspected of eating something man wants become a pest, and in the West these seals are detested by all fishermen. They are captured in traps or shot by hunters from power boats, for their insatiable curiosity makes them easy prey. Pups are killed so that the mothers may be the more easily destroyed while looking for them. Along the eastern coast there are perhaps fewer fish, fewer fishermen and fewer seals, but mankind is still a menace to a friendly mammal.

Harbor seals are no great seafarers and stay close to the coastline, nor do they seem to be able to sleep in the water. They need to come ashore by day or night to rest. For all their rather fishlike form and fancy for fish, they are true warm-blooded hairy mammals, of landed ancestry, that suckle their young and bring them forth alive, breathing air and hearing the sounds of the air. True, their feet are finlike flippers, ideal for swimming and of little use on land, and the body as a whole is streamlined and can writhe with a sinuous motion that is the powerhouse of their ten-knot drive through the water. But they are born ashore and have to be taught to swim, like any other landlubber.

Mating takes place mainly in the fall, among males at least three years old and females two years old, and polygamy is the rule. In the spring the newly born pup may still be wearing its white, soft, woolly fetal coat. This coat is soon shed, and the 30-pound baby is taken into the water. Swimming comes easy to it, and submersion is made easier by the valves in its nostrils and ears that close automatically as the seal goes under. The pups suckle for the most part on shore, for at first their endurance in the water is very limited. They quickly become stronger and spend more and more time in the sea, until after one or two weeks they are strong enough to accompany the mothers on fairly long trips. Nursing goes on for four to six weeks, but during that time the young have to be taught not merely to swim efficiently but to catch fish in quantities sufficient to sustain them when the supply of milk dries up.

The young seals up the river were weaning. The waters were quiet and safe, as salt as the ocean and full of fish, for the alewives were on their spring spawning run to the freshwater streams at the head of the tide. Clams were there too, and this was an ideal training ground, with nearby ledges for frequent rests. Every now and then a great seal reared half out of the water to get a better view of the invaders of her privacy and the safety of her pup.

An hour had passed and no other seal had hit the net. Pups occasionally wandered out from behind the rockweed-covered ledges now becoming exposed. Once in a while one came close to the net, but each time the head of the mother could be seen as she tried to locate it. Then she disappeared and in a few seconds popped up between her baby and the net, driving the pup back to safety and a timely punishment. The waiting began to get a little tedious, and we pulled anchor and went upriver.

As the boat turned back into the narrows our heads craned as she ran up close to the net—there was a pup so far entangled it looked almost impossible to get it into the dory without bringing in the whole net with it. It must have been struggling for some time. The dory was cast off before we came to anchor and at the same time another pup floundered into the other end of the net. The meshed-up pup was dragged in and the net finally released, and the dory pulled quickly along to the other one. Perhaps it was just nature's way of balancing things, but this pup was caught only by a flipper and it was vicious. Our hands avoided its snapping mouth, and at length the flipper slipped out and the young seal swam quickly out of sight.

Three pups were aboard out of a requested five, and the waiting started anew. The tide was now at half ebb, and the gap in the long ledge was closing as the water level dropped. Seals were leaving the higher ledges and coming down with the tide, looking for rocks low enough to rest on and yet slip off into watery safety in a second. Those outside our net were still cautious, but two pups drifted through the nearly closed gap in the ledge. No mothers accompanied them, and they had evidently been recently weaned. One passed out into midstream through the half-open side above the net. The other floated toward the inner side and then, in a moment, was in the net and quickly joined the group already caught.

Those already aboard were now completely dried out, and the wet, sleek, dark-gray coats they brought out of the water were now fluffed up and beautiful. One that had seemed but a little lighter than the others appeared in a soft mantle of creamy yellow, setting off its large round, gentle, inquiring eyes. The engineer was sitting on an upturned tub, which to

A blue shark ravenously tears ten-pound hunks from a dead porpoise. The smell of blood or the sound of thrashing will bring sharks from a distance.

this lovely lady on deck looked like a perfectly good rock. Before he knew what was happening, she had humped herself over to the corner and firmly but irresistibly edged him off and took his place.

The sun was getting low and long shadows from the western bank put half the river in shade. It looked as though four seals were all we were going to have today, and we should be leaving if we were to get through the outer passage before dark. Then, just as the word was about to be given, a pup came out beyond the ledges and swung inshore. Curiosity was its undoing, and the upper marking buoy of the net pulled it off its course and onto the wrong side. It was in, quickly caught, and we had our quota.

The first four pups, like all babies, could stand excitement for only a limited time and were sound asleep. The engine started and a throbbing went through the hull and through the relaxed bellies. It was altogether too much, and with wild, startled eyes and rapidly vibrating insides the recently slumbering pups galumphed frantically round the well of the boat. But most kids are adaptable, and even this frightening novelty wore off, and sleep took over again. Only our last-comer stayed awake and insisted on poking its snout through the water outlet to watch the spray driving by.

The river widened, and we came to its wide mouth at dusk. The wind has been blowing all day and a heavy swell rolled in from the open sea. The boat pitched and shipped water, much to the discomfort of the seals, who could no longer rest in peace but slithered from one side to the other of the careening, wet deck. Rather suddenly we were out of it and passing through the island channels. The red light of Fisherman's loomed up in the gathering dusk and then, all at once, the lighted buoys of the harbor. Venus was setting and we were back, the seals all asleep again. Tomorrow they would be above the clouds, heading air-express for Texas.

THE UNPREDICTABLE SHARK

Jacques-Yves Cousteau with Frédéric Dumas

The shark has changed but little in 300 million years. Across the gulf of ages, this relentless killer has come without need of evolution, armed from the very beginning for the fray of existence. After more than a hundred encounters with many varieties of sharks, I can offer two conclusions: (1) The more we know about them the less we know,

and (2) one can never tell what a shark is going to do.

One day in the Cape Verdes we were finishing a movie sequence on trigger fish, when Dumas and I were galvanized with terror. What we saw made us feel that naked men do not belong under the sea.

At a distance of 40 feet there appeared from the gray haze the lead-white bulk of a 25-foot *Carcharodon carcharias*, the only shark that all specialists agree is a confirmed man-eater. I shouted, and Dumas closed in beside me. The brute was swimming lazily. In that moment I thought that he would at least have a bellyache from our three-cylinder lungs. Then the shark saw us. His reaction was the last conceivable one. In pure fright, he voided a cloud of excrement and departed at incredible speed.

Dumas and I looked at each other and burst into nervous laughter. The self-confidence we gained that day led us to a foolish neglect of safety measures. Further meetings with sharp-nosed sharks, tiger sharks, mackerel sharks and ground sharks inflated our sense of shark mastery. They all ran from us. After several weeks in the Cape Verdes, we were ready to state flatly that all sharks were cowards.

One day we harpooned a small bottle-nosed whale. It was lying on the surface, heavily wounded and bleeding. Dumas and I entered the waters with a camera. He was to pass a noose over the whale's tail while I filmed.

The water was an exceptionally clear turquoise-blue. We were following the harpoon line toward the whale when, in a depth of 15 feet, we sighted an eight-foot shark of a species we had never before seen. He was impressively neat, light gray, sleek, a real collector's item. We swam boldly toward him, confident that he would run as all the others had. He did not retreat. We drew within ten feet of him and saw all around the shark an escort of tiny striped pilot fish three or four inches long.

They were not following him; they seemed part of him. A thumbnail of a pilot fish wriggled just ahead

of the shark's snout, miraculously staying in place as the shark advanced. A "cowcatcher" wave probably held him there. If he tumbled out of it, he would be hopelessly left behind. It was some time before we realized that the shark and his courtiers were not afraid of us.

I was happy to have such an opportunity to film a shark, although, as the first wonder passed, a sense of danger came. Shark and company slowly circled us. I became the film director, making signs to Dumas, who was co-starred with the shark. Dumas obligingly swam along behind the brute. He reached out his hand and grasped the tip of the tail fin, undecided about giving it a good pull. That would make a good shot, but it might also be dangerous. Dumas released the tail and pursued the shark round and round, while I whirled in the center.

The shark gradually led us down to 60 feet. Dumas pointed below. From the abyss, two more sharks climbed toward us: 15-footers, slender, steel-blue animals with a more savage appearance. The blue pair leveled off below us.

Our old friend, the gray shark, was getting closer to us, tightening his slowly revolving circle. But he still seemed manageable. He turned reliably in his clockwise prowl and the pilots held their stations. The blue pair from the abyss still hung back.

Below the blue sharks there appeared great tunas. Perhaps they had been there since the beginning, but it was the first time we noticed them. Above us flying fish gamboled, adding a discordant touch of gaiety. Dumas and I ransacked our memories for advice on how to frighten off sharks. *"Gesticulate wildly."* We flailed our arms. The gray one did not falter. *"Give 'em a flood of bubbles."* Dumas waited until the shark had reached his nearest point and released a heavy exhalation. The shark did not react. *"Shout as loud as you can."* We hooted until our voices cracked. The shark appeared deaf. His cold, tranquil eye appraised us. He seemed to know what he wanted and was in no hurry.

A small, dreadful thing occurred. The tiny pilot fish on the shark's snout tumbled off his station and wriggled to Dumas. It was a long journey for the little fellow, quite long enough for us to speculate on his purpose. Dumas shook his head as if to dodge a mosquito. The mite fluttered happily, moving with

Protected by an explosive-tipped pole, a diver takes a close look at a white-tipped shark and its escort of banded pilot fish. Pilot fish do not guide the shark; while it feeds on prey, they wait for the scraps that fall from the shark's mouth.

the mask, inside which Didi's eyes focused in cross-eyed agony. I saw his hand held out clutching his belt knife. The gray shark retreated some distance, turned, then glided at us head on.

The final moment had come. I had my hand on the camera button and without my knowledge I was filming the oncoming killer. The flat snout grew larger and then before me there was only the head. I was flooded with anger. With all my strength I thrust the camera forward and banged his muzzle. I felt the wash of a heavy body flashing past and the shark was 12 feet away, circling us as slowly as before, unharmed and expressionless. I thought, *Why in hell doesn't he go to the whale we harpooned?*

The blue sharks now climbed up and joined us. Dumas and I decided to take a chance on the surface. We swam up and thrust our masks out of the water. Dizzy and disoriented from spinning around under water, we had to revolve our heads like a lighthouse beacon to find the *Élie Monnier*, 300 yards away. We waved wildly and saw no reply from the ship. Floating on the surface with one's head out of the water is the classic method of being eaten by sharks: Hanging there, one's legs can be plucked like bananas. I looked down. The three sharks were rising.

We dived and faced them. The sharks resumed their circling maneuver. We were nearing exhaustion, and cold was penetrating the outer layers of our bodies. Any moment we expected the constriction of air in our mouthpieces, a sign that the air supply is nearly gone. When it was gone, we would abandon our mouthpieces and make mask dives, holding our breath. That would redouble the drain on our strength, and leave us facing tireless creatures that never needed to draw breath.

Suddenly the movements of the sharks grew agitated. They ran around us, working all their strong propulsive fins, then turned down and disappeared. Dumas and I stared unbelievingly at each other. A shadow fell across us. We looked up and saw the hull of the *Élie Monnier's* launch. Our mates had seen our signals and had located our bubbles. The sharks ran when they saw the launch. We flopped into the boat, weak and shaken. The crew were as distraught as we were.

Later, we watched the sharks twisting in the red water, striking furiously at the dead whale. We hoisted the whale aboard and were impressed by the moon-shaped shark bites. The inch-thick leather of the whale had been scooped out cleanly, ten or fifteen pounds of blubber at a bite. The sharks had waited until we were cheated away from them before they struck the easy prey.

Part Three

This Planet Earth

Chapter One

The Poles

*Life is at its poorest and its richest at the poles. The land, much of it perpetually covered
by ice and snow, supports only the hardiest of plants and animals, but the seas teem
with an incredible abundance of living things—from the microscopic organisms
of the plankton to the mammoth blue whales, mightiest creatures that have ever lived.*

THE TOP OF THE WORLD

Edwin Muller

The North Pole used to be a remote end of the earth. Before World War II only a handful of explorers had been to the Pole. A few Eskimos and other natives lived in the Arctic, and there were a few towns inhabited by hardy pioneers; otherwise the area was empty.

Today things are different. The Arctic is much busier and more populated. Some 6000 Americans live in the extraordinary city of Thule, only 950 miles from the Pole. And there are permanent settlements farther north in Canada and the U.S.S.R. Hundreds of people have flown over the North Pole. Regular passenger flights follow the polar route, and there are routine flights for observing the weather and the condition of the ice pack.

The original reason for all this was, of course, military: The Arctic is the shortest route by which Americans and Russians might bomb each other's cities. And today the Arctic is becoming increasingly populated and busy as a crossroads of world air traffic.

Many of us have misconceptions about the Arctic. We call it an "ocean," but it is actually about a sixth the size of the Atlantic. Over 50 years ago explorer Vilhjalmur Stefansson rightly called it a "mediterranean sea"—a sea surrounded by land. On its shores are the most powerful nations of the modern world: the Anglo-American and the Russian.

We think of the North Pole as the coldest place on earth, but the lowest temperature registered there is some 50 degrees warmer than the South Pole's low of –126.9° F. In summer, temperatures can rise above freezing at the North Pole, but this never happens at the South Pole.

To find real cold in the Northern Hemisphere you have to go some 1500 miles south of the North Pole.

The coldest inhabited place, the northern "cold pole," is the Siberian town of Verkhoyansk, just inside the Arctic Circle. It has recorded 93.7° below. (Incidentally, it gets hot in the summer—temperatures at Verkhoyansk average 60° F.) The lowest recorded temperature in North America was –81.4° at Snag in the Yukon.

The Arctic is variously defined. To some it is the region north of the Arctic Circle; to others, the regions north of the tree line, or the 50° isotherm for the warmest month. But most of us generally think of the Arctic as a land of constant snow and ice. It's true there is plenty of ice, but the annual snowfall of Virginia is greater. Eureka, in central Ellesmere Island, has an annual precipitation of only 1.74 inches, comparable to the deserts of the world.

On the west coast of Greenland, near the Circle, are many lovely meadows. There are no trees—almost none anywhere in the Arctic—but in July and August there is a wealth of shrubs and flowers. These meadows are better to look at than to walk on. Just under the surface is the permafrost, or permanently frozen ground. In summer when the top few inches thaw, the ground is like a saturated sponge. This is just right for mosquito breeding. However, while mosquitoes seem to be the most abundant insects in the Arctic because of their persistent annoyance to man, they are actually outnumbered by midges and root maggots. Bumblebees and butterflies are common too, and the ice worm is not really a myth but actually does live on the surface of glaciers.

The Arctic Ocean is deep, averaging 4200 feet, and is 17,500 feet at its deepest. It is covered with ice floes. Along the coasts in summer there is a strip of water through which steamers can navigate most of the circumference of the Arctic seas. In autumn the shore waters freeze, making navigation impossible.

The Arctic has been described as silent. On the contrary, it is apt to be noisy. The millions of ice floes, anywhere from the size of your hat up to several hundred square miles, are in constant motion. Floe grinds

Polar bears are solitary wanderers on the ice floes of the Far North except during their midsummer mating season. In fact, some of them probably spend their entire lives on the ice without ever touching land. Nonskid soles on their feet allow them to move with great speed and agility, even over jumbled pack ice. By moving quickly and carefully distributing its weight, a half-ton polar bear can traverse sheet ice too thin to support a man.

against floe with a roar that can be heard for miles. When one floe is forced over the surface of another, there is an earsplitting screech.

Nor is the Arctic lifeless. In fact, life in northern waters is abundant, and, as elsewhere, is a pyramid. At the base are phytoplankton. Feeding on them are billions of shrimp and similar organisms, the animal plankton; and at the top are great beasts like the walrus and whale. Eating the shrimp, too, are large numbers of seals. At the apex of the pyramid is the polar bear, who lives chiefly on seals and spends most of his life on the floating ice.

This abundant life was little known up to 60 years ago. When Stefansson proposed an expedition far out on the sea ice, "living off the country," no less a polar authority than Roald Amundsen said it was suicidal. Arctic whalers agreed. So did the Eskimos, not one of whom would accompany Stefansson.

With two white companions Stefansson started north from Alaska, carrying food for one month. In a

700-mile journey they spent three months on the ice far from land. They lived chiefly on seals. The meat provided ample food, and the blubber provided fuel. Drinking water was no problem. Sea ice is salty when it first forms, but it loses its salt and in six months is fit to drink. In a year it cannot be distinguished from freshwater ice. Year-old ice was always available.

Thule, the United States Air Force's northernmost base at the northwest corner of Greenland, has a 14,000-foot ice runway and a complement of more than 6000 men. Established in 1951 on a site leased from Denmark, Thule is now also an outpost for the powerful Ballistic Missile Early Warning System, built at a cost of $500 million over two years. The original town of Thule was established by the Danish explorer Knud Rasmussen as a base for his expeditions. A few years ago the Greenlanders still living there elected to move to another site farther north so that they would be free to continue their own way of life, uninterrupted.

The climate is not so tough as you might think. In summer there are many days when you can take off your shirt and sunbathe. In winter the temperature averages −24° F.

It's hard at first to get used to more than four months of constant day and nearly four months of almost constant night when you are above the Arctic Circle. But even on a moonless night in winter it never gets "pitch dark." There is always enough starlight reflected from the snow to distinguish objects 100 yards away.

Other permanent settlements nearer the Pole than Thule are three of the five weather stations maintained jointly by the United States and Canada on the Canadian Arctic Islands. The farthest north is "Alert" on Ellesmere Island, about 450 miles from the Pole. Since most of the weather of the Northern Hemisphere originates in the polar regions, these stations are of great importance to military and civil aviation. There are also several scientific research stations throughout the Arctic, such as the U.S. Office of Naval Research's Arctic Research Laboratory at Point Barrow in Alaska, open all year round, and the Arctic Institute of North America's facility at Cape Sparbo on Devon Island, open for summer work. Numerous temporary sites were established during the 1957 International Geophysical Year.

About 1,750,000 people live in the North American Arctic and sub-Arctic regions from Alaska to Greenland. On the Russian side there are about 29,500,000. In Canada some 38,000 inhabitants, including about 18,000 natives, live above 60° N. In the Soviet Union about 300,000 people live in the Arctic, but then the total area of the Russian Arctic is much larger than the North American. Russian assets in the Arctic and the sub-Arctic are coal, oil, meat, fur and minerals. In summer, steamers go up and down the three great rivers—the Ob, Lena and Yenisei—and regularly traverse the Northern Sea Route, resupplying the northern settlements. In winter these rivers are highways for tractor-drawn trains. Railroads also run beyond the Arctic Circle to Murmansk and Vorkuta.

People in the travel business are now quite accustomed to planning trips to the Arctic. Of all Arctic scenery, the coasts of Greenland are probably the most spectacular. Few people have seen the east coast, where constant ice makes shipping well nigh impossible; but all summer, supply ships and Danish passenger ships ply up and down the west coast. Tourists generally travel by airplane and helicopter.

The air is usually clear. From 100 miles away the great snow peaks of the west coast begin to rise from the sea. Close in, your ship is dwarfed by dark headlands towering a sheer 3000 feet. Now and then through a gap in a cliff you get a breathtaking glimpse of a vast swelling hump of glittering white. The Greenland ice cap is one of the wonders of the world. Except for a coastal fringe 10 to 100 miles wide, it covers the whole of Greenland (665,000 square miles), with an average thickness of 4800 feet. If the climate were to change enough to melt the ice cap, all the oceans of the world would rise 24 feet, and many of the world's greatest seaports would be drowned.

The ice cap is in a state of equilibrium now—the annual accumulation of snow is virtually balanced by melting, evaporation and iceberg production. Tongues of ice flow down the mountains to the sea. One of them, Jakobshavns Isbrae (glacier), moves more than three feet an hour and discharges millions of tons of ice into Disko Bay in the form of icebergs. Great chunks topple like falling skyscrapers; they cause a deafening thunder and throw out mighty waves.

From a ship's deck in Disko Bay you can see hundreds of icebergs "calved" by the glacier. They tower above you, the visible eighth as big as a cathedral, carved in fantastic shapes—spires and pinnacles and rounded domes. At their waterlines the pounding waves have undercut them: you can peer into lovely blue-green caverns.

Full use of the Arctic as an airway will not come until there is unrestricted travel between North America and the Soviet Union. But Arctic commercial flying hasn't waited for that. Jet airplanes regularly fly over the North Pole, the shortest route between the Scandinavian countries and the Pacific coast of the United States. Emergency landing fields have been established along the route at Thule, Coral Harbour and Frobisher Bay.

Polar flying has shown that Arctic air travel is even safer than present commercial passenger flights across the Atlantic. Theoretically flying is safest at the poles (and the equator), where there are clear skies and an absence of fog, sleet and icing conditions. And if a transocean plane has to come down, it is better off on floe ice than in the open water of the Atlantic.

The under-ice voyages made to the North Pole a few years ago by the nuclear submarines *Nautilus* and *Skate* pioneered a possible route for future commercial shipping. This route, for example, reduced the distance from London to Tokyo by more than 40 percent—from 11,200 to 6500 miles.

So turn your globe over on its side and have a look at the top of the world. You may be there before long.

ANTARCTICA: THE WORLD'S MOST FASCINATING ICEBOX

Ira Wolfert

Exploring is one of man's oldest adventures. Never before, though, has he had a chance to do it the way it's being done in the Antarctic today. In 1961, 12 nations ratified a treaty agreeing to reserve Antarctica exclusively for scientific research for 30 years. As a result, scientists are now busily pursuing an intense program of research and exploration on a year-round basis. It's a fantastic project, unique in the history of science.

On shore to nest, two Adélie penguins exchange ceremonial greetings. When summer begins, Adélies gather in great breeding colonies, called rookeries, around the rim of Antarctica. The eggs are brooded in simple pebble nests; the young hatch in December. In February the birds return to the food-rich pack-ice region farther north.

They're at work in an amazing land, nearly one and a half times as big as the United States. The South Pole itself is in the midst of nothing at all—just flat, blank, snow-covered ice. But elsewhere on the continent there are jagged mountains, with all but their peaks buried in ice and snow; a lake—covered by more than 12 feet of ice—whose depths register a temperature of 80° F.; violet and green ice; a smoking volcano; penguins in rookeries of many thousands, sometimes hundreds of thousands. There were times when I felt that I was walking in the sky because a sunset had encased me, the fields of snow reflecting the hues in the sky with breathtaking accuracy. At other times, when I exhaled, a bloom of tiny, exquisite ice crystals shimmered into the air and fell like a rain of diamonds.

The coldest temperature ever officially recorded on earth was −126.9° F. at one of the Russian bases in Antarctica. The mean annual temperature at the South Pole is 56.7° below zero. Elsewhere, it is −40° or worse most of the time. "It's the world's most fascinating icebox," one scientist said.

Of the Antarctic programs being carried on by various countries, the United States' is the most extensive. Geologists, biologists, meteorologists, algologists, glaciologists, cartographers, scuba divers—in all, more than 3200 Americans—were working on and around the continent during the 1967—68 season. Some 27 million dollars has been spent, seven million by the National Science Foundation, 20 million by the U.S. Navy, on Operation Deep Freeze—logistic support for the scientists.

Is the operation efficient? "They've got it so well organized that a party of geologists can do in two months what would have taken three entire seasons, a few years ago," said Dr. Charles R. Bentley, geologist from the University of Wisconsin.

Weather permitting, never a day goes by that planes and helicopters aren't giving aid to researchers. It is not unusual for eight aircraft to be aloft at once,

With startling abruptness, an Adélie penguin can rocket seven feet out of the Antarctic Ocean and land feet first on an iceberg. Though ungainly out of water, Adélie penguins are nearly as swift and agile as porpoises in the water. Even their "tuxedo" look is indicative of an aquatic way of life: Swimming penguins have the dark-above, light-below coloration common among fish.

flying supplies to the South Pole, doing aerial mapping, reconnoitering terrain for men traveling over land never before trod by human feet, making touch-and-go landings to drop off or pick up field parties.

"A touch-and-go landing," explained Lt. Comdr. Bert Johnson as we were about to make one, "is where you touch the ground to see if it's safe and go like hell if it ain't."

From October to March the daylight lasts 24 hours at McMurdo Sound, and Navy work goes on around the clock in 12-hour shifts. At two o'clock one morning, with the sun shining brightly, the American supply base near McMurdo was alive with typically varied and extraordinary activities.

A traxcavator (an excavating and forklift truck on tracks) lumbered by with a load of snow to melt for water. It was followed by another tractor vehicle hauling materials for the permanent housing (built to last 30 years) going up to replace plywood and canvas huts constructed when exploration was on a may-be-never-again basis. The new housing has electric heating from a nuclear power plant, hot-and-cold running water from desalinated seawater pumped from under the ice, plus refrigerators—to keep food from freezing.

At the time I was there, Arthur DeVries of Stanford University was preparing to trap fish to study their metabolism. He attached one end of a net to a harness, the harness to a seal, then shoved the seal down a hole in the ice. The nearest hole was a quarter mile away. When the seal came up through that one, the harness was unhooked and what everybody else had thought was impossible—spreading a large net *under* ten feet of ice—was accomplished by DeVries without taking his pipe out of his mouth.

Four men took off in a helicopter. Two of them, who called themselves sea-cowboys, were on their way to brand seals in an effort, eventually, to gauge their ages and trace their wanderings. The other two, trying to determine how penguins are able to navigate so precisely over such vast distances across the featureless landscape, were carrying tiny radio transmitters to strap onto the birds so their course could be tracked.

Meanwhile, at the South Pole, ten men were starting out in three tractors on a two-month, 900-mile zigzag traverse, through unexplored territory, toward the abandoned Soviet station at the Antarctic's farthest inland point, sometimes called the "Pole of Relative Inaccessibility." Hooked on behind the tractors were six trailers carrying scientific instruments, spare parts, explosives and three tons of food. The trailers rode on enormous tires in which extra fuel for the trip was stored.

There were more than 60 scientific research projects in the Antarctic during the 1967–68 season. One of the continent's attractions is that it is a land mass surrounded by an ocean, unlike the Arctic, which is an ocean surrounded by land. In the Antarctic, polar conditions and science can meet on a stable platform, where prolonged studies are possible.

Seals, for instance, have become a subject of lively interest in fields as diverse as medicine, sonar and submarine design. Physiologists have found that seals are able to shut off the circulation in their outer surface and extremities to concentrate the blood in the vital organs so they can conserve their oxygen supply. The Weddell seal can hold its breath for more than 30 minutes and can dive to the hull-crushing depth of 1400 feet. It is thought that this seal navigates under ice by making sounds—one of which is hauntingly melodious—and reading the echoes.

Biologists were amazed to find that the Antarctic Ocean supports larger numbers (although fewer kinds) of plants and animals than any other. (Among these is the biggest animal in the world, the blue whale.) Scientists worrying about feeding the world's expanding population are studying this phenomenon with interest.

The Antarctic also provides a window on unknown facets of nature's mechanisms. For example, semi-tropical trees and plants once grew on the continent. In several places, petrified wood 270 million years old and coal beds up to 25 feet thick have been found. The coal is hard, and many slabs are imprinted with different ancient plant fossils. It's like turning the pages of a book.

Is the tropics-to-deep-freeze climate change temporary or permanent? Is it the result of a variation in solar activity? Or of the continent's breaking off and drifting away from some previous position closer to the equator? Or of a change in the position of the Earth's axis?

These questions are of moment to all of us, as about 90 percent of the ice on earth is in the Antarctic. If it were ever to melt, the level of all the oceans would be raised some 250 feet, redrawing the map of the earth. Even a thaw too minor to make any significant change in ocean levels could over the long run affect the global weather pattern profoundly.

Some of the greatest hazards to man in Antarctica occur when abnormal conditions cause one of nature's booby traps to explode in his face. I learned about this in a "whiteout."

I had left camp for a stroll, when the color of the air began to change. I was soon enveloped in a uniform white light that blotted out shadows and made depth perception impossible. Air and ground had become the same color, and I had the eerie feeling that I was wandering around inside a Ping-Pong ball. Explanation: Light was being reflected back and forth between white cloud layer and white snow, destroying all contrasts and making it impossible to tell where the sky left off and the ground began.

The inevitable happened. I put my foot down on what turned out to be empty air over a gully and fell and slid some 20 feet. Fortunately, I had worn two of the three pairs of gloves I had been issued, and after I climbed out of the gully I threw a mitten ahead of me at each step to make sure that what I was about to put my foot on was really there. I was learning that this is still a country where you can walk five minutes in any direction away from a base and find yourself lost.

Then there's the wind. It comes up in nothing flat, and the French reported its reaching a speed of 200 miles an hour before the instruments at their base broke. There's no overture of sound. Abruptly you're engulfed in the drumming and shrieking of a blizzard that goes on and on without letup—for nine days once, while I was there.

"Men haven't conquered nature anywhere, here least of all," said Maj. Adrian Hayter, who was commander of New Zealand's Scott Base. "They've only found the terms under which nature will permit them to operate."

Nature has equipped every living thing in the Antarctic except man, who is an outsider, with boundlessly ingenious natural devices for enduring the harsh climate. The fish have certain chemical substances in their blood which, scientists think, act as antifreeze and keep their body fluids from freezing. The insects, of which some 60 species have been discovered, are active only when the sun has heated their surroundings above freezing. "They have a practically instantaneous reversible hibernation," said entomologist J. Linsley Gressitt of Hawaii's Bishop Museum. "When in cold-stupor, they can be activated simply by breathing on them." If ice forms over their resting place as they sleep, they can wait a long time for it to melt—some insects have revived themselves from hibernations thought to have lasted 70 years.

Do these marvelous devices enable any of these creatures to do more than merely struggle to survive? During a weekend with 60,000 penguins, I found indications that these wonderful birds seem to enjoy a remarkable adaptation to the harsh environment.

The Adélie penguins spend most of their time on ice floes at sea. They feed on shrimp, and, though they cannot fly, they can swim at speeds up to 30 m.p.h. Every October they go ashore to breed, finding their way to the same spot in the same rookery. After the female lays her two eggs, she returns to the sea to restore her depleted body, and the male takes over the domestic duties. He can go without food for as long as six weeks.

At Cape Hallett I saw the females returning to the rookery. Plump, sleek, shining, their white spotless, their black gleaming, they waddled in large groups over the ice and separated to go to their own nests.

I couldn't stop grinning. The Adélies demonstrate emotion for one another graphically in what scientists call "mutual display." In each nest to which a female returned, the male jumped up from the eggs, stood on tiptoe facing his mate, and, with head and neck swaying, let out repeated raucous "ga-ga-ga" noises.

At the end, when the male had started off to feed himself and the female had taken over the nest, I noticed that she would stand up every now and then, look down at the eggs under her and go into mutual display all over again.

On my way back to the United States, I stopped in Christchurch, New Zealand. There I talked with a National Aeronautics and Space Administration representative from Washington who is involved in planning for the exploration of the Moon. "We're keeping an eye on the Antarctica program," he told me. "It's as close as men can come on earth to doing the job we're likely to want to do."

So a great new age of exploration is speeding through its dawn. Once nations looked to their explorers for gold. Today, in the Antarctic or on the Moon, it's knowledge. That is not so different as it seems, for, in the final analysis, knowledge is the goose that lays the golden eggs.

LAND OF FANTASY AND PHANTOM

Thomas R. Henry

Explorers of the Antarctic encounter phenomena far outside ordinary experience. They are eerie and beautiful and terrible, and science still gropes for understanding of many of them.

Antarctica is a land of white darkness, where two men, dressed in white, can walk across the snow side by side and find themselves in a world of complete whiteness. The air is white; earth and sky are white; the wind in the face is white with clouds of snow. Suddenly one man becomes conscious that the other no longer is walking beside him. He has disappeared, as though the thin, white air has dissolved him. Yet he continues to talk as if nothing has happened, unaware that he has become a substanceless phantom. His voice is unchanged; it seems to come from the same direction and the same distance. A moment later he reap-

Intense cold, dry air and seemingly limitless expanses of snow and ice combine to make the Antarctic landscape almost as alien as the face of another planet. Mirages and other illusions are common as the low-slanting rays of the southern sun are bounced and twisted in apparent defiance of the normal laws of optics.

pears—perhaps floating in the air a few feet ahead and at about eye level. Still he talks as if he were walking beside the other man.

These vanishings occur only on "white days," when the sky is overcast with white clouds—which results, scientists believe, in the physical phenomenon of "multiple reflection." At such a time the accumulation of imprisoned light between earth and sky—like the accumulation of heat in a greenhouse—causes vision to become drowned in light. This results in "the complete antithesis of darkness"—absolute whiteness, to which the human eye is little better adjusted than to darkness.

In white darkness there are no shadows. The illumination is so diffuse that there is no perspective by which one can estimate the contours, size or distance of white objects. The feet cannot find the snow underfoot. One staggers and stumbles like a drunken man.

Accompanying the white light is an enormous amount of invisible ultraviolet light that makes sunburn a serious problem. It radiates from all directions, and on a white day the most likely part of the body to become sunburned is the exposed bottom of the chin, or the palms of the hands if the weather is mild enough to discard gloves.

Another apparent contradiction to the laws of physics was first experienced by Dr. Paul Siple, chief scientist of a U.S. Navy expedition. While engaged in surveying an ice shelf two miles from his camp, Siple became aware that the tents had enormously enlarged. The camp loomed before his eyes like a city of pyramidal skyscrapers. Then a cloud drifted across the sun and there was a slight change in the wind direction. In the twinkling of an eye the tents disappeared completely, and before the observer stretched an empty field of snow. Mystified, he dropped to his knees. The camp of brown skyscrapers immediately reappeared. When he arose it disappeared again.

Much of the Antarctic's topsy-turviness can be explained by comparing it to a great hall of mirrors in the sky. The illusions are caused by the refraction of light as it passes through warm and cold layers of air. There are double and triple sunrises and sunsets. Ships sail upside down in the clouds. In the middle of the ice shelf one may see floating vessels, smoke pouring from their funnels, although no open water is within a hundred miles. Wild mountain landscapes, grossly distorted, loom on the skyline. They look as though they could be reached easily in a few hours, but in reality they are beyond the horizon, weeks away.

Antarctica knows no rot, rust or mold. There are no bacteria to spoil meat, no spores to mold bread. In 1947 Rear Adm. Richard H. Cruzen visited the camp at Cape Evans that had been abandoned by Capt. Robert F. Scott more than 35 years before. From the camp's appearance, the occupants might have just left. Boards and rafters of the cabin looked as if they were fresh from the sawmill; there was no rot in the timbers, not a speck of rust on the nailheads. A hitching rope used for Manchurian ponies looked new and proved as strong as ever when it was used to hitch the helicopter. Biscuits and canned meat were edible.

At the Little America camp that he had abandoned

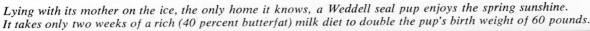

Lying with its mother on the ice, the only home it knows, a Weddell seal pup enjoys the spring sunshine. It takes only two weeks of a rich (40 percent butterfat) milk diet to double the pup's birth weight of 60 pounds.

short-maned, buffalo-sized creatures. Then, right before our eyes, the unbelievable happens—the miracle of birth, Garden of Eden style, no suffering, no bleeding, no distress.

We have been watching a number of females group themselves, heads out, around a bulky matron who is holding her tail out rigid as a rod. Now, to our astonishment, we see two tiny hooves protruding just below it. Mother-to-be seems unaware of her predicament; presently she lies down for a roll in the flowers. Soon we are watching a small head being born and now, as the matron stands up, out slides a brown-black body almost vertically, two little forelegs groping for the ground. In no time a perfect little calf is lying on the flowers, and we watch the mother expertly remove the membrane, snip the cord, dispose of the afterbirth, turn her attention to jacking the baby up onto his wobbly legs. The calf plops down once or twice, but a few minutes later there he is at the milk bar, happily soaking up his first meal. The whole performance has taken about half an hour.

Suddenly the sorority breaks into a frantic dance of alarm. In a moment we see the trouble—a hyena! It is slinking past us, jaws a-slaver, eyes on the suckling calf. Unthinking, we bang loudly on the metal sides of our wagon, stamp our feet, yell, "Shoo! Scat! Beat it!" To our dismay the din scares off not only the hyena but every other creature within earshot. We watch helplessly as the herd canters away, leaving the mother and calf trailing woefully behind. Will this late-afternoon drama end in another killing? No. Through binoculars we finally see mother and child safely reunited with the rest.

Our day ends with a Technicolor sunset. Back at the crater's rim, we look down at the toy trees where weird, sad elephants are hiding; at the swampy lake where flamingos settle in a shell-pink mist; at the vast velvety carpet where little cheetahs attend nursery school and terrifying rhinos snooze like Ferdinand the Bull among the flowers.

A Royal Portrait

From below the Sahara Desert to the Transvaal, the majestic lion holds sway in the game-rich grasslands of Africa. The king of beasts, which has an extremely well-developed hunting instinct, preys on grazing animals ranging in size from small antelopes to zebras. When ravenous, a pride of lions—one family or several combined—may bring down a full-grown elephant, rhino or hippopotamus. But females do most of the hunting, relying less on speed for success than on stealth, cunning and teamwork. The male *(opposite)*, recognizable by his regal mane, is first to eat after a kill has been made.

A lioness carrying her cubs (above) *irresistibly suggests her kinship to the domestic cat. She bears two to four young every other year—the more plentiful the food, the larger the litter.*

Lion cubs enjoy rough-and-tumble play. Their mother rears them away from the pride, so they do not compete with adults for food. At ten months they can stalk but are not yet strong or heavy enough to handle large prey.

These young lions wear the dappled-
sunshine camouflage of their cubhood.
At five years the males will sport manes.

Sprawled on its back, this young lion is
the picture of sleepy contentment. It rolls
in the grass to discourage biting insects.

A lioness (above) *trots casually toward a wildebeest herd, perhaps to stampede it past other members of the pride.*

After her drink this lioness (left) *may hide nearby and wait for prey animals to visit the water hole at dusk.*

Following a successful hunt a pride of lions (below) *sometimes sleeps for as long as four days before waking.*

AUGUSTO RUSCHI'S JUNGLE PARADISE

Allen Rankin

The boy was six when he made his first all-day expedition into his vast backyard—a Brazilian forest. Entranced, he gazed wide-eyed at the towering jacaranda and *paraju* trees, the myriad orchids hiding in their shadows, the swarms of hummingbirds like tiny jeweled darts on speed-blurred wings. "It's wonderful there. Marvelous!" Augusto Ruschi announced to his family that night. "When I grow up, I'm going to spend *all* my time with the birds and flowers!"

To his parents, leading citizens of the little village of Santa Teresa in the state of Espírito Santo, this sounded anything but practical. Yet Augusto Ruschi, now over 50, has done just what he said he would—and is probably South America's greatest naturalist.

In joyously satisfying his insatiable curiosity, Dr. Ruschi has become the world's leading authority on the ways of hummingbirds. He is also an internationally recognized expert on many other exotic forms of life, from the beautiful wild orchid to the hideous vampire bat. His discoveries of previously unknown species or subspecies of flowers, birds and mammals have added appreciably to the science of biology and to the pleasure of nature lovers everywhere.

Ruschi is tall, lank and physically tough as a rattan vine, and his eyes still glow with childlike enthusiasm. "I call this my Eden," he told me, as we strolled through the forest park surrounding his boyhood home, where he lives with his wife and two sons. Orchids of every hue flamed along the garden paths; parrots and gaudier birds flashed and screamed in the pavilions; and dazzling hummingbirds zipped or hovered around us.

The area is a public wildlife museum which draws some 30,000 people a year although it is 45 rugged mountain-trail miles from the nearest city, Vitória. "All I ask," said Ruschi, who developed it largely at his own expense, "is that people look at things closely enough to enjoy them. Because the longer and harder you look at *any* living creature, the more marvelous you find it to be."

Ruschi's own life is a case in point. By the age of 12 he was staying in the forest as long as two weeks at a time, living off wild fruits and the meat of small animals he bagged with a rifle. His closest friends were not schoolmates but the creatures in the woods. His favorite books were tomes on botany, biochemistry, ornithology and other natural sciences, which he learned to read not only in his native Portuguese, but in French, German and Latin.

Augusto's first great teen-age love was the wild orchid. After combing about 400 square miles of wilderness, he numbered, mapped and indexed the locations of 90,000 orchid plants of scores of different species. He kept elaborate records on each of the choicer specimens: what kind of tree or rock it lived on; at what elevation and in what degree of sun and shade; when birds and insects arrived to pollinate it; its size and color at various phases, its peculiarities. Many of the plants literally burst into bloom, with a glorious and quite audible puff. The boy kept track of these, and even when a flower blossomed in the small hours after midnight he was often on hand for the event. Sometimes a series of blossomings would keep him running from plant to plant all night. "Marvelous!" he found it all.

That's what the professors at the National Museum in Rio de Janeiro thought, too, when they received one of the most startling documents ever written by a boy of 15. Hand-penned in scholarly Latin, it revealed that the young prodigy had discovered two new genera of orchids and at least 19 new species. More important, it contained "A. Ruschi's simplified formulas" for the conditions under which many species of the plants

Unique among birds, the male Loddigesia mirabilis *has only four tail feathers: two inner spikelike feathers and two outer paddle-like feathers attached to long filaments which the hummingbird manipulates to attract a mate.*

flourish best. These formulas have helped naturalists, hobbyists and commercial florists in South America and elsewhere to produce healthier, lovelier orchids ever since.

Augusto's father, with 11 other children to provide for, could not afford to send his nature-obsessed son to college. The boy, left free to roam the woods, was delighted. From orchids his interests turned toward hummingbirds. The elusiveness of these minute feathered acrobats, flashing all colors of the rainbow, offered a special challenge to him—especially when he learned that no one knew enough about their habits to get them to live and breed in captivity. At 19 he embarked on studies that would greatly change that situation.

First, he set up an observation post near the nest of a tiny emerald-crowned lady hummingbird. There he kept watch for 35 days and nights, sleeping or dashing home for food only when the mother bird slept. Ruschi saw the mother lay her two eggs and, 14 days later, saw the eggs hatch.

Often, when the mother flew off to get food for her young, he gently borrowed the little ones from the nest. He weighed them (on a pharmacist's scale) and took their temperature. With an eyedropper thrust down their throats, he even took samples of their stomach contents, which—with his remarkable self-taught knowledge—he chemically analyzed. In this way, Ruschi began to learn precisely what hummingbirds must eat to survive—exactly the kind of proteins (insects) and carbohydrates (flower nectars) they must have at various ages.

Through this technique and others, he gradually revealed some of the best-kept secrets of hummingbirds (called *beija-flôres,* "flower-kissers," in Brazilian Portuguese). He learned the exact amount of space that certain species of the birds require to "pair off" and mate in proper privacy. He discovered what flowers the birds need for nutrition, what plants for shelter, what materials—down to the last wisp of spider web—they must have for nest-building.

Putting this knowledge to use, he began to build aviaries and stock them with the finicky little creatures. Soon they were reproducing. Today, in Ruschi's *viveiros* (flower-filled enclosures), some 400 hummingbirds of 95 different species live, breed and perform their sensational aerial stunting almost as freely as in the wild state.

More and more zoos are now providing the "natural" conditions under which even the most exotic hummers can live. In September 1964, for example, 105 tropical hummingbirds, all presents from Ruschi, took up permanent residence at the great San Diego

Hovering like a bumblebee, a female royal woodnymph probes deep into a fuchsia blossom to suck up nectar and tiny insects through her tongue, which is shaped like a soda straw and works like a suction pump. Hummingbirds must eat every 10 or 15 minutes.

Zoo. And an additional 100 or more of Ruschi's prize hummingbirds were offered to the Washington, D.C., National Zoological Park.

Ruschi has contributed thousands of rare birds—and plants, animals and insects, too—to parks and museums, all gratis. "I do what I do for the love of it," he explained simply.

Though the gifted young man did not go to college, the college at nearby Campos came to him. It gave him a scholarship, allowed him to do his "classroom work" in his beloved woods, requiring only that he show up at school for examinations. About the same time, Prof. Cândido de Mello Leitão, a leading naturalist at the National Museum in Rio, urged young Ruschi to work for the museum and get some of his college credits there. Ruschi lasted only a month before he resigned, explaining: "I cannot be pent up by walls. I must go back to my forests."

But the museum directors refused to accept his resignation. Instead, they made a government biological field station of his home in Santa Teresa and paid him for managing it—a job Ruschi has held happily ever since. He also practices law occasionally—a profession he mastered on his own at 35.

Dr. Ruschi still spends much of his time in the wild. To catch a really rare hummingbird, he may camp for three months in the South American mountains or jungles. The task of finding a creature smaller than one's thumb on a largely unexplored continent of close to seven million square miles requires the most knowledgeable kind of detective work.

Consider, for example, the case of the missing *Loddigesia mirabilis*. No specimen of this gorgeous fancy-tailed hummingbird had been recorded since 1933. The species was feared to be extinct, but Ruschi thought not and in 1962 set out to try to rediscover it.

Because he knew that the bird had lived at an altitude of over 6500 feet, he selected an appropriate area in the Peruvian Andes. Then, figuring that the *Loddigesia* would prefer foliage thick enough to hide in but thin enough so that it would be in no danger of snagging its elaborate tail, he narrowed his search to areas with relatively thin underbrush. It took two months of hunting, but suddenly, hovering before a flower, a female of the missing species appeared.

Then, to Ruschi's delight, the cock bird showed up, his long twin tails spinning and interlacing like the blades of an ethereal eggbeater to impress his lady. *Tat-tat-tat-tat!* drummed the tails and wings in rhythm as the bird performed his courting dance. Ruschi was so enthralled that he waited until the half-hour wedding ceremony was over before catching the two lovers.

Dr. Ruschi's enormous curiosity about all phases of nature has led him to astonishing bits of knowledge. Once, for example, he followed a single ant for 30 hours just to see where the insect was going. At long last the ant—a giant two-inch-long Tocandira—reached its home colony and joined its fellows there. Until then it had been generally believed that this ant was nongregarious, spent most of its life alone. Subsequently, Ruschi became an expert on Tocandira's busy homelife.

To peek in on the nesting habits of a marsh bird called the small diver, Ruschi hid neck-deep in swamp water for three days and nights, his head and face masked by a hollow gourd in which he had punched two holes to peer through. He watched the bird dive to feed on something at the lake bottom. What was she eating? Ruschi later seined the muck and brought up some 5000 tiny frogs of a kind he had never seen. No wonder, Stanford University zoologist Dr. George Sprague Myers told him later; this animal was a primitive frog that gives birth by opening up its back. The species had never been found so far south before.

For his contributions to the natural sciences, Ruschi holds six major decorations, including the Brazilian government's highly prized Award of Dom João VI. He has lectured at international scientific conferences all over the globe. But he is still happiest when coaxing yet another secret from his forests.

"Isn't it marvelous," he asks, "that this is such a great world that we can never solve all its mysteries—and that the secret of an exciting life lies not in the finding of wonders but in the search for them?"

BARRO COLORADO, TROPICAL NOAH'S ARK

J. P. McEvoy

Back in 1909, when the Chagres River was dammed to create Gatun Lake for the Panama Canal, every living thing fled before the rising waters. Many of these tropical refugees wound up on the highest peak in the lake—Barro Colorado.

Here in six square miles of jungle was a wealth of teeming plant and animal life: pumas, ocelots, peccaries, toucans, capuchin monkeys, black howling monkeys, sloths, coral snakes, the deadly fer-de-lance. It was a tropical Noah's Ark, ready and waiting for scientific study.

Fortunately a wide-awake scientist named James Zetek, who had been working on malaria control in the Canal Zone since 1911, recognized the importance of this island sanctuary. He was largely responsible for getting it set aside in 1923 for tropical research, under U.S. protection. During 40-odd years of devoted toil in the tropics, Zetek was the fairy godfather of the island's exotic fauna and flora. Guide, philosopher and host to distinguished scientists from all over the world, he was also the dogged money-raiser who helped keep this modern Noah's Ark financially afloat.

Hundreds of scientists have prowled this open-air laboratory and have taken home new-found knowledge to enrich natural-history textbooks, educational films and classroom teaching.

On Barro Colorado, year after year, the murderous campaigns of army ants were followed by noted authority Dr. T. C. Schneirla. Here Zetek himself, with Dr. Thomas E. Snyder, pioneered invaluable research in termite control and continued to report new findings on the voracious appetites of those chew-it-yourself craftsmen. Here the U.S. Armed Services tested GI equipment and rations for jungle warfare, and here a giant corporation—Eastman Kodak—struggled to outwit a microscopic fungus that etched camera lenses in the tropics. Here Dr. C. R. Carpenter observed the adult delinquency of howling monkeys and told all with Kinsey clarity.

This tropical island paradise is a unique zoo-in-reverse, where animals roam as they please through the primordial jungle while human visitors, as they walk the narrow trails, inevitably feel that their presence is merely tolerated.

When I sat down to my first meal in the dining room, also used as the laboratory, I was fascinated by the shelves of canned goods and pickled vipers, and I envied the aplomb of my companions—all famous scientists—who looked upon life-in-the-raw around them with professional detachment.

"I hear the wild pigs are quite vicious. . . ." I volunteered offhand to no one in particular. My neighbor said, "The white-lipped peccaries, the more vicious of the two species of wild pigs on the island, have been known to charge, especially if you happen to get between the female and her young, in which case . . ." His remarks trailed off as if the outcome was of no importance.

I made a mental note to observe the traffic rules of the peccaries and pointed across the dining room to a large glass jar containing, tastefully coiled in alcohol, a six-foot fer-de-lance, the deadliest serpent in this Eden.

"How about snakes?" I asked. "Like that?"

Another scientist replied: "Oh, that one. I killed her last year with a machete. When I dissected her

she had 47 little ones in her. They are born alive, with venom and fangs, you know."

"Naturally," I said.

He turned to discussing the fertilization cycle of army-ant queens with the lady scientist across the table, down from Columbia University to study sex determination in certain monophlebine coccids, if you'll pardon the expression.

"But those pumas," I said, during a lull, "they're pretty big, aren't they? Do they really run wild out there?" And I pointed up the hill to the trail that I had promised to walk with Dr. Schneirla after lunch.

"Pumas?" Dr. Schneirla came back with a visible effort. "Oh yes! Fellow here last year from the Middle West, collecting fungi. Suddenly saw a puma

Toucans, like this Swainson's toucan in the Barro Colorado rain forest, use their brightly colored beaks to pluck fruit. Honeycombed with air spaces, toucan beaks are strong but surprisingly light for their size.

right in front of him on the trail. Not more than 20 feet. Zetek made rules for visiting scientists: 'Don't panic. Don't run. You can stare your puma down.'

"This fellow kept thinking about his wife and children and how they would miss him. But he stared his best and seemed to be holding his own, when all of a sudden there was a second puma, about the same distance, but off to the right. So now he had two pumas to stare down. Says he got so cross-eyed he must have frightened the pumas because suddenly they were gone."

Many miles of narrow trails crisscross the wild and rugged island, all named and marked every hundred meters, starting with zero at the laboratory. I walked a trail with Dr. Schneirla, who was looking for one of his army-ant colonies. "They are not easy to find," he said. "And even when you find them it's easy to lose them." I asked how you could lose 60,000 ants on the march and he said, "Do you see any ants on that vine?" I looked and said, "No."

"That's what I mean," he said. "Look closer and you'll see a single file of them. They come to a ravine like this and cross on one of these long lianas like a suspension bridge. They don't make any noise, and a single file of ants, unless you've had experience seeing them, can disappear right under your eyes."

"How do you know one colony from another?"

"I mark the queens," he said. "Snip a little nick in the back of their necks. I kept track of one queen this way for five years. That's a record." He went on to say that army ants are blind and pretty stupid. They follow a scent laid down by the scouts and each queen has a scent of her own. "I've got so I can distinguish different queens by their smell."

"How about the popular notion of army ants cutting a wide swath through the jungle and killing everything as they go?"

"An army-ant colony on the march will travel less than one mile an hour on a front up to 50 feet wide. And it is true that everything gets out of their way. They bite viciously and will overwhelm the largest victims by sheer numbers and ferocity."

Barro Colorado is ideal for studying army ants. They can't get off the island, so you can keep track of them and build up a year-to-year record. Schneirla had studied ants in other tropical countries but always came back to Barro Colorado. "In no other place," he said, "can the scientist find such perfect conditions for tropical research. Here you are close to modern transportation and communications. Food, shelter and sanitation are cared for and you can spend your time and energy doing research instead of hacking trails, building huts, battling mos-

Capuchin monkeys, once favored by organ-grinders, are the cleverest of American primates. In captivity they exhibit a remarkable ability to solve practical problems and to use and improvise tools. Some of them have been able to paint pictures; others have watched movies attentively.

quitoes, toting supplies, and just keeping alive."

Schneirla told me that all the big cats of the tropics follow the Barro Colorado trails, including the jaguar, which doesn't live on the island but swims over to poach. Automatic cameras with trip wires across the trails have taken flashlight shots of nocturnal prowlers, and occasionally ocelots and pumas have been detected taking parallel strolls with the scientists. "Just curiosity, I would say," remarked Schneirla.

When Zetek first came to Barro Colorado, he had to paddle across the lake in a native dugout canoe and camp out on the bare ground. Later he started cutting trails and building termite test-houses, combining shelter and research.

"After more than 20 years of continuous research we are still learning about termites," Zetek once said. "We have 59 species on the island. They not only eat practically every kind of wood, but will chew their way through wire insulation, inferior concrete, and even lead sheathing."

Thomas Barbour, the great naturalist, was the first patron saint of the island, according to Zetek. "He

A three-toed sloth peers out at the world through myopic, sleepy eyes as it labors up the branch of a Cecropia *tree, its habitat and the primary source of its food. The sloth rarely leaves the tree; much of the time it hangs upside-down, with its claws hooked over a horizontal branch. During the rainy season, green algae grow in its fur, providing camouflage for the sloth and food for small moths that also inhabit the fur.*

contributed generously out of his own pocket and came to our rescue time after time. We named one trail 'Harvard' after his alma mater and the first distance stake 'Harvard O.' An eminent zoologist from Yale stayed with us shortly after, and when he left we found he had committed what might be termed the only 'sabotage' on the island: Under 'Harvard O' he had painted 'Yale 6.'

"Since our job is conserving and understanding life instead of thinking up new ways to destroy it, we are way down at the end of the table when it comes to financial support. We have survived precariously through the years by passing the hat among our friends.

"But I feel optimistic for the future. More and more our nation is becoming involved with far-flung problems around the world, many of them related to tropical conditions. Here on Barro Colorado scientists can do valuable work in the future, as they have in the past, when they were happy to contribute time, experience and knowledge at no expense to the Government.

"Years ago a simple Chiriqui Indian who had never worked in concrete before made, singlehanded, the 198 steps you climb from the dock to our laboratory. He proudly signed the last step: 'Made by Donato with all possible economy.' You might say that is the motto of Barro Colorado."

Life of the Rain Forest

In the equatorial regions of the New World, eons of torrential rains and hot, humid weather have nurtured a lush tropical forest. The interwoven branches of its trees form a canopy over 100 feet high, so dense that only occasional shafts of sunlight can penetrate. Below the canopy, spindly young trees struggle upward, and above it a few wide-crowned giants rise as high as 200 feet. Birds, monkeys, sloths, lizards and snakes live their entire lives in the branches; peccaries and tapirs forage on the floor; myriads of insects flit through the motionless air and crawl across the foliage. Everywhere woody vines, many as thick as a watermelon and over 200 feet long, hang from the trees. Countless orchids and other flowering "air" plants grow on rotting logs and in the damp crannies of living trees. Acre for acre, the tropical rain forest harbors a greater variety of life than any other land area.

King of the rain forest's birds of prey, the harpy eagle (above) *glides through the trees in search of sloths and monkeys.*

The twelve-inch golden conure (above, right) *of eastern Brazil is one of the forest canopy's most colorful inhabitants.*

A versatile predator, the jaguar (right) *feeds on peccaries, fish, and even alligators.*

The howler monkey (above), *whose lionlike roar can be heard for a mile, never descends from the trees. When thirsty, it licks wet leaves.*

Anchored by its prehensile tail, a tamandua, a tree-dwelling anteater, tears bark off a dead branch with hooklike foreclaws and picks up termites on its long, sticky tongue.

A tree frog perches precariously on a Heliconia plant. This gaudy amphibian (shown about six times life size) sleeps all day and hunts insects by night.

Working their jaws like scissors, Atta ants snip pieces from leaves to carry back to their nest. There the ants will chew the cuttings into a pulpy mulch in which they grow an edible fungus.

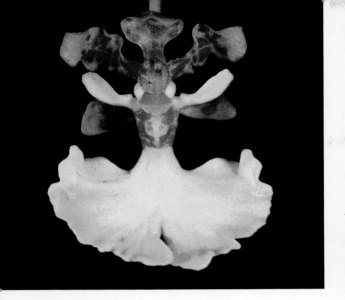

A foot-long giant anole lizard (above) preys on one of its insect-eating smaller relatives. Both of these tree-dwelling reptiles are related to the chameleons sold in pet stores.

Flowers abound in the rain forest, sprouting profusely from tree trunks and climbing vines. The butterfly orchid (top) grows on a long, thin stalk so well hidden by foliage that it seems to hover in midair. The passionflower (middle) is the bloom of a woody vine. The petals of the ginger flower (bottom) catch water in which frogs and insects breed. This blossom has attracted an inch-long Euglossid bee.

Chapter Three

The Seasons

As each year passes, life awakens with spring's promise of renewal and growth,
blossoms into summer fullness and ripening, reaches a climax in the blazing colors
of autumn and retreats before the icy onslaught of winter. As year follows
year and season follows season, life constantly prepares for what is to come.

THE AWAKENING

Franklin Russell

Once again the Northern Hemisphere tilted slowly toward the sun. Great masses of warm air rolled north over the continent, and hordes of migrants moved with and ahead of it. Now the skies over our pond in Ontario, Canada, became a turmoil of rain, snow, high winds and the wild calls of birds, communicating the expectancy of a new season.

An eastern rain wind began blowing tentatively across the pond, its warm vapor condensing into water until the snow was saturated with it. That night parts of the snow began discoloring and collapsing. The mice hurriedly abandoned their tunnels and sought safety in trees as their corridors disappeared.

Next morning the sky cleared and the sun sent down the first palpable heat in 100 days. The ice still sealed the unstirring pond firmly against its own banks, but a small quantity of aerated water seeped into the earth, down wormholes, along roots, through shingle and shale. It appeared in the pond as tiny bubbles, which revived a few of the suffocating creatures. Throughout the pond area could be heard the gurgle and skirl of melting snow and running, flooding water.

The pond has been asleep in ice, and it awoke in a flood. The brooks broke their frozen skins and the ice cracked and floated in the center of the pond. Water flooded the top corridors of ant mounds and trickled into raccoon burrows and skunk holes. Gashes of black earth spread through the trees as the snow retreated, revealing bird and animal bodies, the winter's casualties. A frozen cottontail rabbit came into view in the remains of a snowdrift. A weasel had killed her in midwinter and hidden the body in the snow. But the weasel herself had been killed by an owl soon after, and now the thawing rabbit belonged to the pond's scavengers.

A dull splotch of red emerged from another patch of snow: the breast feathers of a cardinal, who had scarcely glimpsed the glaring eyes and spread talons of a plunging sparrow hawk before he was ripped off his perch and finally dropped into the snow.

All surviving life was now pushing out of its winter sheath for a place in the growing warmth. In the pond a tiger salamander heaved out of the mud in a cloud of debris and swam sluggishly upward, the sun firing his vivid yellow spots. He climbed onto a patch of ice and was still struggling to dispel the sleepiness that had kept him under the mud for 150 days, when he was seized by a mink. His death was a small incident.

Following the salamander came an avalanche of waking creatures. The mud of the pond bulged and swirled as frogs kicked free and headed for the spring air. Peepers began singing. Skittering turtles sped through the water and swooped down in search of sleeping larvae. In the forest a box turtle pushed out of the crusty soil under a tree. The ground cracked and fell away from his upthrusting head. When he lurched into a patch of saxifrage, his shell was almost invisible in the multiple patterns of earth, plant, shade and sun. He would lie in wait there for other sleepy wakeners—beetles, snails, spiders, flies.

The snails dropped in thousands out of the melting ice, some to rot on the bottom, others to extend their viscid bodies and begin foraging. A bluebottle fly groggily preened his wings; a mourning cloak butterfly wakened from his sleep in a hollow tree.

In and around the pond, the shadowy beginnings of new life were moving in egg cases, seeds, larvae, burrows, caves and tunnels. The sodden earth sprouted a million shafts of grass. In a distant tree, a fox sparrow sang a tinkling song of exquisite and expectant feeling.

A succession of warm days sent dogwood buds bursting into newborn leaflets, and a hint of green blurred the stark outlines of deciduous elms. Now plants pushed from under the debris of the forest floor. Green tips of toothworts, bunchberries, bloodroots and foxgloves appeared, and the trilliums' broad green leaves seemed to leap into sight. Then an overwhelming profusion of plants drove out of the earth: anemones, bugbanes and violets; orchids and adder's-tongues; mayflowers and bedstraws. The early skunk cabbages were now flowering, and the blossoms were packed with drinking gnats and sluggish flies and bees.

In the crevice of the granite rock, the queen bumblebee stretched her legs and wings, breathed deeply and stretched again. Then she droned waveringly toward the bright light at the entrance. Though weak, she unhesitatingly launched herself across the pond, flying low over the water until she saw some tree catkins and headed up toward them. She thumped heavily onto the first catkin, sending it swinging wildly, sucked nectar from it, and bumped to other flowers. Then, smeared with pollen, she headed along the bank of the pond, buzzing into piles of leaves, around tree trunks, hunting every crack and crevice in the ground for a burrow in which to begin a new colony.

In a hollow tree 38,000 drowsy, fertilized female mosquitoes began stirring. When they emerged, they would search urgently for their first meal of blood, obtained, perhaps, from a sleeping bird. This would prepare them for the task of laying clusters of eggs in still patches of water around the pond.

Underground, the ants were laboring to clear jammed and collapsed tunnels, working closely behind the retreating ice. One ant mound lay under a rivulet of thaw water. The ants struggled to stem it, but the water carried the ants with it, driving them deep into the soil. Their tunnels collapsed and only stray ants were left, wandering on the surface.

The hare was changing color, turning blotchily from white to gray and brown. The old muskrat looked young and sleek, standing erect on his rough shelter and wrinkling his grizzled snout. A multitude of warblers, tanagers and grosbeaks moved brilliantly in the sun, and red-winged blackbirds clackered in the marsh. Two kingfishers appeared one morning and dived for fish, smashing into the calm water in a shower of stars. The earthbound eye could see only part of the arrival of the birds, but at night the air was filled with the whisper of wings, and on pink evenings the sky was marked with flowing lines of ducks and geese moving north. On some days the marsh held 100,000 birds, who took to the air in sinuous columns and clusters, riding across the rays of the setting sun into the north.

The red-tailed hawk watched the fliers from a high point in the sky and screamed at them, sometimes smashing them to earth in showers of feathers.

Even the awakening around the pond was not as spectacular as the awakening within it. The stream

This field mouse has taken refuge in the branches of a sapling. Like many small animals that live on low ground, it was displaced temporarily when torrential spring rains flooded its home.

feeding the pond brought in 14-legged sow bugs, each as big as a large fly, to feed on rotting vegetation. Eighty thousand came into the pond in one day, and the crayfish emerged from their tunnels and began to eat them. Great diving beetles rose from the mud, their sheeny purple skins reflecting the spring sun, while from slimy vegetation bronze-colored whirligig beetles kicked swiftly for the surface and jerked back and forth there, two of their four eyes watching above water, two beneath. Water boatmen and slender, long-legged water striders burst to the surface and darted across the pond. The bottom of the pond was alive with the crawling nymphs of creatures who would later leave the water on wings.

The appearance of great numbers of nymphs, beetles and bugs in the pond coincided with the multiplication of the incredible, invisible animal and plant life around them. The diversity of life in this miniature universe seemed infinite. Throughout the fast-warming shallows, microscopic desmids and diatoms rose from debris at the bottom. The desmids headed for the warm sunlight and fastened their soft bodies to the stems of plants. Collectively they looked like a fine green film, for they sprang to life in billions. Unlike the unicellular jelly blobs of the desmids, the dia-

toms had hard exterior cases, which, when attacked by beetles or nymphs, would crack open. Despite their billions, few pond creatures could see them, even in the mass. But these organisms were a prime source of food to many of the pond's creatures. Together with other equally small creatures, or plants, they would form the algae of the pond, which would appear as

slime on rocks and brown stains on plant stems as their numbers multiplied again and again.

Water mites and water fleas and many different worms appeared now in the pond. Planarian worms undulated gracefully through the water; tiny tubifex worms protruded waving, questing heads from projections on the bottom of the pond.

All this life appeared against countless blunt shoots springing from the bottom, from old roots, from dormant seeds. Cattails sprouted in the shallows. Bulrushes, pondweeds, duckweeds and water lilies headed urgently for the surface.

This was the awakening in the pond, a prodigious expansion of life, diversified but interrelated, with common animation of spirit and objective.

FROM SPRING TO SUMMER

Edwin Way Teale

March 20. It is officially spring! But what an anticlimax! Gust-driven rain is slashing the trees under a sullen sky; the air is raw and chill. I recall Henry van Dyke's observation that the first day of spring and the first spring day are not always the same thing.

To me spring was marked this year by the return of the male redwing blackbirds, who came back with a rush a month ago. Almost overnight the drear stretches of our winter swamp were filled with life. Everywhere, with scarlet epaulets flashing, the blackbirds have been singing and darting about, chasing each other, shooting up like rockets, whirling like pinwheels. It is a kind of Oklahoma land rush. Before the females arrive, each male stakes out a homestead, and then with spectacular aerobatics defends and holds as much of the territory as possible. The air rings with their wild xylophone calling. It is an exultant, jubilant call, a fitting voice for a season of flowing sap and awakening life.

March 24. The time of baby squirrels is at hand. Each year around this time I see gray squirrels stripping off the dry bark of cedar limbs and carrying it away to their nesting holes. And now I also see them carrying bits of newspapers.

I wonder if there is some untaught wisdom that

Ears cocked for danger, a young white-tailed deer pauses in the shallows of a woodland pond before taking a cool drink. A fawn born in April or May loses its spots by September but, not yet fully mature, it stays with its mother until it is nearly a year old.

leads the squirrels to the cedar tree, and makes them prefer newsprint to other paper. Cedar protects clothes from moths, and newspapers are sometimes used for the same purpose. Do they also help keep a squirrel's nest free from vermin?

March 26. At sunset I walk along the swamp path. Only a few weeks ago the frozen earth appeared hard and dead, yet now I see the beginning of a flood of life that nothing can halt.

Because growth in plants is a gradual thing, we often overlook the power that is contained in the rising shoot and expanding seed. I once saw peas, planted in a flowerpot, lift and thrust aside a heavy sheet of plate glass laid over the top. Another time, when peas and water were tightly sealed in thick glass bottles, the germinating seeds developed pressures sufficient to shatter the glass. An explosion, in slow motion, had occurred within the bottles.

March 28. In the breeding season the starlings' mimicking of other birds reaches its peak. One male has been sitting in my silver maple today giving the calls of such varied species as the crow, catbird, meadow lark and killdeer, and even the quacking of a flying mallard duck. Also, a neighborhood child has been blowing a shrill police whistle, and now the starling imitates that sound, too—a little softer perhaps but unmistakable.

March 31. As I walked up through the old orchard late this afternoon I looked back and caught the different shades of green in new grass clumps and young leaves, all suddenly brilliant in the sun, which had just emerged from behind a cloud. In the same way, the peculiar illumination before a summer thunderstorm brings out special details and alters a whole landscape. As I stood there, an old saying took on added meaning: "To see it in a *new* light."

April 4. A long soaking rain before daybreak, and earthworms are stranded everywhere on the inhospitable cement of sidewalks, in imminent danger of early birds or drying sun. So my morning walk is slowed by stops to put earthworms back on the ground, where they belong. People probably wonder what treasure I am finding when they see me stoop so often.

And, in a way, I am dealing in treasure. A silver fox may sell for hundreds of dollars; a racehorse may be insured for a quarter of a million. Yet the world's most valuable animal is the earthworm—a humble burrower, nature's plowman!

April 15. At 6:30 this morning I watch a velvet-coated bumblebee begin hunting for a nest site. I see her investigate every possible opening near a pile of moldering fence rails. Zigzagging, hovering, alight-ing, she peers into a rusting tin can in the weeds, explores under a maple root, in a knothole. She investigates the region around my shoe, and then along a bit of board lying in the grass. She will continue searching for hours and days, and may consider thousands of sites before she decides where to establish her nest. She is the founder of an insect city, and the fate of her colony depends to a great extent upon the wisdom of her choice.

April 21. Just before I start for a walk in the misty dawn this morning, the radio is filling the airwaves with the troubles of the world. But out-of-doors the news is good. All of nature is a going concern. The business of spring is prospering. I stand for a long time beside the swamp stream in a fairyland setting of low-lying mist, glowing and tinted with the pink of the sunrise. Such a sight sets us to rights again. For the disturbed mind, the still beauty of the dawn is nature's finest balm.

April 22. This is the time of robins bewitched. People write me letters about robins that peck endlessly at shiny hubcaps, that spend their days fluttering against windowpanes and pecking at the glass. Have the birds gone crazy? What ails them?

Wherever robins are nesting, the same thing is taking place. Males are defending their nesting territories. Catching sight of his own reflection in a window or a shiny metal surface, the male robin dashes to drive the intruder away. He may battle this phantom rival for days on end.

Only windows with darkened rooms behind them, turning the glass into a mirror, attract the birds. Merely turn on a light in the room or hang a white cloth in the window and the bird's reflection will disappear. The robin imagines it has vanquished its rival and, in high good spirits, returns to the normal life of a redbreast in the spring.

April 29. Rain in the night, and this morning the fallen white petals of the pear trees lie scattered across my path like confetti. Mingled with the gray rain has been the green rain of descending maple flowers as well. They dot the sidewalks and form yellow-green windrows at the edges of the puddles. Leaf-fall in the autumn and flower-fall in the spring!

May 2. Someone dumped the limbs and trunk of a willow tree beside the road and they have been lying there a good part of the winter. Today I noticed that innumerable sprouts have pushed out all along the length of one of the discarded logs. The sight recalled the experience of a man I know who left rustic willow chairs out in his yard all winter. In the spring he discovered that every chair had taken root!

May 13. This evening I saw the spectacular aerial

A male redwing blackbird perches on a cattail. Adult males are the first to reach the marshes in spring, and each establishes a territory. The duller-colored females follow and prepare nesting sites, then advertise their presence to the males. The first-year males, just beginning to show adult plumage, arrive last and rarely mate.

mating of a pair of tree swallows. The birds flew wildly, almost like swifts. Then, 50 or 60 feet above the ground, the swallows met face to face, fluttered for a moment, and then, with wings widespread to break their descent, dropped straight downward through the air for 40 feet or more! They were hardly ten feet above the ground when they disunited, to rise up and up again into the sunset sky.

May 18. Through my glasses, I watched a female redwing working at a cattail stem floating in the water, stripping away fibers for her nest. But fibers and other time-honored construction materials are being supplemented these days with a surprising number of modern odds and ends. Near here, a wood thrush made use of torn-up bus tickets; another wood thrush, nesting near a refreshment stand in an Indiana park, collected discarded pop-bottle straws. Small nails, carried from a building project to a birdhouse, formed the steel nest of a house wren, while a redstart made its nest entirely of insulating material.

May 24. All along the shallow eastern edge of Milburn Pond the sunfish have been scraping away the silt to provide bare, clean patches of gravel for spawning—a sign that the water's temperature has risen to

68°. Over each of these scoured patches was a guardian fish that rushed toward every interloper. Where two patches overlapped, the guardians kept rushing back and forth in a seesaw battle. The fury of the attacker waned quickly as it advanced into the defender's territory, while its courage seemed to mount when it was pursued into its own. Thus they continued as long as I remained at the pond.

All the defenders were males. They build the nest, guard it, fertilize the eggs—often laid by several females—and defend the young that hatch there among the pebbles.

June 1. Outside a little after five on this first morning of June. The machinery of nature, with its winds and dews and dawns and morning mists, produces poetry as well as seasons and growth and change. The functioning of nature's cogs has created dewdrops and veils of luminous mist caught among the cattails. Before the work of the day, taste the poetry of the day!

As I crossed the hillside, a small patch of dry, yellow grass caught my eye. Carefully I pulled aside the grass and the soft gray blanket of fur I found beneath, and exposed the little ears of a nestful of baby cotton-

Born blind and helpless, baby cottontails spend the first 12 days of their lives in a fur-lined nest. No more than two of the five or six babies will reach adulthood, but a mother may have five litters a year.

tails. Just as carefully I replaced the fur coverlet and the grass. In a little while, now, I will see rabbits hopping about my hillside.

June 4. One of the gray squirrels that shares our yard is using a crutch. It injured a hind leg somehow and, although it gets about on three legs fairly well, when I throw it a peanut it is unable to sit up to eat it. So the crippled squirrel carries its nut to a branch that fell from a dying maple and braces itself against that. Thus supported, it can eat its nut sitting up, in the traditional squirrel fashion.

June 12. To the sea moor at sunset, to witness again one of the most ancient dramas of the earth: the coming of the king crabs to the shallows to fertilize and leave their eggs. This is the great annual event in the lives of these "horsefoots," as the baymen call them. They are among the oldest dwellers in the sea, creatures that have lived on and on after some of their early contemporaries have become fossils.

Moment by moment the water creeps ahead as the tide runs in. Shadowy at first, the crabs appear from the murky water; they come linked together, the smaller male behind. Farther and farther they push up into the shallows to deposit the translucent little globes of their eggs. These events, as I watch them in the twilight of this June day, are the same as they were a hundred million years before the dinosaurs. In an unbroken chain they link the Atomic Age with the primeval world.

June 14. Who can doubt that it "feels good" to the turtle to sun itself on a log; that it "feels good" to the flicker to rap its bill on hollow wood; that it "feels good" to the muskrat to dive into water? Pleasure and pain, comfort and discomfort, these are the push and pull of instinct.

June 19. Glistening globes of white, each about the size of a pea, shine out from the grass tangles of the hillside this morning. Each mass of froth, like beaten egg white, is produced by a tiny immature insect inside, using a mechanism unknown elsewhere in all of nature. For millions of years these insects, commonly known as froghoppers, have literally been saving their lives by blowing bubbles. Safe within its little foam castle, the insect lies moist and hidden, sucking sap from the grass stem. Later it develops wings and flies away, a nondescript brownish little bug that is rarely noticed. Its great achievement, its claim to fame, is this shining house of foam that is produced during its earliest days.

June 21. This is the hinge day of the seasons. Today the yearly tide of light reaches its flood. Tomorrow it will begin the long rollback to the dark days of December. I heard robins singing this morning shortly after four, Daylight Saving Time, and they are still singing at nine o'clock at night. A robin uses up all the daylight, even on this longest day of the year.

In the later sunset of this final day of spring, my wife and I walk to the bay. As we stand there, in the quiet of the evening and with the smell of the sea all around us, a faint mist forms in the air. Twilight here is doubly impressive for we are face to face with twin mysteries—the mystery of the sea and the mystery of the night.

Thus ends another spring—rich in the small everyday events of the earth as all springs are for those who find delight in simple things. The institutions of men alter and disintegrate. But in the endless repetitions of nature—in the recurrence of spring, in the coming of new birds to sing the ancient songs, in the continuity of life and the web of the living—here we find the solid foundation that underlies at once the past, the present and the future.

AUGUST BOUNTY

Hal Borland

August ripeness creeps across the land, a continuing event. Traveling west, you see the harvest in all its stages, and the seeing is a fresh reminder of this season's variety and its ever-amazing bounty. The corn everywhere, from the patchy little fields of the East to the vastness of Illinois and Iowa cornfields. The deep, rich green of soybeans, and the oat fields, the rye and barley and wheat fields, golden stubble now, clipped and thrashed of their grain. And, as one approaches the western mountains, the endless, ordered fields of garden-fresh sugar beets.

And the hay everywhere. Timothy and clover and alfalfa and native grass. Hay in bloom, hay cut and baled, and hay in fresh windrows curing in the sun. Stacks of hay, bales of hay, millions of tons of hay.

You travel, and you see this creeping harvest, and you know again the reality behind the statistics. For here is the diet, the nutrition, the plenty that statistics can only hint at. Here is the storehouse, the grain bin, the bounty of the land ripening in the August sunlight.

August is the year at early harvest, a farm wife

From October to May this algae-covered snapping turtle may hibernate underwater, but for now it enjoys August bounty: aquatic plants, insects and small fish. Though it looks placid, the snapper is irascible— much more so on land than in water. It captures its food with a strike as powerful and swift as a rattlesnake's.

with a baby napping in the crib, a preserving kettle on the stove, fryers in the freezer, new potatoes in the pot, and a husband in the hayfield baling the second cutting. August is tomatoes ripening and the insistent note of the cicada puncturing the midafternoon heat.

August is the flame of phlox in the dooryard and hollyhocks down by the roadside. August is a falling star in the evening. It is a languid river and a springhouse brook reduced to a trickle. August is baby rabbits almost grown, and pilfering in the garden; it is fledglings all feathered and on the wing; it is a cow, her spring calf forgotten, chewing a leisurely cud in the shade of an elm at the side of the meadow.

August is the heavy grapes in the vineyard, and the lacy leaf where the Japanese beetle feasted. August is a hastening sun, earlier to bed and later to rise. August is summer thinking of the cut and color of her autumn costume.

The quiet ponds are scummed over now and full of algae, and one gets the feeling that anything could happen in such waters, any kind of life arise from them. Here, in the dead heat of late summer, is the marshy margin and the primordial ooze, and he who approaches it might be walking backward in time toward remote beginnings.

Even the pond creatures and those along its margins belong to another time. Of the reptiles, the snapping turtle is one of the ancients, armored like a creature of the Silurian age. The frogs are primitives, tadpoles that have shed gills and tails and crept up onto land. The water snakes are still slithering through the vanished age when pterodactyls had not yet grown wings. And in the air drift and dart such dragonflies as can be found as fossils in rocks older than coal.

The pond water is tepid with mud warmth, a kind of protoplasmic soup full of strange and struggling uncertainties. But the hills look down, and the hills are certainty itself, for they are the land risen from the muck, the rock, the soil, the maturity of an age reflected briefly in the stagnant pond.

In the evening, there's warmth to an August moon and the fullness of midsummer. It is a generous moon that lights the green hills with a kind of ripening-apple glow. There is a mellowness about a moonlit night in August that is a sweet antidote for the cicada heat and the dusty glare of the sun.

Katydids scratch the night, but there is also the silent beat of moth wings. And on a distant hill is the tentative bark of a fox, testing the air for some faint hint of autumn. Summer it still is; but summer passing the peak, reluctantly starting the long, leisurely

glide toward frost and November. Early windfalls scent the breeze from the orchard, not quite a cider tang but the promise of cider to come.

Now, in late August, a miracle declares itself in every field and garden in the land—the wonder of the seed, the means of reproduction, life that will somehow endure beyond this one season. Everywhere you turn you see it. The uncut grass comes to head and ripens its seed. Pods begin to form where the milkweed hung its sweet lavender bloom so recently. The sweet clover at the roadside is not half so fragrant now that its blossom has gone to seed. Cattails lift brown thumbs of packed seeds to ripen in the southing sun. Thistle heads begin to turn to fat tufts of floss that delight the goldfinches.

Garden beans grow too tough to eat, hastening the seed toward ripeness. Sweet corn, ready for the pot today, will be too ripe by day after tomorrow. It is a race now between the succulent prime and the too-ripe seeding, a race the gardener inevitably loses, for the seeding is inevitable. This is the miracle itself, the insistence of the seed, the persistence of the mysterious germ that is life.

AUTUMN FLIES HER FLAGS

Donald Culross Peattie

All summer a tree has spread its green tiers of foliage outside your window, spray on spray of airy leaves that set the sun and shade to dancing on your floor. In the night wind it whispered to your roof. Through the long summer you came to take it for granted, and almost ceased to see it.

Now, suddenly, what was only a tree has turned into a radiant presence. As the sun shines through its autumn tints, the light in your room is colored, as if a cathedral window had been set there, and the faces within glow a little with that unearthly beauty.

Across the street your fiery sugar maple is matched by an oak burning with the embers of all summer's pyre. And next door is a purple dogwood, and beyond a poplar, carelessly dropping its gold pieces into the gutter.

And so it is all up and down the street—any street,

Leaves from a red maple tree carpet the forest floor. One of the first trees to herald the coming of autumn in eastern North America, the red maple often wears a resplendent mantle of crimson and gold when other trees around it are still clothed in summer green.

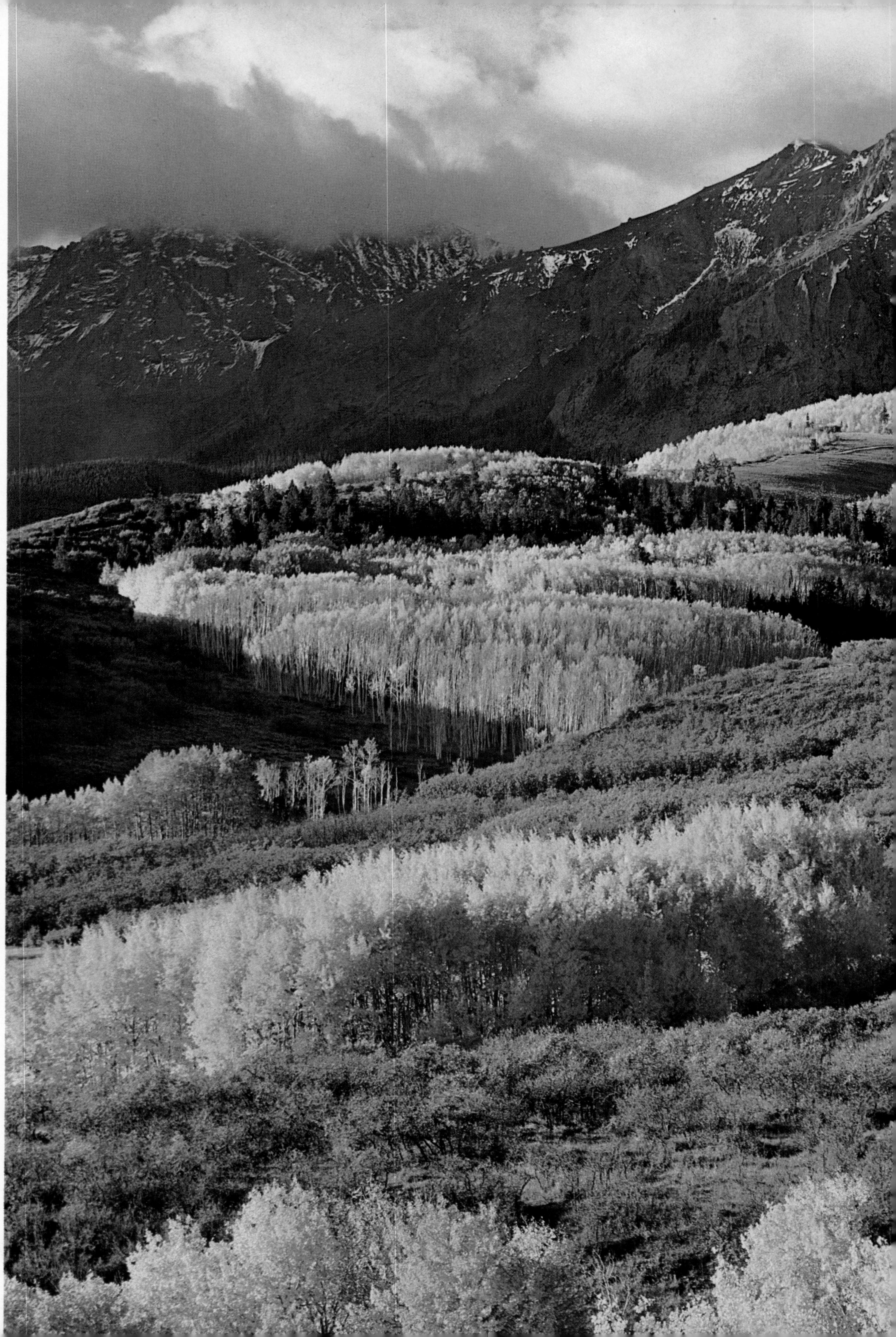

in every town of the North American hardwood zone. The North has its Christmas trees all year round, and the South has palms and live oaks that never go bare, but in the heartland between them summer dies in a glorious national pageant.

Out in the country, where the first hoar frost rimes the angry purple of the blackberry leaf, are heaped the spoils of the season. At the door of the white farmhouse the soft maples, gold above and silver below, scatter their wealth. The sumacs, like savages in war paint, besiege the well-stored barn. Field after field, the landscape fills with the russet of the turning grasses. Crickets chant; a last bobwhite calls. The hedgerows burn with a low running fire of blueberry bushes. But in the oaks, craggy against October sky, nature plays out the climax of the great drama, in salvo after salvo of changing color.

That it is North American, above all, foreign travelers agree. All British reserve left Lord Bryce as he spoke of the fall he saw here. Mrs. Trollope, who liked almost nothing else here, admitted that at this season the countryside goes to glory. Our autumns are startling to the newcomer, for the cold rainy autumns of Europe preclude gorgeous colors. Even the native maples there only pale sadly. To achieve autumnal vistas like ours, the English have imported North American species. Virginia creeper is their favorite, but they have even been known to play with the hellfire flickerings of poison ivy!

Only regions with drop-leaf, or deciduous, trees can have autumn coloration. This confines nature's handiwork to the temperate zones. But temperate Europe lacks variety in hardwoods, and red and purple in its autumn hues. China is too largely deforested to rival us seriously.

If I could transport some of my foreign friends here, I would have them come in the fall and start on a journey, beginning in September in the north woods of the East. I would have them see aspens shining gold against the closed ranks of dark spruces and firs, and white-limbed birches standing like nymphs in the shower of their own gold hair. Then I would have them travel southward with the living fire of the sugar maples as it lights the whole landscape from the forests where they grow wild to the villages where, planted, they march two by two up the hill to the meeting house.

Turned to blazing gold by the afternoon sun's slanting rays, quaking aspens gild the slopes of the Colorado Rockies in autumn. Remarkably widespread, these hardy trees grow in the west from Alaska to Lower California and in the east from Labrador to Kentucky.

South of the belt of maple and birch comes the great band of American oaks, stretching from the Atlantic to the prairie. And of all these I would choose to show my visitors the oaks of the Indiana dunes along Lake Michigan. Not that autumn isn't fine in Pennsylvania or Quebec, in Wisconsin or Ontario, but there is something special about the zest of "dune weather," when the lake comes foaming up the beach, filling the stately painted woods with its roar and its fresh breath. There is something incomparable, too, about the way the sumacs flame there, and the Virginia creeper, clambering to the highest trees, pours down molten color.

You would do well, also, to show foreign visitors the dreamy Indian summer distances of the Ohio Valley, where the pawpaws, amid clear lemon leaves, ripen their dark-skinned fruits. Or to take them to Arkansas, just for the sake of its blazing hawthorn trees and the beaten gold of the Osage orange leaves, or the sulky beauty of the smoke bush.

In November the southern Appalachians catch fire. Besides the vivid sugar maples and oaks and sumac, there are sassafras, its gaudy orange and scarlet intermixed with the glossy green of leaves not yet turned color, and sourwood, beloved of the bees for the fine honey it makes. And there are the tulip trees, casting the glowing squares of their foliage upon the chill spring bubbling at their feet. For colors more subtle still there is white ash that turns mauve and bluish-bronze, or the wild hazel, soft salmon and rose-pink.

The Far West is best famed for its conifers, its pines and firs. But there is a subtle beauty in an Oregon maple, trembling like a splendidly dressed bride before the towering strength of redwoods. And when you round the corner of some Colorado trail through Engelmann spruces, you'll come abruptly upon an aspen, the purest gold in all the world, breathtaking as some angelic apparition.

Were you told, as a child, that Jack Frost paints the leaves? Actually a severe early frost kills the leaves before they can turn color. The yellow pigments in almost all foliage are present in the interior cells, but are masked all summer by the rich green pigments. When the life in the leaf cell goes, so does the green, and the gold comes out. So leaves turn yellow in a drought. In fall the tree cuts off life from its leaf by growing a row of brittle, corky cells at the base of the twig, cutting off circulation of sap. Summer's green disappears and the latent yellow gets its chance to shine through.

Light is as essential in bringing out reds and purples as it is in bringing out an image on a photographic plate; thus sunny autumns are the most brilliant. A dearth of nitrogen is also conducive to high color. Where this plant food is abundant, as in heavily manured soils, leaves may stay green until so late that a final frost kills them colorlessly. In consequence, the poor, rocky, acid soils of New England and the southern Appalachians and the sands of the Great Lakes dunes are ideal for artist Nature's purpose.

Sugar in the sap is especially inducive to reds; that's why the sugar maple is the king of autumn foliage. It is the same with acidity; at time of cell death, acidity spreads through the leaf. And as acids turn litmus paper pink, so they turn leaves red.

Three chemicals account for most fall tints. Tannin in the leaves produces the browns. Xanthophyll, which is also present in egg yolk, gives most of the yellows. This pigment is water-fast. But the reds and purples, produced by the anthocyanins, are water-soluble; they are mere stains, and are found only in the superficial cells of certain leaves. These are the ones that most need the sun to bring them out. Sometimes when a leaf or a whole tree that is normally red is denied sunlight it will fall back on the underlying yellow. That's why the swamp maples, for instance, may be red or yellow, and the same maple that was red one year will in another, cloudier season be yellow only. Orange, of course, is due to what artists call overpainting. That is, the underlying yellow is shining through the overlying red, and makes the blended shade.

It is essentially death that causes all the brave show. But it is a glorious one, and Americans and Canadians may feel proud when their countries are hung with the battle flags of a triumphant year.

THE DAY THE BEARS GO TO BED

Jean George

Her grave face turned into the wind, the female grizzly bear jogged swiftly through a lonely pine forest in Yellowstone National Park. Snow was gusting around her that November 5, 1963, when she reached her den at the base of a fir tree. For a moment the behemoth hesitated; then she pushed her head beneath the fir roots and shuffled in.

Sinking down on a bed of boughs she had gathered days before, she fitted her back into the rounded earth, rolled her nose into her belly and covered her head with her paws. Her body relaxed, she growled softly and began to pass into the deep and mysterious

A grizzly bear lounges and yawns, the first signs that its metabolism is beginning to slow down as winter approaches. Soon, responding to a mysterious inner clock, the bear will retire alone to a den it has prepared for the long winter, not to emerge until March or April. If it is a female, it will be accompanied then by two-month-old cubs.

sleep that would lower her temperature and slow down her heartbeat and breathing. In hibernation, a state devised by nature for protection, she could live through Yellowstone's cold and foodless winter.

Unknown to the grizzled sleeper, a small radio transmitter in a yellow plastic collar around her neck beeped on. Three scientists, following the beeps, trudged up the steep slope in the spinning snow. Then the signal weakened; it could barely penetrate the earth from the den. Dr. Frank Craighead, Jr., naturalist, president of Environmental Research Institute, grinned at his snow-covered companions, Dr.

John Craighead and Maurice Hornocker. "She's in. The old gal's gone to bed!"

Five years of work had come to a victorious climax. For the first time in history a grizzly bear had been tracked into its hibernation den by radio.

Frank scanned the blue-white wilderness near Trout Creek to see what signs had told the bear that tomorrow's dawn would rise on a snow-locked world that would not release its grip until spring. Although the snow was whiting out the canyons and forest that day, and the great gray owl huddled somewhere against a tree, these signs of winter had come before during Yellowstone's erratic autumn. Each time they had said winter to the men, but not to the bears, who had stayed up, knowing by some mysterious sense that these preliminary snows would soon melt and the air would warm above freezing.

But today all the grizzlies on the Yellowstone plateau would go to bed—hundreds of them. The Craighead brothers knew from previous years that when darkness came this night, every grizzly bear in the park would be snowed under the roots of some lonely tree. Yet the country looked for all the world like any other snowy day in autumn. Why had the bears chosen *this* day? And which of the components of the day—temperature, barometric pressure, vanishing food supply, snow—had triggered the biological clocks in the bears? Or had these environmental stimuli only appeared to put the clocks in action? The Craigheads and their team of scientists felt that they could now answer some of these questions.

That day ended the fifth year in a seven-year study of the grizzly bear, *Ursus horribilis*, conducted by the Craigheads. Sons of a naturalist in a family of naturalists, they had grown up in Washington, D.C. Their lives were literally cliff-hangers, from dropping down canyonsides on ropes to study eagle and falcon eyries, to being abandoned on a Pacific atoll by the U.S. Navy as part of a research project on survival in the jungles. It was on that island that they decided they would work together, through wildlife research, to help keep intact the natural environment man needs for his physical and spiritual welfare.

When, years later, they learned that the grizzly bear was vanishing from the West, they urged the National Geographic Society, the National Science Foundation, Philco Radio Corporation and the U.S. Fish and Wildlife Service to help them make a comprehensive study of the bears in Yellowstone. The information they and their team of doctors, physicists, engineers and biologists uncovered is now being used to give the grizzly the kind of management he needs for roaming and denning, for food and shelter.

The Craigheads were among the first to employ the new space science of bio-telemetry, gathering distant information on animals through radio transmitters and receivers. Frank said of the technique, "The bears wander far into inaccessible country, and they are most active at night. We could not follow or consistently observe them without radios."

Even with bio-telemetry, facts were not easy to get. The bears had to be trapped, anesthetized and color-tagged for identification—by snapping numbered plastic tags of different colors into each ear. Then the enormous animals had to be weighed, measured,

Fatter now than at any other time of year, a grizzly makes its last prehibernation prowl. With the coming of winter, bears leave their lowland feeding grounds and move off alone into higher mountain forests.

sexed. Several were fitted with collars carrying the transmitters that pulsed at different rates for each individual.

Four of the instrumented bears were monitored from the laboratory in Canyon Village, where the radio beeps could be picked up for a distance of 12 miles, 24 hours a day. The others could be monitored at will by receivers in the field. When a transmitter began to give off odd sounds, the Craigheads would get compass bearings, then hike as much as ten miles or more into the dense forests to see what the sounds meant. An on-off signal was found to be a bear digging or entering a den, an irregular signal indicated walking and moving around, and a conttinuous rhythmic beep was a nap.

A strong trap made from heavy steel sewer-piping and a dart that injected a drug were used to capture the bears. The anesthesia had to be carefully administered as there were no known dosages for bears. Once, when a cub got too much, John had to give him artificial respiration. Also, there were some radio troubles—one bear sat down in a stream and shorted her transmitter. Eventually, however, some 300 grizzlies cooperated by walking into traps.

Several summers ago I drove with the Craigheads toward a bear that had just been trapped. He was put to sleep, then lifted out of the trap by four men and placed in a cargo net. When he was cranked slowly up for weighing, the scale read 500 pounds. "Just a little one," Frank said, as they tagged the bear, measured his ears and body length, and took a blood sample. Meanwhile, the crew was making imprints of the bear's glistening teeth and paws in plastic, from which a technique to determine age was developed.

Then Bear 114's eyes opened! In a few minutes he sat up, shook his head and arose. Although some bears would charge the team of men, this one just gave us a bored glance and then hurried off.

In the laboratory in Canyon Village, bear-paw imprints, maps and radios lay on the long tables. A map for each bear hung on the walls. As the men tuned in on the bears, their locations were marked on the maps. Eventually their home ranges were obtained in this way. Some had large ranges, 14 miles by four. But one bear, Number 40, required only five miles by three in which to eat and nap.

By 1965 the Craigheads were on their way toward understanding the secrets of prehibernation. They knew that the bears went off to bed simultaneously but on a different calendar day of each year studied: October 21–22 in 1961, November 5, 1963, and November 11, 1965. All were days of storm, cold and low barometric pressure.

The dens were warm and ingeniously chosen. Some were located on slopes that could be death traps to humans when the snow came; some were on canyon walls. All were on slopes facing north, exposures that did not thaw during the brief warm spells. All were dug by the bears themselves under the roots of big trees. No den found was ever used the following season.

All the dens were lined with pine and fir boughs, the region's best insulation, raked down by the bears and carried to their dens in their teeth. It seemed that expectant females fashioned deeper and softer bough beds than barren females and boars; and the cubs, conceived in June, were born to a drowsy mother who may have been snoozing through the process in December.

The bears know that the day is coming and prepare their cavities many weeks ahead of the last storm. Then they all wait for that final trigger.

In the last autumn of the study, a series of unusual weather conditions unlocked some answers to the question of what the final trigger was. Until then, winter had always come to Yellowstone gradually, in snows and thaws and slowly increasing cold before the final blow. But that September 15, when Frank was chopping wood, he noticed that the temperature was dropping swiftly. The thermometer registered 12°F. This was unusual for September, and even more so when the cold front stayed for eight bitter days. The bears, however, did not move from their summer areas.

October 15 was another unusual day. The morning dawned warm and sunny. Birds sang, rivers ran free. At noon, however, it grew cloudy and Frank flipped on the laboratory receiver. He and assistant Bob Ruff were startled by what they heard. Number 202 had left his Sulphur Mountain summer bedding area and was clipping along Elk Antler Creek.

John tuned in on other bears. They were all on the move. Number 181 was splashing across the Yellow-stone River; 65, a barren female, was trotting toward a canyonside. At four o'clock that afternoon snow dropped silently on Yellowstone.

But though the bears had gone to their dens, they had not gone inside. Some were digging, a thing they never did on hibernating day. Perplexed, the brothers waited all night while the transmitters sang on. Three days later the sun came out again and rapidly melted away the thin blanket of snow.

From that day to hibernating day was a lonely vigil in the Yellowstone wilderness. Frank tracked a sow and saw her sitting on her big haunches on an isolated ledge desperately fighting sleep. He had never seen this before. The lethargy of hibernation had set in, but she would not den. John found that her son, 202, was also having trouble. The receiver beeped as he went into his den and came out, went in and came out—waiting for something, he knew not what.

Finally, on November 11, 1965, a storm rode into Yellowstone. When Frank flipped on the receiver, erratic beeps came from the bear radios. One was giving the weak signal that meant that the bear had denned. However, 202 was some little distance from his den. Frank set out to find him. As he fought his way for six miles through dense timber, he watched the ground for paw prints. Number 202, the receiver indicated, was close by, but Frank could not see his tracks.

Then 202 was just ahead of him, marching hard. Frank watched his feet, for now he was certain of what the bears were instinctively waiting for—a drifting, blowing storm that would cover their tracks as they hurried to their dens. By morning the radios were all transmitting their "underground" signals. And there was not one visible bear print to tell which way the bears had gone.

In the laboratory the Craigheads put some of the facts together and speculated. The cold snap of September 15 had set off the first bell—drowsiness. A month later the second bell went off—the urge to be alone. That day grizzlies had gone off to their dens in the canyonsides and forests. They had not denned up, for the final alarm had not yet sounded—the drifting, blowing snow that erased their footsteps and sealed the plateau until spring.

As Frank looked out at the white wilderness, he thought that even though he and John and their colleagues had taken many secrets from the bears, the most awesome one remained unknown—the "feel" of that final storm that would bind the lakes in ice, slow the rivers and close the roads until spring. Perhaps that secret was theirs forever, buried in instinct and old bear wisdom from millions of years of listening to the murmurs from the earth.

SNOW IS TO LIVE WITH

Jean George

Trudging home in a December snowstorm, flakes blowing, air snapping, I was astonished to hear a bird singing softly in the wild twilight. I plunged through a drift, lifted a hemlock bough and saw a small sparrow on a brown twig. Piled on needles and cones, the white snow stood around him like a shrine, and he, puffed like a ball, made comfortable chirping sounds. He probably had not been so warm since winter began as now on this first evening of snow.

As I gently replaced the bough I understood why the sparrow sang. Most people, as they growl and dig with their snow shovels, forget that, in the world of the birds and beasts and plants, snow is not a nuisance, but welcome as the rain and the sun. It is an insulator, a warm shelter—and a vital stepladder.

I became aware of this last use of snow while my husband and I were visiting a friend in central Ontario. Around his home were many snowshoe rabbits, big white hares of the North that have developed wide furry feet to stay on top of the snow. The rabbits had almost eaten themselves out of food—every twig they could reach was snipped off with the slanted bite of their teeth. I asked if there was danger of their starving. My friend squinted up at a typical snow cloud with its soft fuzzy edges and said that they would all be fine in the morning.

"There'll be another rung on the snow ladder," he commented. "There's about a foot of snow in that cloud. It'll lift the rabbits to fresh twigs and stems."

Sometimes wildlife can't wait. One winter day I watched a grouse pick dried grapes off a vine in a nearby woods. He ate until there were no more grapes in reach, stretched to one above, hopped for it and missed. Then, whether in frustration or knowledge, he scratched in the snow. The flakes piled into a mound, the bird stepped on it and snatched his prize.

The birds and beasts have developed some clever devices to keep on top of the snow. Some species of grouse have little horny scutes, or comblike points, that spread out on either side of the toes and act as snow rafts. The ptarmigan grows feathers on his feet. The Canadian lynx has enormous paws, more than twice as big as those of his cousin, the bobcat.

Creatures less specialized for snow than the lynx and ptarmigan have been forced to make use of one of the outstanding physical properties of snow—its poor conductivity of heat. Mice, several species of birds, porcupines and shrews go down *under* the snow, where the white crystals hold their body heat like a mountain of insulation.

Pheasants and quail often flutter their wings and wedge themselves into a snow pocket; grouse fly headfirst into a snowbank for the night. The danger is crusting, and often birds are iced under the snow. If the crust is not thawed out within a day and a half, they may never get out.

Snow is one of the best insulators for many plants. One year we all wondered why every forsythia bush in town bloomed only at the bottom two feet. Finally we recognized that the blossoms marked the snowline of the past winter. All the buds buried by a deep snow bloomed radiantly. Those above had been frozen to death by a week of unusual sub-zero weather.

For the creatures unspecialized for dealing with snow, it creates a new environment that must be coped with. Deer and moose, cottontails and squirrels beat down trails for easier travel, as deliberately as you shovel your walk. My uncle, on a hunting trip in the mountains of Pennsylvania, awakened in the night during a snowstorm to hear a herd of deer tramping nearby, snapping twigs and limbs as they kept their yard open. In the morning he found their acre neatly packed, with grasses and mosses showing above the snow. Like wheel spokes, other trails led out into the hills to pantries of grass they needed to keep alive.

To a hoofed animal a heavy snow can mean danger. Coyotes find hunting easier when there is a heavy snow with a light crust—strong enough to bear them, but too thin to support a deer. A coyote will then chase a deer off his trail and bog him down in the deep snow where he can be taken easily.

The most fascinating use to which snow has been put by the creatures of the wild is its development as cities. Under the snow are millions of rooms, tunnels and roadways—drilled, packed, dug and bitten there by wintering animals, until a cross section of a week-old snowstorm would look like Swiss cheese. For, to almost every animal that digs in the ground, here is a medium just as warm, just as safe, but one which can be tunneled and carved with a nose or a hot breath. To the hard-digging beasts of the earth it is a glorious relief.

On the rock slopes of the West and the North, the pikas, or conies—relatives of rabbits, with short ears and no tails to get cold—live their daily lives under tons of snow. They make sitting rooms, zigzag halls and corridors leading to barns of sweet grasses that they have cut, dried and stored during the short summer months.

Life in cony town is vigorous. A naturalist traveling

with his dog team along an Alaskan riverbank heard a squeak. He looked about him but saw only snow, six feet of it, lying everywhere across the land. He listened, and the air was busy with cony voices. Then he realized he was hearing the cony town under his feet. The little animals had heard him coming and, six feet below, were scolding him.

Mice, shrews, weasels and otters all carve roads and rooms beneath the snow. The star-nosed mole makes cloverleaves and roller coasters, turnpikes and apartments—and he does it faster than anyone.

A friend of mine was mapping a mole's tunnel for a science journal. He told me that he could not dig with a shovel one half as fast as the mole digs with his nose and feet. The tired mammalogist declared the snow to be the mole's true medium. "He gets downright inspired," he commented, "when he is released from the confines of earth to the relative freedom of the light crystals."

Most wild animals, dogs and children love the snow. Mink and weasels play in it, leaping like darning needles in and out, diving into the snow like wa-

Snow piled up on a small bush provides safety for a cottontail rabbit. Like many small animals, cottontails stake out temporary shelters all over their territories, so they are never far from a refuge. When they sense danger, they scurry to the nearest shelter and remain motionless for as long as necessary.

ter. They also travel through it, and perform their mad deeds of death under its cover.

But on a winter's day when the air is clean and the sun bright, it is the top of the snow for me! For upon this white paper of winter are written—in marks of talon and claw, hoof and nose—the most dramatic who-done-it stories I have ever read.

My favorite is the story of the missing pheasant, written in a Michigan farmyard. I came down the farmer's lane early one morning to see that a pheasant had walked under the rail fence in the early dawn. He found a bite to eat, a rose hip. He picked out the seeds, scattered the pulp and walked on. Then something frightened him—his steps were far apart, running. Whatever was following him must have vanished, however, because his steps became close soon again.

But now I saw that the pheasant was not long for this world. A fox track—one round hole behind the other in single file—fell in behind his. I walked forward to read the sad ending; but it was not there. Suddenly the fox trail turned and walked away. The pheasant trail went on.

Then down near the fence, I read in the ruffled snow the ending of the tale: Slashes, struggle marks, footprints and feathers said the pheasant was dead and gone. But the fox had not done it. Wondering what had, I looked closely at the marks in the snow, and made out the fuzzy footprints and finger wing marks of the great horned owl of the forest. He had snatched the prize before the fox could strike, and winged away.

There are other stories in the snow, like the one written by a meadow mouse under my woodpile. On an icy day, in sleet and cold, he ran out a few steps, looked at the dreary world—and clearly said, in three returning footsteps, "It ain't fit out for man nor beast."

Now it is winter again. I wait for the quiet snow to fall so that I can go walking in it and feel the cold crystals on my cheeks and lips. To me as to the birds and beasts, the snow is as much a part of this world as the night, and like the night is lived with gently.

A herd of elk crosses a snowy meadow in Yellowstone
National Park. The elk's summer range is higher
up the mountains, but in winter they seek lowland areas
with snow cover thin enough for them to reach
dry grass underneath. Before the spring migration the
bucks will have lost their soaring five-foot antlers.

An unlucky field mouse is spotted by a young red
fox and tries to escape by burrowing into the snow, but
to no avail. This series of photographs tells the
story: The fox flushes the mouse (far left), chases
it (center), leaps into the air (left) and pounces.

Chapter Four

Water on the Move

Whatever form it takes—whether a placid meadow stream or a majestic mile-wide river, a splashing mountain brook or a thundering thousand-foot waterfall—moving water invariably has about it a fascination and an enchantment all its own as it proceeds on its endless journey back to the sea.

COLOSSUS OF RIVERS: THE AMAZON

David Reed

High in the Andes of Peru, more than three miles above sea level, a blue-tinted glacier clings to the face of a mountain. Wind shrieks through icy crags, and every few moments the glacier rumbles and booms as it inches its way down the slope. From the lower edge of the icefield a tiny rivulet tumbles out. It looks like any mountain stream, yet this is the beginning of the greatest river in the world. For here, on the frozen roof of South America, about 70 miles from the Pacific Ocean, the titanic Amazon is born. Ice-cold and crystal-clear, the Amazon is only ankle-deep. But as it cascades down, other rivulets race to join it. It picks up speed. Soon it is a full-fledged river, churned muddy-brown by its furious descent. For hundreds of miles it roars through mountain gorges. Then, with explosive force, it bursts into the green hell of the jungle below.

As the Amazon surges across the torrid wilderness, hundreds of tributaries pour their waters into it. Torrential rains swell the flood. Now the Amazon is no longer just a river; it is virtually a moving inland sea that drains nearly half of South America. The Amazon knows no channels; it tolerates no obstacles; it rips away its banks with brutal fury to pour its turbid waters across thousands of square miles of jungle, drowning and obliterating everything that stands in its way. In places, its ultimate banks are 60 miles apart; the main channel itself is often so wide that you cannot see the far shore. So great is the river's power that, even when it reaches the Atlantic, the Amazon refuses to die. It floods the ocean with fresh, muddy water for up to 200 miles offshore.

Everything about the Amazon is colossal. Its basin, estimated at 2,772,000 square miles, extends to six countries, covering most of northern Brazil, as well as portions of Bolivia, Peru, Ecuador, Colombia and Venezuela. Only the Nile, 4145 miles long, has a greater overall length than the Amazon, estimated at about 3900 miles (including the Ucayali). And the Amazon is by far the world's longest river for navigation by oceangoing ships. Vessels make regular voyages all the way across Brazil and into Peru, a total distance of 2300 miles.

Of the Peruvian rivers that form the Amazon proper, the Marañón is considered by many experts to be the true parent stream. To see the birthplace of the Amazon, therefore, I set out by car from Lima, and headed up the Pacific slope of the Andes. Just over the Continental Divide, at an altitude of 15,350 feet, is Lake Santa Ana, with mountains rising almost perpendicularly from the water's edge. Cascading down from the west into the lake is a small brook. With much huffing and puffing, I followed the stream up the mountain on foot—past a second lake, then a third and fourth.

Finally I came to a fifth lake. There, at an altitude of 16,075 feet, I found that tiny stream pouring out from the foot of a glacier—the ultimate headwaters of the Amazon.

Next morning, accompanied by three cowboys, I set out on horseback to follow the infant river on the first leg of its long journey to the Atlantic. For hours we rode along the foot of a row of towering glacial peaks known as the Seven Caballeros. Springs bubbled from every slope, and waterfalls cascaded hundreds of feet down rock cliffs. Twice we forded the river, here knee-deep to the horses. One of the cowboys played sad, lonely tunes on a harmonica. Once we passed a man on horseback; once we came near a herd of llamas; once, too, a condor circled overhead. But otherwise it was a silent, empty land. Late in the afternoon we arrived at a sheep ranch on the shores of Lake Lauricocha, where we spent the night.

From Lauricocha, last in a chain of lakes leading down from Santa Ana, the Marañón-Amazon emerges as a mature river. For the next several hun-

Fed by mountain streams high in the Peruvian Andes, not far inland from the Pacific, the Amazon flows for 4000 miles across Brazil before spilling more than 3 billion gallons of water per day into the Atlantic. Amazonia, the region drained by the river and its tributaries, encompasses parts of six countries—Venezuela, Colombia, Ecuador, Peru, Bolivia and Brazil—and covers nearly one twentieth of the earth's land area.

dred miles the river tumbles through inaccessible gorges, unnavigable even by raft or canoe. So I left the Marañón and set out eastward across the Andes, first on horseback, then by bus and finally in a small plane, bound for Iquitos and the jungle.

At Iquitos, in the northeastern corner of Peru, the Amazon proper has already been formed by union of the Marañón and Ucayali rivers. Now there are no more cataracts or rapids. As it passes Iquitos, situated on a bluff overlooking the river, the young giant is several miles wide.

To the traveler just down from the Andes, the jungle climate comes as a jolt. It is never as hot as a summer day in the midwestern United States. Temperatures of over 100°F. are unknown. At night one sleeps under a light blanket. But the humidity is awful. Everything drips moisture. Clothes, books and papers are continuously damp. Worse still is the inescapable monotony: Every day is as sticky as the last. Soon even the most energetic visitor yawns, mutters, *"No importa,"* and acquiesces to the snail's pace of life in the tropics.

Iquitos, though 2300 miles from the Atlantic, is jokingly called "Peru's Atlantic port"; it is regularly visited by ocean vessels. Getting a ship up the river takes all the skill its pilots can muster. There are virtually no buoys or other navigation aids but, even if there were, they wouldn't help much. The Amazon is

so powerful that it continually creates new routes. A pilot will steer to the left of an island on one voyage, then to the right on the second. On the third voyage, he will sail right through it—the island having disappeared.

At Iquitos I hired a small outboard motorboat and set out downriver. As we put-putted along, breathtaking panoramas unfolded. The sky was brilliant blue and the muddy, red surface of the river shimmered in the sunshine. Every few minutes a freshwater dolphin leaped from the water, then fell back with a splash. And, all the while, the vivid green jungle—100 feet high and so dense I could see only a few yards into it—marched past in silent, savage splendor.

Gazing at the wilderness, one feels as if one were looking into eternity itself. The entire region has scarcely changed since the beginning of time. There is not a single bridge or dam on the main river. People live only along the edge of the Amazon and its tributaries, in little clearings hacked from the forest, where they hunt, fish and gather rubber, cacao, fruits and nuts.

Fifty miles downstream from Iquitos the pilot headed up a small tributary, the Manatí, and I went ashore. A guide walked ahead to hack out a path with a machete. The ground underfoot was like sponge rubber—one walked on a mass of sodden

The cat-size uakari monkey lives high in the canopy of the Amazon jungle and seldom descends to the ground. When it is angry or excited, this rare short-tailed monkey blushes a bright scarlet and makes sounds resembling hysterical laughter.

The morpho butterfly (above), common in the high forest canopy of the Amazon Basin, attains a wingspan of more than seven inches. Its glittering color is caused by sun reflected off a mirrorlike film on its wing scales.

The garish scarlet macaw (opposite) is one of South America's largest parrots: It often measures three feet from its head to the tips of its tail feathers. With a strong sickle-shaped beak and a prehensile tongue, it can even extract meat from the rocklike Brazil nut.

leaves. The jungle was roofed over, like a great cathedral. Enormous trees, among them cedars and mahoganies, soared upward for a hundred feet or more. Occasionally a ray of sunshine dazzled down through the canopy, but otherwise the jungle floor was immersed in twilight. Monkeys squeaked, gorgeous blue Morpho butterflies flitted past, birdcalls filtered down, and I caught glimpses of hummingbirds.

Elsewhere in the jungle one sees gaudy, raucous macaws, comical toucans with huge beaks, parrots, parakeets, and bellbirds that let out an ear-piercing call sounding like a dozen hammers beating on anvils. Not a breeze stirs. The air is heavy with dankness and decay, mixed with the intoxicating fragrance of exotic fruits and flowers. Orchids bloom on tree trunks, and at times clusters of other brilliantly hued flowers can be glimpsed. I remembered that Charles Darwin called this jungle "one great wild, untidy, luxuriant hothouse."

At nightfall the jungle, seen from the river, was a wall of blackness. Frogs, insects, birds and monkeys raised a furious uproar. All the latent horror of the jungle swelled to crescendo. Armies of unseen snakes and other reptiles were on the move. One evening, as our boat glided through the tropical night, I shone a flashlight at the riverbank. Every few moments a pair of red eyes glowed back, like the coals of hell. These were caimans, an Amazonian relative of the crocodile and alligator. The river seemed to be alive with them.

Apart from the caimans, the jungle horrors, though real, are seldom seen. Some Amazon bugs are truly awesome—spiders with bodies two inches wide and hairy legs six inches long; wasps with four-inch wingspan. One particularly revolting individual, known as the rhinoceros beetle, has a 2¼-inch-long body and a long curving horn. That is distressing, but the creature flies, too. When it hits a window screen, it sounds as if someone had pitched a rock.

Wild yarns are told of Amazonian monsters, yet the truth is fantastic enough. Among the jungle creatures, the anaconda, up to 25 feet in length and the longest snake in the Western Hemisphere, is capable of swallowing a deer whole. More feared by river dwellers are the bushmaster, which averages ten feet in length, and the smaller fer-de-lance. Highly venomous, both are pit vipers, guided to their prey by the victim's body heat.

Leaving the Manatí, I continued down the Amazon in a speedboat, accompanied by two French Canadian missionary priests. As we passed the mouth of one of the Amazon's great tributaries, the Napo,

another Amazonian phenomenon appeared—a floating island. These islands, many of them with big, living trees, are torn loose from the banks by the rampaging current and swept along downstream.

Outwardly the Amazon is as peaceful as a millpond, and the traveler is tempted to plunge in for a swim. But the river is filled with unpleasant creatures, including the piranha fish, ranging from a few inches to more than a foot in length, with bulldoglike jaws and razor-sharp teeth. Stories of people and animals reduced to skeletons in minutes by these fish are legion, yet I never found anyone with firsthand information on that score.

The Amazon also is infested with electric eels, which deliver stunning shocks, and with poisonous sting rays. Then there is the insufferable little fish (called the *candirú* in Brazil and the *canero* in Peru) that insinuates itself into body orifices. A series of spines in the fish's body prevents its being pulled out; often it has to be cut out.

The upper Amazon is Indian country. Even today, some tribes have had no contact with the outside world. Here live the Jivaros, once noted for shrinking the heads of their enemies to the size of a man's fist—a practice stamped out by the governments of Peru and Ecuador. (The shrunken heads sold to tourists in Lima and Iquitos today are artificial.)

At an encampment of Yagua Indians near Iquitos, I saw a demonstration of the nine-foot blowguns

Near Manaus in north-central Brazil, the "white" waters of the Amazon River meet the "black" waters of the Río Negro. The turbid Amazon is colored yellowish-white by clay sediment, whereas the transparent Río Negro is tinged dark green by billions of microscopic organisms that require sunlight and could not survive in turbid waters. After meeting, the white waters and the black flow side by side for several miles before mingling.

with which the Yaguas hunt birds and animals. Each man took a dart only a little larger than a piece of straw, twirled cotton around one end to make it fit airtight—then *whoosh!* The dart would be quivering in a tree trunk 50 yards away. Because the weapon is silent, a man with a blowgun can pick off five or six monkeys in a tree before the game is frightened off.

After a day's journey downstream from San Pablo in a dugout canoe, we went ashore at a little clearing to visit my skipper's brother, a barefoot, ragged man, who greeted us with dignified cordiality. His wife killed a chicken, and we feasted by the light of a kerosine lamp while American jazz blared from a transistor radio. Like most of the river people, the man eked out a living from "slash and burn" agriculture. He would cut down a few acres, then burn it off for planting. But the jungle soil is poor and farming methods are so primitive that only one or two crops can be grown; then the clearing is abandoned and a new one is hacked from the wilderness.

A few days later I entered Brazil at the border town of Benjamin Constant and from there flew to Manaus, on the left bank of the Río Negro, 1400-mile-long tributary of the Amazon and itself one of the world's great rivers. Fantastic Manaus, situated in the middle of the wilderness 1000 miles from the sea, is a thriving community of 210,000. Very few roads lead to Manaus—few more ever will—yet it is a city of ten-story buildings, air-conditioned homes and offices, crowded docks and hurrying traffic.

Setting out from Manaus in a chartered 50-foot diesel launch, the *São Joaquim*, I soon came to the spectacular meeting of the inky waters of the Río Negro with the now-yellow Amazon. Like giants in a death struggle, the two rivers battled each other furiously. There was a sharp line where they surged together, marked with whirlpools and swirling debris. Several miles downstream the line disappeared—the Amazon had finally subdued its rival. Now the river, its main channel usually at least two miles wide, was roiled with whitecaps, and the *São Joaquim* rolled almost to its beam ends.

At Santarém I paid off the skipper of the *São Joaquim* and wangled passage on a small river freighter, the *Euclides da Cunha,* bound for Belém, 90 miles from the Atlantic. The *Euclides,* loaded with foul-smelling balls of rubber, had no passenger accommodations; but, being by now an experienced Amazon traveler, I brought aboard a box of food and a case of beer and slung my hammock on the afterdeck.

Two days later we passed the mouth of the last of the great tributaries of the Amazon proper, the Xin-

gú, which is over 1200 miles long. Now, swollen by the Xingú's flood, the Amazon was at its greatest volume. As we entered each new reach, there was nothing but water on the far horizon. Even the main channel was five to ten miles wide.

On the third day we entered the Amazon delta. Now the river was breaking into dozens of distributaries. The delta is so vast that just one island, Marajó, is larger than Switzerland.

A golden dawn broke through the early-morning mists on the last day of the journey. We were heading down the Río Pará, along the southern shore of Marajó. The river was filled with sailing ships, many with red and orange sails.

As the *Euclides* neared Belém, black clouds collided in the sky, and for perhaps the hundredth time since the beginning of my Amazon journey a blinding storm beat down on the river. The pilot rang for half speed, and the ship slowed for a shoal. A crewman, drenched in rain, took soundings. Then, as we came safely over the shoal, the storm abated. The afternoon sun appeared faintly in the mist. A rainbow formed. Beneath it the skyline of Belém took shape.

Nearly two months had passed since the day when I stood knee-deep in snow in the Andes, watching as the Amazon trickled from the foot of a glacier. Now, on the other side of South America, the drama had reached its finale. The greatest river on earth was rolling through the delta and surging out into the Atlantic. In its time the Amazon had swallowed up hundreds of other rivers. Now, far offshore, the titanic river was coming to its own inevitable end. From the sea, the source of all water, the Amazon came. And now to the sea it was returning.

WHAT A GIGANTIC, ALMOST-LIVING THING!

Wolfgang Langewiesche

Last spring I spent a couple of weeks flying over the Mississippi and watched it flow down its winding course to the sea. From the ground you see small parts of it, not the river itself—the thing is simply too gigantic. But studying it from the air, I began to understand it.

I started at Cairo, Illinois, where the Mississippi takes in the Ohio, doubles in size and begins its final march to the sea. Down to this point it has been just another river, though a big one. From this point on it is unique, the classic river of Mark Twain, the

A stern-wheeler plies the Mississippi between Hannibal and St. Louis, Missouri. A mile and a half at its widest point, the river begins as a 12-foot stream that flows from its source, Lake Itasca, in Minnesota.

Cotton Delta, the gilded showboats—Old Man River.

Right there at Cairo it starts to wind, to meander. Sometimes it flows almost around in circles—and for no apparent reason. No hills are in its way. The country is flat, an immense plain that slopes imperceptibly toward the Gulf of Mexico, 600 miles away.

Thanks to the U.S. Army Corps of Engineers, river wobbling has become less of a mystery. They built a laboratory river, fed by city water, which ran 150 feet on an inclined floor covered with sand. To begin with, they gave it a straight channel. Yet in due course it developed all the peculiarities of the Mississippi—meander loops, sandbars, deeps and shallows. Using patches of colored sand as tracers, the engineers studied everything.

It now seems that the fundamental cause of meandering is the power of flowing water to pick up and carry earth material. As a river flows through loose, fine-particled soil, it eats into the banks; a bank caves in somewhere; a sandbar forms downstream of it. Then the water has to detour around the bar. As the current on the outside of the curve speeds up, it eats into the riverbank on that side, undercaving it. At the same time the water on the inside slows down, loses dirt-carrying power and drops some of its sand load. So the sandbar grows. In this way the river shifts its channel farther and farther outward.

Through the years, the original slight detour becomes an exaggerated loop. And where the river comes out of that loop and turns back toward the sea, the same things now happen in reverse: The river pushes its channel out to the opposite side. One loop causes another, which causes a third, and so on down the river. That's how a river starts its amazing dance.

But there's more. Not only does the river swing back and forth in curves; the curves themselves keep moving, squirming, snaking. The whole river country is a maze of former river courses, now abandoned, all curving and swinging and crisscrossing each other. Geologists have sorted them out and dated them quite accurately back to the time of Christ, fairly accurately for 4000 years before that!

Each meander loop, once formed, moves downstream slowly, so many miles per century. Occasionally one loop gets into tougher soil and its motion slows up. The loop next above catches up with it in a sort of rear-end collision: As the two touch, the current short-cuts, and a whole curving loop of river, now abandoned, becomes a lake. You see them by the dozen in the Mississippi Valley, beautiful crescents and loops of water. "Oxbow lakes," they are called. They are one of the South's many unsung treasures, and they are especially beautiful from the air.

Another river motion is the formation of chutes. When a meander loop has become too much of a detour the river gets impatient and, during high water, starts flowing across the bend. A sort of gully forms, called a "chute." Over the years, the chute becomes the main channel.

But now the current, no longer coming around the bend, flows into the *next* bend at the wrong angle. So now *that* bend must change its shape and, after it, all other bends all the way down. This makes the river an almost-living thing: It squirms, writhes and

thrashes; it never gets comfortable in its channel.

That's why civilization stays away from its banks. The river flows in solitude. Few roads go near it. Most towns are well away from it, except for the few, like Memphis, Vicksburg and Natchez, that are on bluffs. The levees—flood-control dikes—are set back at a respectful distance from the river, sometimes over five miles away. The country between is the flood plain—a wild country, mostly woods, old river branches, oxbow lakes—no people.

Floods on the lower Mississippi can be gigantic. The river drains more than one third of the United States, from Virginia and New York to the Rocky Mountains; also, one small section of Canada. The runoff from all that area flows down this one slot below Cairo.

On so big a river, floods are not directly caused by heavy rain—it's the small river that floods in response to rain. Big rivers flood when too many tributaries happen to have high water at the same time.

Normally, the timing of the Mississippi tributaries dovetails. The Ohio's high water passes Cairo between January and April; that from the upper Mississippi and Missouri between April and July.

The biggest flood in the lower Mississippi occurred in 1927. The Ohio was late and poured into a river that was already full. The Mississippi rose 20 feet above "banks-full," and the levees gave way.

These levees form an almost unbroken earth dam, hundreds of miles long. Back in colonial days each landowner along the river built his own piece of levee, three or four feet high. By 1888, under the control of levee districts, the levees were nine feet high. Now the levees are a responsibility of the Army Engineers, and they average 30 feet high. The more effective they are, the more they have to grow! If a levee really holds, it keeps the water from spreading out sideways. That makes a flood higher. So the levees have to be built higher to contain it.

Naturally, I wanted to see a flood. The Mississippi was not performing, but one of its tributaries was in flood—the Red; and also *its* tributary, the Ouachita.

One thinks of a flood as a raging thing. I found it to be more of a soggy mess. Only along the main channel of the Red was the current strong, the brown, muddy water angry and rippling. Mostly I saw just water standing in the woods of the floodplain.

Here and there the muddy water of the Red had actually flowed up the side rivers for a mile or so and, backed up, these streams were now beginning to overflow. This backwater flooding puts a great burden on the flood controller. It's not enough to build a levee along the river; he must branch out and build more levees along the tributaries, and along *their* tributaries, until he gets into the hill country. If he leaves any low spot unprotected, the main river flood, backing up, will find it, break out there and come running down on him from behind.

Now I understood for the first time the great problem of flood control: The place where the damage is done is not the place where the damage can be prevented. To protect his house, a man might have to build a levee on someone else's property, perhaps in some other state. He might have to build a flood-control dam that would drown out half a county. To do these things the local citizen (or his small flood-control district) lacks the knowledge, the money and the legal power. Flood control requires big tax areas, big jurisdictions, big force.

When the Mississippi decides to change its course, the levees are no help. Levees, after all, are only earthen dams, designed to hold back slow, standing water, not the main angry current. So the Army Engineers decided to put the river into a straitjacket. Here and there along the banks are fields where they have been casting concrete blocks by the millions. With these blocks they are, in effect, paving the riverbanks and the river floor.

A "revetment," this is called, and its object is to hold the river channel where it is and thus protect the levees. Revetments don't depend on just brute force. By paving the banks so the current can't cave them in, they starve the river of sand with which to build bars. In this way they interrupt the whole meandering process.

In recent years the Army Engineers have also shortened the river 152 miles by making artificial cutoffs.

The new river cuts across the lovely old meandering river, straight, cold and efficient—it makes a landscape something like a dollar sign. This, too, is flood control. On the upper part of a river you hold a flood back with dams. On the lower river, you shorten the route and shove the flood on—get rid of it.

All this involves tremendous effort. But when the river is fixed, the rewards are great. Not only are the levees safe; the ship channel also is improved. More industry is able to locate along this newly vitalized waterway. Already Memphis and Vicksburg and other river towns have increasingly developed their industrial waterfront areas.

Thus life on the Mississippi, as elsewhere, tends toward management and control. But sometimes the river wriggles out from under. For several years it poured more and more water into Old River in Louisiana, where it discovered a new route to the sea, 173 miles shorter than the present one. The new route was the Atchafalaya River. This distributary had always been there—it was seen by De Soto's men—but in its original state, choked off by a mass of dead logs, it didn't amount to much. Then the steamboat came in the 1850's, and local people, with enormous labor, cleared out the logs. The flow speeded up. Now, 100 years later, we saw the result.

Each year at flood time, more Mississippi water poured down the Atchafalaya. Each time the channel was deepened so it drew more water. By 1970, if nothing were done about it, the new route would have become the main river. Then the present lower Mississippi would silt up fast; factories, harbors, ship channels would be laid dry; New Orleans and Baton Rouge would wither.

But the Army Engineers started to tackle the Atchafalaya in a big way with bulldozers, draglines and lots of concrete. They made big canals with gigantic floodgates, spillways, locks for shipping. Now there are two passageways for flooding waters: the West Atchafalaya and the Morganza floodways. In time of flood the engineers can open floodgates and let a lot of water out of the Mississippi down the Atchafalaya ways. This is one of the great safety valves for the lower river, assuring flood protection for New Orleans and Baton Rouge.

As I followed the Mississippi down I saw why this safety valve is so important. In the lowest section, below Baton Rouge, the levees are set hard against the river edge. With no floodplain to spread the water sideways the river cannot handle the floods. And with plantations, towns and cities lining the shores, the situation would be impossible without the Atchafalaya safety valves.

All this comes to a dramatic point at New Orleans. Here the city is on one side of the levee, the river is right on the other side, and sometimes higher than the city. What's more, the river does not merely flow past the city but halfway around it, in a big curve. Flying over, you recognize this curve: a typical meander loop. And you can see the river would just love to make a chute right across town! To make quite sure it doesn't, there's another floodway just above the city—the Bonnet Carré, which at flood time can bleed water out of the river sideways into Lake Pontchartrain, which connects with the Gulf.

Below New Orleans the river flows another 100 miles, while on both sides the country fades away in a twilight zone between land and sea. In the end the river flows through the sea—incoming ships meet the muddy water 30 miles out. In the old days, it is said, a steward would dip up a pail of the stuff and serve it around the deck in glasses. The passengers would then drink a patriotic toast with it.

A steamship was coming in now and I flew a few miles out over the Gulf to circle it. Its churning propeller was bringing clear seawater up from underneath, and you could see how the river really still maintained its identity—now as a thin sheet of muddy fresh water, spread over the heavier salt water of the Gulf.

That's what I saw along the Mississippi, air-age style. For 600 miles I was looking the river straight in the face. I came to feel its presence like that of a person. I kept looking at the Mississippi with a stupid feeling of: What a thing! What a gigantic, almost-living thing!

TWENTY TIMES HIGHER THAN NIAGARA

Michael Scully

Jimmie Angel had no urge to carve his name on the map when he nosed his little Flamingo plane up that wonderful Venezuelan canyon back in 1935. He was just a journeyman flier, class of World War I, looking for a river full of gold in the chaos of stone and jungle called the Guiana Highlands.

In Panama a few years before, a secretive old prospector named Williamson had hired Angel to fly him to Venezuela and inland to Ciudad Bolívar on the Orinoco River. Williamson had pointed out a zigzag course over the Orinoco llanos, a vast grassy basin studded with iron hills that jerked the compass into impotent jitters. Farther south they entered a mad land of mesas, rearing thousands of feet from the

emerald jungle and split by plunging streams. Finally they lurched to a stop on a grassy opening and the old man went off to the river nearby. An hour later he returned—with about 20 pounds of gold nuggets.

Jimmie Angel's skill got them safely home again, and he was paid $5000 for that flight into fantasia. A short time later Williamson died.

Angel returned to Venezuela. First he flew from Ciudad Bolívar, scouting from mesa to mesa. But that took too much time and gasoline, so he built a camp and cleared a landing strip near Auyán-Tepuí —Devil's Mountain, 150 miles closer to his goal.

Auyán-Tepuí is a giant among mesas. Its flattish top covers 250 square miles and bears a peak nearly 10,000 feet high. Eons of erosion have cut a crooked, V-shaped canyon into its northern face, and from this surges a stream that stirred Jimmie's curiosity. He had found a few nuggets and diamonds, but nothing like the rucksack load that Williamson picked up in an hour. Perhaps he could never locate the golden stream again, but there must be others like it, and this canyon looked inviting. So he poked the Flamingo's nose between its blue-brown walls, and flew into an unexpected kind of immortality.

From high in the wall on his right, a stream spurted and plunged to the jungle below. From a higher hole beyond it another one dived. Then another; then four side by side. And more beyond, right and left. The flier soon lost count.

Then, as he rounded a promontory, Angel came upon an unbelievable sight—a vertical river plummeting from the clouds above him, its roar drowning the sound of his motor. He craned to see the white column vanish in a mass of foam where it crashed into the valley. He went down perilously close to the jungle floor and made a rough calculation of the fall's width. It was perhaps 500 feet. He climbed again, trying to estimate height by his altimeter. Somewhere between a half mile and a mile, he calculated. Even a half mile would make it the great-grandfather of waterfalls.

Angel made a layman's guess that there was nothing else like this in the world. He was right. When in 1949 a National Geographic Society expedition finally measured the august marvel named Angel Falls, it found that the great cataract was 3212 feet high, *20 times the height of Niagara*; almost three times as high as the Empire State Building. The first straight drop is 2648 feet; then the column bounds from a ledge and falls another 564 feet.

For centuries men had skirted and probed the region—a place where geography is so mad a river flows in two directions. Baron von Humboldt, in 1800, followed the Orinoco, which empties into the Carib-

bean, to a point where the upper river splits and one branch, the Casiquiare, is shunted southward via the Río Negro and the Amazon into the Atlantic. A few years later, Robert Schomburgk climbed Mt. Roraima, far to the east, and found a plateau jungle of plant life unlike, and older than, any other known to science. When Conan Doyle fictionized such discoveries in *The Lost World*, he scarcely exaggerated the realities of this region.

Before the airplane came, Auyán-Tepuí, 300 miles from Humboldt's trail and half as far from Mt. Roraima, was only a piece of mapmakers' guesswork. Moreover, it was shielded by superstition. Its name, Devil's Mountain, had real meaning for the few jungle Indians of the region. The awesome thunderstorms it brewed were adequate proof that the devil himself lived there, and Indians gave it wide clearance.

In Caracas, Gustavo Heny, a veteran mountain climber, and Felix Cardona, a Spanish explorer, were the first to become actively interested in Angel's story of his discovery. In 1937, in separate expeditions, they explored the canyon and saw that this was no orthodox waterfall: It was the end of an underground river roaring from an enormous tunnel 200 feet below the mesa top. How could that lost plateau, measuring only 15 by 22½ miles, produce the immense daily flow from the great falls and its satellites, which, they found, numbered nearly 100?

From the nearest point accessible on foot, Heny and Cardona, who had met at Angel's base camp, set out to climb the cliffside. Aided by Angel, who dropped food from his plane, they reached 4000 feet. But horizontal progress from there was impossible. Ages of erosion had cut away the soft surface rock, leaving an insane pattern of fissures, some hundreds of feet deep, between jagged ridges of sandstone.

The mesa is a colossal natural condenser, squarely in the path of the almost ceaseless trade winds from the Caribbean. As these meet the warm air rising from the low forests, they produce a constant mist. Precipitation is estimated to range up to 300 inches a year, and this may be the wettest area on earth. The honeycomb of deep fissures serves as a gigantic reservoir, feeding the underground rivers that form the falls.

Heny and Cardona spotted through their field glasses a level stretch in the far distance. If they could land a plane on it, the major falls might be accessible.

In a series of spectacular leaps, the world's tallest waterfall, Angel Falls, drops 3212 feet from the rim of a mesa to the floor of Venezuela's Gran Sabana (Great Plain) region. Its longest segment, fully visible here, is a 2648-foot plunge down a sheer cliff.

Angel scouted the spot and decided that a landing might be possible, barely.

It was agreed that Heny and Angel would make a try, while Cardona would man the camp radio to keep contact and, if necessary, summon help. But when Jimmie's wife, Marie, who was also in camp, discovered their plan she delivered an ultimatum: "You are not going up there without me!"

The three landed safely, but the grass hid a soggy surface, and the wheels quickly mired. Angel found that a takeoff was impossible. It was also impossible, they soon saw, to reach the falls. They surveyed their chances, then called Cardona by radio, describing the route by which they would try to escape.

In answer to Cardona's radioed appeal, William H. Phelps, American businessman of Caracas, chartered a plane and started out the next day. The Venezuelan army sent another. But shifting cloud masses and their shadows made a maddening kaleidoscope of the vast patchwork of ravines and saw-toothed ridges; spotting three tiny human figures proved impossible.

Cardona and the rescue fliers had all but lost hope when, after two weeks, the two men and Marie Angel dragged one another into camp. They had carefully rationed the food, and water was no problem, but their boots were shredded by the savage rocks, their clothes were torn away and their bodies were tortured patterns of cuts and bruises.

Jimmie Angel's plane sits today on the mesa where it landed in 1937. A few years ago my wife and I flew just above it with Capt. Charles C. Baughan, an aerial veteran of both World Wars, who has put his wheels down on as many unlikely spots as Angel, excepting one. The little Flamingo marks that spot.

Like so many trailblazers, Angel was unrewarded except for the satisfaction of giving his name to the world's highest waterfall and the fact that his find focused attention on a region that is now proving fabulous in raw wealth—diamonds, gold, iron ore.

Of the few persons who have ever seen Angel Falls from its base, most were with the National Geographic expedition of 1949. A few other determined souls have made the one-week, round-trip journey by dugout canoes, leaving from Canaima, site of a small rustic tourist camp some 40 miles northwest of the falls. Hundreds of tourists have viewed the falls from the air on regular excursion flights.

Jimmie Angel died in 1956 as a result of a plane crash in Panama. As he had requested, his ashes were scattered over the falls. Four years after his death, the Venezuelan government commemorated Jimmie and his magnificent discovery by proclaiming the still-mired Flamingo a national monument.

Chapter Five

Our Ocean of Air

As the Earth spins on its axis and circles the Sun, heat pours in and drives the prevailing winds of the world. These great globe-girdling currents in our 20-mile-deep ocean of air create the weather in all its variety—from spring's soft rains and gentle breezes to the screaming fury of a hurricane or the deadly suction of a tornado.

THE WONDER OF THE WINDS

J. D. Ratcliff

The wild wind can be a demon out of control, a bearer of death and destruction. But day in, day out, the wind is the earth's breath of life—an awesome wonder that shapes and blesses our lives in a hundred different ways.

As bearers of rain, the winds determine which portions of the globe are habitable and what crops can be grown. They keep northern Europe from being a polar waste and moderate the heat of South America's west coast. Winds virtually created one country: the Netherlands. They spun 9000 windmills that ground grain, sawed wood, pumped out the sea. And they helped make tiny Holland one of the world's greatest trading nations, driving her windjammers to every corner of the globe.

For centuries winds determined where men could go, and but for them civilization might have been stillborn. They made settlement of Virginia and Brazil easy, settlement of Oregon difficult. Bostonians still "go *down* to Maine," since Maine is downwind from Boston.

The names men have given to winds have an allure —the poison wind, the doctor wind, the barber wind, the wind-of-120-days; the roaring 40's and the howling 50's; Alaska's *knik*, Japan's *narai*, Argentina's *pampero*. Hurricanes, typhoons and tornadoes make the headlines. But the real stars are the great wind *systems:* the monsoons that water southern Asia; the westerlies that drive the Gulf Stream and warm northern Europe; the antarctic winds that push the cold Humboldt Current with its enormous cargo of sea nutrients up the west coast of South America—giving rise to some of the world's greatest fisheries.

Early sailors hugged the shore. The Romans were among the first to note wind *patterns* and take advantage of them. Rome had to have 20 million bushels of Egyptian wheat a year to survive. Roman sailors observed a prevailing wind blowing up from Egypt across the Mediterranean in the spring. In summer the wind reversed and blew from the north. They did most of their hauling in spring.

We say we live *on* earth. We also live *in* a vast sea of air. At times this sea around and above us is calm as a millpond; at others it moves with a speed greater than a .45 bullet. The cause of this unrest? The wind has two great propellant forces. First, there is a constant interchange of air between the warm tropics and the polar ice caps. Second, the earth exerts a rotational force—at the equator it moves at about 1000 m.p.h., dragging a sea of air behind. These two forces generate the great primary winds that flow in regular paths over thousands of miles.

In the North Atlantic and North Pacific these winds flow in a clockwise pattern around high-pressure areas, pushing before them the great sea currents—the Japan Current, or Kuroshio, the Gulf Stream. In the South Atlantic and South Pacific they flow counterclockwise, pushing along the Humboldt, the Brazil and other great currents that have enormous impact on world weather.

The famed North Atlantic trade winds are part of the pattern, blowing with amazing constancy from North Africa west. These winds frightened Columbus' sailors. How would they ever get home? They didn't know that, farther to the north, the westerlies blew in the opposite direction, from America east.

Ferdinand Magellan, on his epochal round-the-world exploration in 1519–21, rode the trades across the Atlantic and down the east coast of South America. Then below the 40th parallel, approaching Cape Horn, Magellan encountered the roaring 40's that howl around the earth in an easterly direction at speeds up to 50 knots! After bucking these terrors he found another set of gentle trade winds, in a new ocean that he named "Pacific."

Ships followed the great pathways of the primary

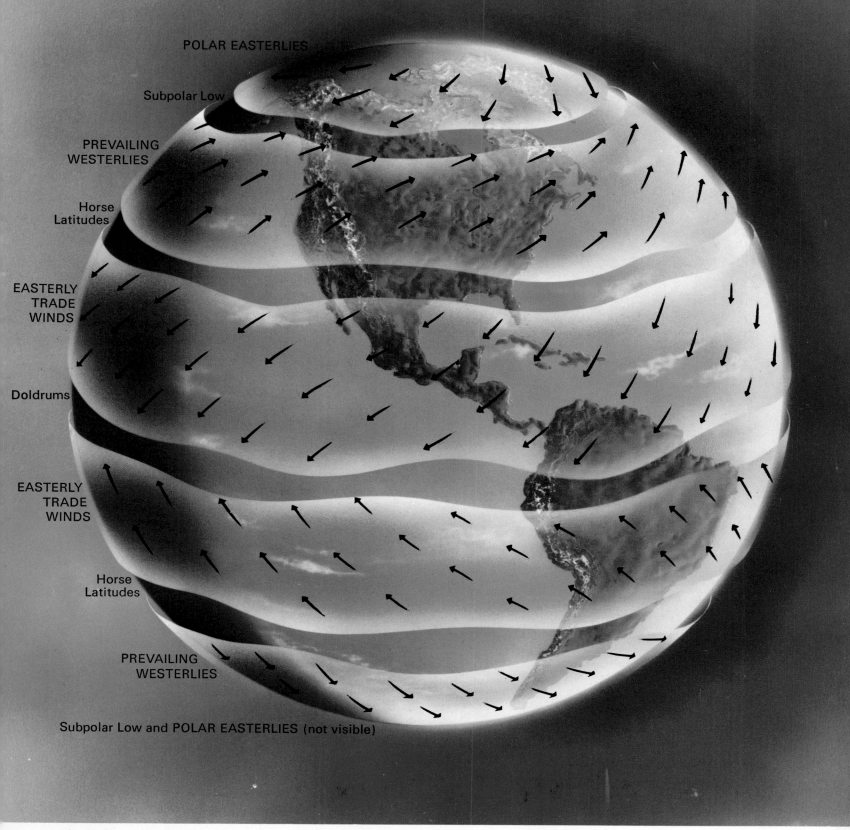

POLAR EASTERLIES

Subpolar Low

PREVAILING
WESTERLIES

Horse
Latitudes

EASTERLY
TRADE
WINDS

Doldrums

EASTERLY
TRADE
WINDS

Horse
Latitudes

PREVAILING
WESTERLIES

Subpolar Low and POLAR EASTERLIES (not visible)

This highly simplified diagram shows the prevailing surface winds that girdle the globe; the arrows indicate the direction in which they blow. In the hot, sticky doldrums near the equator, there is little wind. The air, warmed by the equatorial sun, rises straight up while cooler air from north and south moves in to take its place as the easterly trade winds. With average speeds of 10 to 15 knots, these trade winds are the most constant on the planet. The horse latitudes, or belts of subtropical calm, are zones of downward vertical air movement where warm air earlier forced up from the doldrums returns to the Earth's surface and divides into two streams. One stream moves toward the equator again as part of the easterly trade winds. The other joins the prevailing westerlies as they blow poleward. At the poles, meanwhile (the South Pole is not shown here), cold air in the polar easterlies starts toward the equator. The subpolar lows, where these winds meet, are among the stormiest places on Earth.

winds to open the world for trade and colonization. One route: from England down to Africa on the wind-driven Canary Current, with a cargo of trade goods; thence to the West Indies on the trade winds with a cargo of slaves; then home on the westerlies with rum and molasses.

It was Matthew Fontaine Maury, a U.S. Navy hydrographer, in the mid-19th century, who began putting the global wind picture together. He collected thousands of ship's logs, noting set of the wind at specific spots on specific dates. Maury showed that a roundabout course often provides the quickest passage. If an English ship bound for Australia, for instance, rode trade winds to the coast of Brazil, then dropped down, passing around the Cape, it often took only half the time—although the route was thousands of miles longer than the trip down the African coast.

Nothing demonstrates man's utter dependence on the winds so well as the monsoons. In summer the great central land mass of Asia heats up; air becomes light, and a vast low-pressure area forms, which sucks in air from as far away as Australia. Passing over seas it picks up moisture and drops it as rain on Malaysia, India, Japan and other areas. With astonishing regularity June marks the arrival of the rainy season, and planting can begin. Indians by the thousands pour out into parched fields and streets to let droplets splash in their upturned faces, to give thanks for this ever-recurring miracle.

In winter, as the Asian land mass cools, the air over it cools; a great high-pressure area forms, and the outward flow of air begins. When it strikes the towering fence of the Himalayas, it drops moisture as snow. By the time it arrives in India the air is dry, cloudless. For six months the sun will shine. Rainfall figures tell the story: In March Bombay has virtually no rain; in July it has 25 inches!

Among the most interesting of local winds are the foehns. Passing over mountains, damp winds rise, cool, drop their moisture; then, as they tumble down the other side, they become compressed and heat up. (Remember how a bicycle pump gets hot as it compresses air?) Thus a cool, wet wind on one side of a mountain becomes a hot, dry one on the other.

The foehn effect is noted at dozens of places around the globe, but the chinook, which sweeps over Montana and Alberta, is the most spectacular example. On western slopes of the Rockies this great sea wind drops snow or rain, to feed rivers and irrigation ditches. Then it tumbles down eastern slopes as a hot, dry wind whose performance is almost past belief. In Havre, Montana, it shot the temperature up 31 degrees in three minutes. Calgary, Alberta, reported an incredi-

bly precipitous rise one February some years ago: from −14° to 76°F.

Great deserts are powerful wind breeders. Iran's maddening, desiccating wind-of-120-days often carries enough sand to bury whole villages. Southern California's Santa Ana wind, which sweeps in from the desert, heats up as it drops down the Pacific slope of the Rockies. It withers vegetation and opens the way for raging brush fires. The sirocco, born over the Sahara, sweeps northward, picks up water crossing the Mediterranean and strikes Spain, Italy and France as a hot, sodden, enervating wind cursed by all.

The northers are winds that occur when low-pressure systems suck in polar air. Most great land masses in the Northern Hemisphere have east-west chains of mountains that block the flow of polar air. North America doesn't. Hence the devastating northers that sweep down from Siberia and Alaska, chilling air as far south as Central America. With some degree of accuracy, Texans say there is nothing between them and the North Pole but a barbed-wire fence. In a few hours northers have dropped Texas temperature from 75° to 22°F., destroying millions of dollars' worth of citrus fruits and winter vegetables.

France's famed mistral, sucked southward by low-pressure areas over the Mediterranean, is a norther. It has overturned trucks and blown chains of parked railroad cars for miles. In southern France houses present a solid stone wall or only small windows to the anger of the wind, and most village main streets run east-west.

Although we have accumulated a vast store of wind knowledge, great areas of mystery remain. For instance, the drought that plagued the U.S. northeast for more than five years has been traced to an unexplained shift from normal wind patterns. Nor is anyone sure what causes a tornado. That's why the greatest study of world weather ever undertaken has gotten under way. More and more Tiros, Nimbus and other satellites are sending to earth TV pictures of the wind-driven cloud patterns.

The World Weather Watch of the World Meteorological Organization is now being formed, and observations from land stations and ships at sea are being planned. The data collected will be analyzed with the aid of high-speed computers located at meteorological centers in Washington, D.C., Moscow and Melbourne. There are also plans for providing more effective international communication systems for transmitting information about the weather.

The winds have been great shapers of human destiny, and man does well to continue in his attempts to discover what the wild winds are saying.

THE MIRACLE OF LIGHTNING

Ira Wolfert

When you see lightning, it has already missed you. When you hear thunder, relax; the show is over. The noise is just the audience rushing for the exits.

One of the great figures in thunderstorm exploration, the late Dr. Karl B. McEachron, used to reassure nervous laymen that way. If a big stroke were to hit you, you'd never know it. In the meantime, enjoy the spectacle.

Lightning is one of the most dramatic examples in nature of the ill wind that blows good. It is true that it kills more people in the United States than any other natural disaster: an average of 400 dead and 1000 injured yearly. It destroys 37 million dollars' worth of U.S. property annually—and this figure does not include the losses from some 8000 forest fires started by lightning. Yet it is also true that without lightning plant life could not exist.

Eighty percent of our atmosphere is nitrogen—an essential food for plants. About 22 million tons of this nutriment float over each square mile of earth. But in its aerial form nitrogen is insoluble, unusable. Before plants can take life from it, it must undergo what our food undergoes in our digestive machinery: a series of chemical reactions. Lightning touches off the series.

This extraordinary process was described for me by Dr. M. F. Fogler, formerly executive vice-president of the Nitrogen Division of Allied Chemical & Dye Corporation. Air particles are made white-hot by lightning. They reach temperatures as high as 30,000° C. Under this intense heat, the nitrogen combines with the oxygen in the air to form nitrogen oxides that are soluble in water. The rain dissolves the oxides and carries them down to earth as dilute nitric acid. You can smell this acid—the pungent, tingly odor that hangs in the rainy air of a thunderstorm. Reaching the earth, the nitric acid reacts with minerals there to become nitrates on which plants can feed. Here is a wonder, indeed: Lightning, which meteorologists estimate to be bombarding the earth at a rate of more than 100 times a *second*, transforms the upper air into fertilizer for plants!

The story of lightning is one that sings the greatness of science. Children are taught in school that the story began with Benjamin Franklin and the kite, which led to his invention of the lightning rod. That simple device, basically unchanged since Franklin's day, must be included in any list of great inventions.

Very little more was learned about lightning until an August afternoon in 1920, when a bolt struck a gnarled "snake tree" a foot away from an unoccupied shack owned by Charles P. Steinmetz, "the wizard of General Electric." The bolt bounded off the tree and broke a window; it splintered a worktable, then leaped across the room to shatter a mirror. Discovering the debris, Steinmetz had every fragment and splinter of the mirror collected and fitted together between two sheets of glass. It was the first time that the pattern struck off by a lightning charge had been studied.

Now scientists devised instruments to measure and record bolts. They hunted lightning, trapped it on film, learned how to make it in the laboratory. They even developed a camera that takes what amounts to a slow-motion picture of a lightning bolt.

Scientists were urged to make these studies because of the growing dependence on electric power. Lightning plays rough when it hits electric lines, and it hits frequently. (In the U.S. Midwest every mile of a 100-foot-high power line is hit once or twice a year.) Lightning can run along the line directly into expensive machinery in the powerhouse or transformer station or, if it makes an arc to the ground before it travels that far, it can be followed into the earth by all the electricity in the line, until the line is drained or shut off.

The scientists eventually discovered how to control

A unique time exposure, taken in Castleford, England, records this weird phenomenon—a "ball" of lightning bouncing off a brick chimney and exploding in front of a house. Ball lightning has never been satisfactorily explained (and a few scientists deny it exists), but it appears to be formed of electrified gases resembling those on the Sun.

Two strokes of forked lightning, the most common and the most powerful kind, are caught in this rare time exposure. Their characteristic zigzag is blazed by "leaders," which travel downward from the negatively charged base of a thundercloud—to be met by "streamers" rising from the positively charged earth beneath the cloud. Sheet lightning, which sometimes illuminates the whole horizon, is a reflection on nearby clouds of lightning strokes flashing far away. Heat lightning, which can occur in a cloudless sky, is thought to be either a reflection of storms going on below the horizon or the result of electrical discharges high in the sky.

the power failures by learning how lightning strokes are formed. To begin with, a thundercloud gets under way when warm, humid air rises from the earth in a steady updraft, generally over a hill or mountaintop. The humidity condenses as the air cools on rising. We see the tiny water droplets as mist that gradually assumes the familiar shape of a cumulonimbus cloud. Sometimes looking like a huge cauliflower, sometimes an enormous white anvil, the cumulonimbus is often topped by a "cirrus umbrella." It is composed of billions of minute ice crystals.

These formations can be enormous—up to 50,000 feet or more in height. They can contain as much as 300,000 tons of water. In them is a so-called chimney current—a column of air rising at a full gale force of about 100 feet a second. The moisture in this column condenses rapidly, and the droplets are swept upward to freeze into hailstones. The hail-

stones do not fall. They dance on the chimney current like celluloid balls on a gushing fountain, rising steadily higher until, near the top of the cloud, the force of the current is exhausted. There the hailstones shower out in all directions, carrying cold air with them as they descend. Frequently they are sucked back into the chimney current, to be dissolved and re-formed again and again.

In this turbulent motion something still unexplained happens. There is a separation of electric charges. The smaller particles near the top of the cloud become charged positively, while the raindrops in the lower portion are charged negatively.

Meanwhile, on the surface of the earth directly below the cloud, there is a corresponding buildup of a positive charge. As the cloud drifts, a positive charge on earth follows it like a shadow, climbing trees, church steeples, towers, poles. It races into houses,

Cirrostratus clouds, formed of ice crystals high in the atmosphere, throw a halo around the moon, foretelling the approach of a warm front with heavy rains.

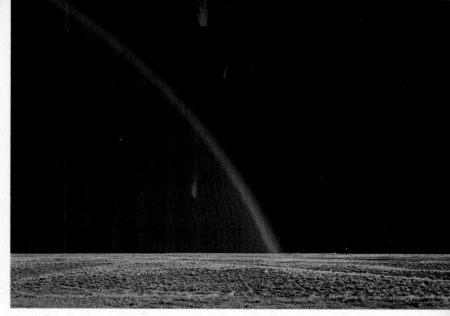

A rainbow in the east means that clouds blown by the west wind have passed over and fair weather is coming; a rainbow in the west means that rain is on the way.

the rain clouds have moved to the east and should continue to move in that direction. If rain has been falling, it is over for the day. On the other hand, the *rising* sun can produce a rainbow only by lighting up water droplets to the west. This means that the cloud system laden with moisture is to your windward and probably moving in your direction. Rain will soon come.

See what basis in science this slogan enjoys:

> *Mackerel sky,*
>   *Not yet wet, not yet dry.*
> *Mackerel sky and mares' tails*
>   *Make the ship lower lofty sails.*

These couplets, taken together, turn out to be surprisingly accurate. A mackerel sky by itself is an indeterminate condition: It means only that moisture has been swept by strong winds high into the atmosphere. There it floats in the form of cirrus clouds, in layers, resembling the scales of a fish. A mackerel sky is not enough to indicate real change *unless,* as pointed out in the final couplet of the proverb, mares' tails accompany the formation. These great wisps, strikingly like the tails of gigantic flying horses, occur at a lower altitude—and the combination is characteristic of the slope of an advancing warm front, which is almost sure to bring rain or snow within 24 hours. It is of course important to note in what direction the mares' tails are flicking. It is when we are in the path of the east-moving mackerel sky and mares' tails—*i.e.,* when the high-level formation is to our west—that we had better shorten sail.

Some signs are hard to miss. Consider the halo around the moon or, in rare cases, around the sun. This phenomenon is expressed in such folk sayings as, "When the moon or sun is in the house there is

rain without." It is, again, visible evidence that moisture has been borne aloft into the higher and colder reaches of the atmosphere where it has been converted to ice-crystal form. In thin, wispy clouds called "cirrus" the ice crystals refract incoming rays of light, concentrating them in a visible ring around their source, the moon or sun. These high cirrus clouds—arriving earlier because the winds aloft are much stronger—are the precursors of a warm front with its lower, heavier clouds, and storms.

In his ballad, "The Wreck of the Hesperus," Henry Wadsworth Longfellow has an old sea dog plead with the ship's captain to put into port, cautioning him with the words:

> *Last night the moon had a golden ring,*
>   *And tonight no moon we see!*

The skipper ignored the warning, "and a scornful laugh laughed he." But the storm had the last laugh, and the *Hesperus* was wrecked on the reef of Norman's Woe.

Longfellow's meteorology was better than his history. The *Hesperus* was actually in Boston Harbor the night of this storm. But the advice of the old sea dog was sound. Increasing clouds had moved in, changing the thin cirrus and halo around the moon to a heavy overcast—an even more immediate harbinger of a storm.

The usefulness of weather proverbs has been long admitted in the U.S. Army, and official cognizance of folk sayings was taken as early as 1880 when Gen. William Bancroft Hazen was appointed chief signal officer of the War Department. Hazen asked Army posts to send him "popular proverbs and prognostics used throughout the country by all classes and races of people."

Not all dealt with visible signs in the sky. Here is

one from New England and the Middle Atlantic States:

> *Winds blowing from the East*
> *Bode no good for man or beast,*
> *Winds blowing from the West*
> *Please everyone the best.*

Meteorologists explain that all major storm centers are areas of low barometric pressure around which the winds blow—counterclockwise in the Northern Hemisphere. Most storms that affect the eastern coastal states come up from the south, moving northeastward. So when a storm hit the early mariners (and other weather watchers) in the Middle Atlantic or New England areas, it was the northernmost edge of the whirling storm system that hit them first—the edge where the winds are blowing from east or northeast at peak velocity. (For this reason, a "nor'-easter" has always been the New England mariner's most dreaded storm.) As the storm passes over, the direction of the wind changes until, by the time it is blowing from the west, the storm has passed and clear, dry weather is forthcoming.

Windjammer sailors and pre-tractor farmers knew nothing about cold fronts or low-pressure areas or great counterclockwise winds or weather systems. But they used their eyes and they felt things in their bones. They were conscious, observant. And they passed on their views in apt prose and verse. If we, too, but lift up our eyes and scan the skies, we will feel a companionship with those who have built up the folk wisdom of the past. We may be able to add a few observations of our own and increase our awareness of the world around us.

RIDING HERD ON THE TWISTERS

James H. Winchester

Patrolman Louis Watkins kept a wary eye on the sky as he cruised the streets of Leavenworth, Kansas, on April 12, 1964. Thunderstorms and possible tornadoes were forecast.

By midafternoon rain, hail and winds were heavy. Then came an ominous lull. Within minutes a tornado was reported moving toward the city, and the fire siren atop City Hall began to wail. "Take safety precautions," warned the local radio station repeatedly. Patrolman Watkins started plowing a pattern through the streets, his car's eerie warbler siren wide open.

Every two blocks, by loudspeaker, he exhorted: "This is a tornado warning! This is not a practice."

He was still sounding this urgent warning later when the tornado swept across the town like a giant vacuum cleaner. The whirling, 100-mile-an-hour winds caught his car, spun it around and pushed it sideways for a block. Some 1300 homes and business buildings were damaged or destroyed, 2000 trees uprooted and hundreds of cars smashed. Damages totaled over a million dollars. But *no one was killed, and only three persons were hospitalized with minor injuries.* Amply forewarned, the town's 25,000 residents were safely buttoned up in cellars and shelters.

Making such alerts possible is the U.S. Weather Bureau's National Severe Storms Forecast Center in Kansas City, Missouri, which sounds the alarm well in advance for a high majority of the nation's yearly 600 to 900 full-blown tornadoes. The results are evident: In the first half of this century tornadoes took an average of 200 lives a year in the United States. The ten years since 1954, when this service began operations in Kansas City, were peak ones for tornadoes, and property damage increased greatly with denser populations. Yet the average annual death toll from such storms dropped nearly 50 percent.

Until recent years, the basic cause of tornadoes remained a mystery. All of them seemed to come out of thunderstorms, but not all thunderstorms created tornadoes. With an estimated 44,000 such storms lashing the earth's surface every day, some 1800 of them in action at any given moment, tornado forecasts could only be guesswork. For a long period the U.S. Weather Bureau refused to issue any tornado forecasts at all, reasoning that their unreliability might do more harm than good by causing unnecessary panic. Said one veteran weather forecaster, "The surest way to get fired was to use the word 'tornado' in a forecast."

A breakthrough came in 1948, when an unpredicted tornado mauled Tinker Air Force Base outside Oklahoma City, doing ten million dollars' damage. The winds were still howling as Tinker's meteorologists, Maj. Ernest J. Fawbush and Capt. Robert C. Miller, were called on the carpet. "We can't predict something we don't understand," they explained.

The two Air Force scientists began studying weather conditions existing before the storm. The next week they noted the same conditions again, and they forecast a tornado. As a precaution, Tinker flew its planes to bases out of danger. Everything else was tied down. Seven hours later, a vicious tornado, stronger than the previous one, materialized as predicted. Tinker's damage this time, because of the early warning, was far less. "This was probably the first tornado ever accurately pinpointed," says the American Meteorological Society.

Encouraged, Fawbush and Miller probed deeper. Hundreds of old weather charts were studied. Slowly a pattern emerged. Nearly always, they found, tornadoes had occurred where a warm, wet wind from the south collided with a cold, dry current from the west. Adding other data, such as temperatures at varying heights, wind speeds and the direction of large air-mass movements, they devised a workable method of forecasting tornadoes. Their forecasts, about 40 percent successful, were available to the military's Air Weather Service and to the civilian Weather Bureau.

Then in 1953, on two successive days in June, disastrous tornadoes hit Flint, Michigan, Cleveland, Ohio, and Worcester, Massassachusetts, killing 223 people and injuring 2555 others. The U.S. Weather Bureau was sharply criticized for its failure to give adequate warning. In the wake of these episodes, additional emphasis was placed on tornado forecasting.

With tons of dust swirling up its funnel, a tornado twists across the Kansas plains against a lowering sky. Destructive twisters like this one are formed when a vortex drops out of a thundercloud and sucks into its vacuum air or anything else in its path. Tornadoes passing over ponds and streams sometimes drain them dry. Those passing over larger bodies of water become waterspouts and suck up great columns of water as land tornadoes suck up dust, trees and buildings. The winds in a tornado's funnel may reach velocities of from 300 to 600 miles per hour, and are thus the most powerful winds on Earth.

The Forecast Center was enlarged and moved to Kansas City, nearer the midwestern "tornado alley."

Today, 650 weather-observing and radar stations feed over 1,750,000 bits of data daily into the Center in Kansas City. Temperatures, humidity, pressure and wind directions come from ground stations and weather balloons. Weather-satellite signals give the center a picture of clouds and their movements over the North American continent. Electronic computers take all these clues and process them. Information from about 350 different reporting points, arriving by teleprinter, can be automatically compiled and analyzed by processing machines in just 20 minutes.

Since it is still impossible to predict exactly where and when a tornado may strike, the Weather Bureau has helped set up hundreds of local observation networks to give residents on-the-spot warning when a tornado is actually developing. The effectiveness of such a setup was demonstrated in the great Topeka tornado of June 8, 1966. At 6 a.m. that morning, the Forecast Center circulated a warning of severe thunderstorms in eastern Kansas, western Missouri and Oklahoma. At 11 a.m. a tornado watch, on a 60-mile-wide path that extended from southwest of Hutchinson, Kansas, to east of Kansas City, Missouri, was issued. The first tornado was reported by a civilian observer near Alden, Kansas, at 3:05 p.m.—one of eight or so reported that day. Meanwhile the Topeka office of the Weather Bureau was tracking the storms by means of its radar and volunteer spotters, and the public was kept informed by frequent TV and radio bulletins that also included rules for self-protection during severe storms. The local Civil Defense units in Topeka were alerted for action, and at 6 p.m. volunteer observers took up prearranged positions around the city.

The Topeka tornado was first spotted snaking down to the ground 19 miles southeast of the city. By 7:02 it had approached to within seven or eight miles of the city limits, and the Civil Defense sirens began to sound the "take cover" signal. The storm, moving from southwest to northeast at 30 to 35 miles an hour, was not unusual except perhaps for the length of its 22-mile path, but when it struck the city of 127,615 persons it made history. The angry black funnel plowed through the city's heart, leaving a path, eight miles long and four blocks wide, of almost total destruction—the worst single tornado ever to strike a community. Damage was estimated at more than $100 million; 800 houses were reduced to matchwood; an additional 1200 received varying degrees of damage. Every major structure on the campus of Washburn University was destroyed or severely damaged. Over 550 persons

were injured—but only 16 were killed. This amazingly low toll was attributed to three factors: early official notice of potential storms, a network of spotters, and almost constant warnings and instructions to the public as the storm approached.

Fortunately this tornado occurred during the daytime. People were awake, *available* to be warned. In tornado forecasting, the real challenge is in the states east of the Mississippi, where storms usually hit late at night. The winds that create tornado-spawning thunderstorms ordinarily build up over the Southern and Central Plains in the daytime, then move eastward, arriving over Indiana, southern Michigan, or the southeastern states when people are asleep. Radio warnings are useless. In such cases the Forecast Center attempts to make early predictions for those areas, so people learn of possible trouble before going to bed.

There are still great gaps in the meteorologists' understanding of tornadoes, but a concentrated scientific assault on tornado ignorance is helping the Center better its odds for more accurate forecasts. The U.S. Weather Bureau coordinates a joint civilian-military effort through its National Severe Storms Laboratory in Norman, Oklahoma, an ideal location for tornado studies. Though tornadoes occur all over the world, no place is more favorable for their formation than the flat plains east of the Rockies. A majority of all U.S. tornadoes strike here in a wide corridor stretching from Texas to the Canadian border.

In the laboratory's tornado research, instrument-crammed, high-flying jets have been widely used. Pilots are called "rough riders," and with good reason. According to those who have flown both types of missions, penetrating a hurricane is child's play compared to tornado hunting.

One afternoon several years ago, for example, Maj. O. Patrick Arquilla and Lt. Ed Miller arrived over Yukon, Oklahoma, in their F-100 interceptor to ride herd on a series of thunderstorms. From the laboratory in Norman a radar controller talked them toward their target. At 25,000 feet, Arquilla twice pushed his plane at about 300 knots into the storm cell. "Light turbulence, rain, snow, slush and hail," he reported. "Very mild."

"Try again," the controller ordered. "Roger," Arquilla replied, and headed back into the turbulence. Suddenly the colors inside the storm changed from almost black to yellowish. Lightning flashed, and heavy hail and rain engulfed the plane—"like flying in a waterfall."

"Updraft!" Arquilla reported. Faster than any express elevator, the heavily loaded F-100 shot 6000 feet straight up. Instinctively Arquilla pushed forward on his controls. At the same instant a downdraft hammered him earthward. The plane dropped 10,000 feet, almost in a spin, before he could recover. In the fluctuating air pressure the jet intakes couldn't get enough continuous air to keep the engine compressor going, and it stalled a dozen times. Lightning played along the craft's skin like fireworks.

Then, as quickly as it appeared, the turbulence, rain and hail abated, and Arquilla was once again in clear air. While he was inside the thunderstorm, a tornado had whirled out of it, touching down to the ground outside Yukon.

Rough-rider flights in the past have come back with hail dents punched in the planes' metal skin in dozens of places. Stabilizers have been burned by lightning, and rain at a pressure of 17,000 pounds per square inch has curled up and broken off rivet heads along the leading edges of the wings. This time Arquilla's plane escaped severe damage and was able to fly again the next day.

The rough riders have brought back astounding records of what actually goes on inside such a severe storm, but a thousand questions about tornadoes still baffle researchers.

When the answers are in, National Severe Storms Laboratory hopes to know enough to tame tornadoes before they can destroy man and his property. Orbiting weather satellites could watch for telltale vortexes in cloud covers. Ground stations could monitor suspicious thunderclouds for electrical fluctuations. Then high-flying pilots, or even rockets, might "seed" the clouds with dry ice or other agents, which speed condensation and thus drain the clouds of their moisture.

"Before that, though," Dr. Edwin Kessler, head of the Severe Storms Laboratory, said, "our work is to prove what causes thunderstorms with tornadoes and hail, and, knowing this, to know more about predicting them. Then we can protect ourselves because we'll have a much better idea of what's ahead."

HOWL OF THE HURRICANE

Benedict Thielen

Between the trade winds of the North and South Atlantic lie the doldrums—a belt reaching across the ocean from French Guiana in the west to the bulge of Africa in the east. It is a place where breezes falter, a place of calms but not of peace. Behind the calms there is a restlessness. The slowly heaving sea, shivering from time to time with flurries of wind or brief showers, glistens pale as lead. Gray curtains of distant cloud and rain form, drift and disappear below the horizon. Sometimes, in the hot summer months, they form and grow.

The heated air, saturated with water, rises slowly from the sea. As it rises, other air moves in to take its place. This motion in the calmness is imperceptible at first but growing, as the misty air is drawn off the sea like smoke up a chimney. The Earth, too, is moving, spinning; and as the air moves, it takes on the movement of the Earth as well. Around the hollow center the air begins to spin and spiral. Rising, the warm air expands, cools; and the water it is charged with condenses as rain.

So the air column grows, spinning in one place like a top, with occasional erratic darts forward or to the side. Presently, touched by the edges of the trade winds, the column begins to move westward. It moves slowly at first, sometimes stopping altogether as it sucks up the hot dampness that is its fuel. But a direction has been set. Out of motion a shape has been born. It will become a hurricane.

On a distant shore, a thousand miles away, the sound of the sea changes. The light, quick rhythm of the breakers becomes heavier and slower. When the long swells, visible far out on the horizon, reach the shore, they fall with a deep, reverberating boom, grave as a tolling bell. Hearing the sound, a man who remembers other storms will look to the sky. It is clear, with a still and luminous clarity that seems to stem from an immense innocence. Far above, a few wisps of high cirrus cloud gleam with a pearly luster. The sunset will blaze more splendidly than usual.

Many men and instruments have been watching the sea and sky. From weather satellites in orbit above the Earth and from men on freighters, liners and tankers at sea comes information about the changing weather conditions. High in an office building in Miami, at the National Hurricane Center, men analyze this data.

Next morning the waves are breaking against a lighthouse on an offshore reef. A breeze is blowing now, but instead of blowing off the sea, it blows from the land. Yet it is not a land breeze, dry and smelling of dust and late summer flowers. It is heavy and damp, and there is salt in it, bitter on your lips.

The sky is no longer clear but veiled in a milky haze. As the day wears on, the veil thickens, grows yellowish. As the sun sinks, the sky is streaked with unusually brilliant orange-and-red light.

At sea, the air has begun to hum and throb. The dark mass has moved forward, as the confused wa-

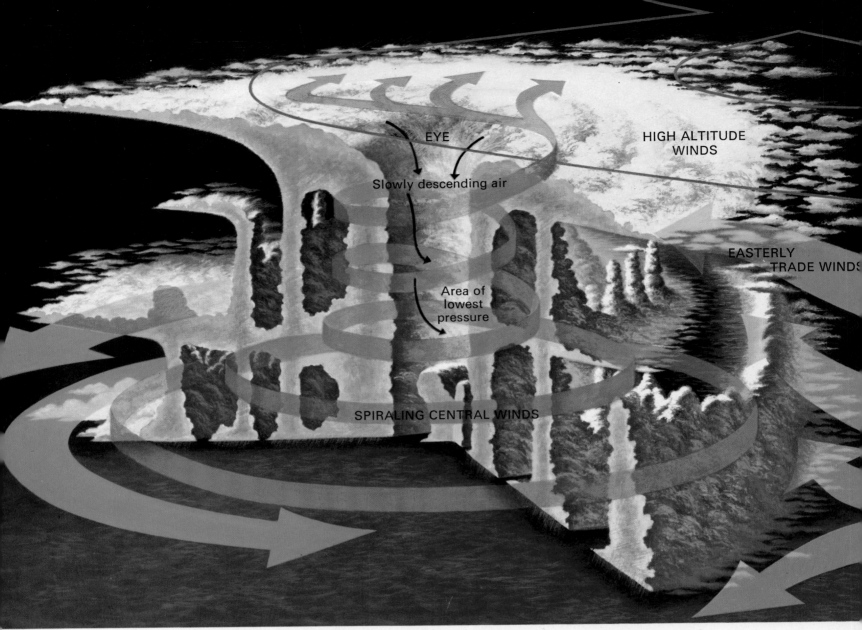

EYE

HIGH ALTITUDE WINDS

Slowly descending air

EASTERLY TRADE WINDS

Area of lowest pressure

SPIRALING CENTRAL WINDS

This cutaway view of a hurricane is exaggerated vertically: Hurricanes are less than ten miles high but may be 400 miles wide. Once a tropical storm becomes strong enough to cause the easterly trade winds (green arrows) to turn in on themselves, spiraling central winds (orange arrows) may accelerate to velocities of 75 miles per hour or more, and the storm is then officially termed a hurricane. Acting like an enormous pump, a hurricane takes warm, moist air from just above the ocean's surface, swirls it up to great heights around a calm low-pressure core called the eye, and releases it into the path of high-altitude winds (red arrows). As this air rises the moisture in it condenses, releasing heat that produces strong updrafts and creating long spiral cloud bands from which torrential rains fall.

ters are lashed by the rain and wrung and twisted by the wind. The clouds spin faster, advance faster, rumbling like distant guns. Coming in low above the churning water, a plane flies straight into the eye of the storm. A long time after, it reappears, wings quivering. Then it wheels, rises and sends its message to shore.

In Miami the man at the drafting board can now mark the exact center of the storm. The radar grilles swing to face it, and men bend over the screens waiting for its picture to appear—the hollow center with its spiraling cloud arms, the octopus shape. Now the storm is given a name. It has become a personality, malevolent and dangerous, a criminal at large. At the Hurricane Center the teleprinters click faster.

As the storm approaches, the air ahead of it be-

comes charged with an unaccustomed tension. Not knowing why, people become more aware of the beating of their hearts. They feel a restless need to be doing something and at the same time a difficulty in concentrating on the thing to be done. Fear twitches. It was fear that gave the hurricane its name: *hurrican*, the Carib Indians' word for "evil spirit."

The storm now spins at a hundred miles an hour— an immense, shallow disk, its top curved with the curve of the Earth, its center filled with sunlight and plunging air. It still advances slowly, at ten or 12 knots. As it moves west and north, its outer edge strikes a well of air, the great oval of high pressure that covers the Atlantic from Bermuda to the Azores. Unable to go farther north, it heads due west. The westward-flowing winds urge it faster on its course.

Watchers on the shore can see it approach now. Through the milky veil a grayish blur appears on the horizon, shot through with a coppery light. Other clouds, broken, fast-moving, come like outriders at its side, scudding low across the sea. As it nears, the body of the storm becomes black, swelling and rising, blotting out what light still lingers in the sky. The driven rain rakes the sea, and for a long time gusts punch and pound at the torrents of rain, now pausing, then striking again.

The pauses grow gradually longer. Finally, only gentle airs drift about. The sky clears, and the sun comes out. The air is warm and dry and very light. This is the eye of the storm. For perhaps half an hour the quiet persists. Then from far away comes a faint humming. Clouds creep over the rim of the sea and begin to spread across the sky. The wind returns, at speeds of 150 miles an hour and more.

Now, with the passing of the center around which it spins, it blows from the opposite direction. Trees that had bent before it are jerked back. Like someone kicking and gouging an opponent who already lies gasping, the wind clutches and shakes the helpless land. Then, as the blackness touches the zenith, the whole world seems suddenly to burst apart. From someone's throat comes a cry as the sea, piled up by the wind, breaks from its own weight, and falls—obliterating houses, boats, trees and, here and there, the small running figure of a woman or a man.

The water flows over the defeated land. When a tree falls, its splash is lost in the universal thundering. The flight through the air of a roof, an oar, a bucket is without sound. There is no sound as a splinter no bigger than a matchstick penetrates the skull of a man. Now again, though, the sun comes out. The air smells fresh and clean with the sweetness of crushed leaves. Boats and houses lie broken and scattered along the shore. Some people are dead. . . .

To the meteorologist the hurricane is a "cyclonic vortex," a circulation of air revolving around a core of low pressure. It spins clockwise below the equator, counterclockwise above. To be classed as a true hurricane, it must have a circular speed of at least 75 miles an hour; speeds of 160 miles an hour are not unusual. Above this point, wind-measuring instruments are generally carried away, but there have been storms with gusts estimated at 250 miles an hour. It was to express this, the inexpressible, that a shipmaster once entered in his logbook, "Winds infinite."

A hurricane's course is influenced by neighboring areas of pressure, for it takes the path of least resistance. If a body of high pressure lies on both sides of a storm path, the hurricane will move up the channel created between. It was through such a channel that the hurricane of 1938 tore into New England at the unheard-of speed of a mile a minute.

It has been 23 years since that disaster ushered in an era of destructive storms. With each succeeding one—the Great Atlantic Hurricane of '44; Carol, Edna, Hazel in '54; Donna, surging from Florida to New England in '60; Carla, devastating the Texas coast in '61; Betsy, hitting New Orleans in '65—people have wondered whether a new and permanent pattern has been set.

Once having listened to the rising wind or watched the rising sea, one can never again enjoy quite the same feeling of security he knew before. In Massachusetts I have seen the red, black-centered warning flags fly many times, and in Florida as well, where I have sat in a shuttered house and listened to its shingles being riffled like cards by the wind, while coconuts thudded like cannonballs against its sides. But when I think of a hurricane, it is not Carol or Edna or Connie or the two Key West storms of 1948 that I think of. It is still my first one—the New England hurricane of 1938.

At five o'clock on the afternoon of September 21 the house I lived in on Martha's Vineyard stood on a strip of beach. Behind it lay a large saltwater pond; in front of it dunes faced the sea like ramparts. An hour later no trace of the dunes remained, and the house was floating toward the far shore of the pond. I can still hear the crash of glass as a wave broke in the front window. I feel the water, ankle-deep, then waist-deep, then bottomless in a single huge surge. I see the point of land toward which I am swimming disappear. The wind, blowing at 90 miles an hour, whips the surface of the water into spray and drives it down my throat. It crosses my mind that I may drown. But, finally, slow strokes and the wind carry me to a hillside; I grasp the thorny branches of a wild rosebush and slowly pull myself out and beyond the reaching sea.

In places where hurricanes occur often, they say that people get used to them. In a sense it is true. They know what precautions to take—what supplies to have on hand, which windows to close and which to leave open. But there is always the feeling of ultimate helplessness.

In a small Cuban town I once asked a friend what people there did when a hurricane came.

"Why," he said, looking at me in surprise, "we get drunk."

I can think of no more reasonable course of action.

Chapter Six

Nature's Mightiest Forces

We live precariously on the thin, shifting crust of a turbulent, changing planet, the liveliest in the solar system. Our destiny has been shaped by such incomparably powerful forces as volcanic explosions, shattering earthquakes, upheaving mountain ranges and mile-deep ice sheets that grind inexorably across entire continents.

AN ISLAND IS BORN

Sigurdur Thorarinsson

On November 14, 1963, a fishing vessel was cruising some four miles west of Geirfuglasker, Iceland's southernmost offshore island. About 7:30 a.m. the skipper, engineer and cook felt the boat sway irregularly as if it were caught in a whirlpool. A strange odor of sulfur permeated the atmosphere.

In the distance, toward the south, the skipper spotted dark smoke coming from the ocean surface; he trained his binoculars on what he thought might be a burning ship. Instead he saw the black columns of a volcanic eruption rising grotesquely upward.

Although he could have no inkling at the time, Capt. Gudmar Tomassón was witnessing the very beginning of an awesome miracle of creation. Spewed out of a submarine volcanic eruption, a new island was being born before his eyes. Now, for the first time, scientists with 20th-century instruments would be able to observe, record and analyze each stage of a volcanic island's emergence from the sea and its struggle against the might of the waves to retain a place in the sun.

The birth pangs of the new island, soon to be named Surtsey after a legendary Norse giant, were violent. Days before, a volcanic fissure had rent the basalt ocean bottom 425 feet below the surface. Embryonic cones and vents breathed forth from the bowels of Earth the fearsome gases and solids that started building a solitary islet. Now, at the surface, the eruption column was spewing gas and steam thousands of feet toward the skies, while black columns of ejected solid particles called "tephra" rose hundreds of feet into the air.

That night Surtsey was born. The incredibly new land reached a height of 33 feet above the waves by morning of the second day of the eruption. Four days later, the isle was 200 feet high, 2000 feet long. Ex-

plosions were catapulting incandescent lava bombs 4000 feet away into steaming gravelets in the North Atlantic. During the long arctic nights, residents of Iceland's capital city of Reykjavik, 75 miles away, could see the awesome eruption.

One of the first of the international group of scientists to arrive on the scene itself was Icelandic geologist Sigurdur Thorarinsson, who wrote:

"Few hours of my life do I treasure as much as one late afternoon near the volcano. Waves washed our small coast-guard vessel from stem to stern. The eruption column was rushing continuously upward, and when darkness fell it was a pillar of fire, and the entire cone was aglow with bombs which rolled down the slopes into the white surf around the island. Lightning flashes lit up the eruption cloud and peals of thunder cracked above our heads. The din from the thunderbolts, the rumble from the eruption cloud, and the crashes of bombs into the sea produced a most impressive symphony. High in the sky the crescent moon rushed headlong between racing clouds. How hopelessly beyond my powers it is to do justice to such a grandiose performance of the elements. To do so one would need the romantic genius of a Byron or a Delacroix."

In the weeks and months that followed, Surtsey continued to grow until the tephra cliffs towered hundreds of feet above the Atlantic. Finally came the day when Thorarinsson actually set foot on Surtsey:

"Seven of us, including two women, stood on the sandy beach. We had not stayed there many minutes when Surtsey began to fire warning shots, and we saw water spouts in the sea off the beach. They came from lava bombs crashing down, which soon began to fall all around us. Under such circumstances there is only one thing to do—suppress the urge to take to your heels and endeavor to stand still and stare up in the air, trying not to dodge the bombs until the very moment they seem to be about to land on your head. When the biggest bombs, almost a yard in diameter, crashed on the wet sand, they cupped out holes that

A soaring five-mile-high tower of steam and volcanic ash heralded the violent birth of the island of Surtsey off Iceland's southern coast in 1963. This spectacular event has given scientists a rare opportunity to observe plants and animals colonizing a barren habitat entirely cut off from other land by the sea.

An aerial view reveals the open vent of the infant island of Surtsey as molten lava was explosively turning seawater into steam. Static charges in the rapidly rising eruption sometimes produced brilliant lightning.

soon filled with water which boiled against the red-hot lava.

"After we had stayed on the island for an hour and a half, these bomb showers relented enough so we could row our dinghies to our ship. It was an experience none of us will forget, but no further attempts were made to go ashore while an explosive vent was still active."

Tephra is too unstable a substance to withstand the pounding of waves, and Thorarinsson was elated when, at the end of the explosive phase, lava began to flow in April 1964. Since lava cools into hard rock, the permanence of the island was assured. At the end of the last lava flow, in June 1967, Surtsey boasted noble dimensions: height, 567 feet; length, 1.3 miles; area, more than one square mile—almost twice that of the Principality of Monaco.

The last and most portentous stage in Surtsey's evolution occurred like a quiet postlude to a thunderous symphony. After months of breathtaking pyrotechnics, a miracle wrought silently by wings and fins and seed-bearing currents brought life itself to Surtsey. A creature from the depths of the sea began wriggling

on a sandy beach, and a first plant grew in a rocky cranny on this new Atlantis. The creation of Surtsey, son of the sea, was now complete.

But its evolution continued. By summer of 1967, other plants had rooted, and the newborn cliffs were alive with birds. In June the first flower bloomed—a white sea rocket. Even human beings had found a place for themselves—a hut for international scientists, who arrive and depart in minuscule airplanes, keeping watch on how the world is eternally created anew.

Fiery rivulets of lava solidified to form the island of Surtsey. Only a year and a half after it was formed, Surtsey harbored its first leafy green plant. Within five years, scientists visiting the island had identified 23 bird species and 22 insect species.

WHEN KRAKATOA BLEW UP

Ernst Behrendt

The world is awed by the blasts that devastated Hiroshima and Nagasaki, but there was an explosion once that was incomparably greater. Those atomic bombs flattened two cities, yet people a few dozen miles away were oblivious of the fact.

When the East Indian island of Krakatoa blew up, on August 27, 1883, the whole world knew about it. The noise was heard 3000 miles away. The great waves the explosion caused in the sea reached the shores of four continents and were recorded 8000 miles away. An air wave generated by the blast traveled clear around the world, not once but several times. And where had been a mountain half a mile high was now a hole a thousand feet deep and miles across.

Red-hot debris covered an area the size of Texas, to a depth of sometimes 100 feet on land. For nearly a year afterward the dust of the explosion, blown upward for 30 miles, filled the high atmosphere over almost the whole globe. Even though there were no large towns within 100 miles of the volcano, 36,000 persons lost their lives.

The biggest blast in history was caused by nothing more mysterious than the old-fashioned force that rattles the lid on a teakettle. But the fire under the kettle was a mile-long pocket of seething lava and it changed a cubic mile of ocean into superheated steam. The lid blew off, and the kettle exploded as well.

Krakatoa was a volcanic island of about 18 square miles in the Sunda Strait, in what was then known as the Dutch East Indies, between Java and Sumatra.

Early in the spring of 1883, there were warning signs. Smoke and steam poured from recent fissures in the rock. A river of lava cut a wide swath through the tangled jungle. But the Dutch in Java and Sumatra were not alarmed. Old Krakatoa had puffed and rumbled before. Even when the Dutch Captain Ferzenaar arrived in Batavia in August with a report that two new volcanoes had appeared on Krakatoa, the Dutch were not impressed. There were scores of volcanoes in the East Indies; besides, Krakatoa was almost a hundred miles away.

"The ground was so hot it burned right through the soles of my boots," Captain Ferzenaar said. Well, if it was that warm on Krakatoa the few natives who lived there would have to take to their boats and wait until the island cooled off.

Captain Ferzenaar was the last white man to set foot on Krakatoa before the eruption. By this time navigation through Sunda Strait was becoming difficult. Several skippers turned back when they saw the narrows covered with a foot-thick layer of cinders. But the captain of one American freighter battened down the hatches and calmly sailed through the hissing sea. His cargo—kerosene!

No one after him attempted the passage. By now Krakatoa's rumblings had grown into a continuous, angry roar heard along the entire east coast of Java. In Buitenzorg, 61 miles from Krakatoa, people were seeking shelter from what they thought was a gathering thunderstorm.

"In the afternoon of August 26," R. D. M. Verbeek wrote in his description of the catastrophe, "the low rumbling was interrupted by sharp, reverberating detonations. They grew louder and more frequent. People were terrified. Night came, but no one thought of sleeping. Toward morning the incessant noise was drowning out every other sound. Suddenly, shortly before seven, there was a tremendous explosion. Buildings shook, walls cracked, and doors flew open as if pushed by invisible hands. Everybody rushed into the streets. Another deafening explosion, and then everything was quiet as if the volcano had ceased to exist."

The volcano *had* ceased to exist. Seething with the expansion of its gases, the white-hot lava found temporary outlets in the two craters seen by Ferzenaar, which normally acted as safety valves. But the pressure became too great. Unimaginable energies were straining against hundreds of feet of solid rock overhead. The rock heaved, buckled; on the evening of August 26 it cracked open like the wall of a defective caldron.

With all the fury of a primordial cataclysm a stream of lava burst forth in a deafening roar. Seconds later the ocean rushed into the opening. On contact with the hot lava the water changed into superheated steam. Colossal blocks of granite and obsidian rocketed upward amid a cloud of dust and smoke. Again the ocean rushed in, battling the pent-up lava, changing into expanding, exploding superheated steam, breaking down barrier after barrier of rock.

No one knows how many times the white-hot magma pushed back the ocean and how often the ocean returned to the assault. In the end the water won. Early in the morning of August 27 the ocean reached the volcanic center of the island. Even the fury of the previous explosions was but a faint prelude to the final cataclysm as the heart was ripped out of Krakatoa and 14 cubic miles of rock streaked upward into the sky.

The sun was blotted out behind a curtain of ebony torn by jagged lightning. Miles away, Krakatoa's pyrotechnics awed the sailors of the British ship *Charles*

Bal, who saw the island shoot up over the horizon, "shaped like a pine tree brilliantly illuminated by electric flashes." The sea was covered with innumerable fish, floating belly up on the churning water.

Long afterward came the noise—the loudest ever heard by human ears. "The concussions were deafening," wrote Lloyd's agent in Batavia. They hammered every eardrum in Java and Sumatra and put fear into the hearts of Borneo's headhunters. People in Victoria Plains, Australia, 1700 miles to the eastward, were startled by what seemed to be artillery fire. The sound waves traveled 2968 miles westward to Rodrigues Island near Madagascar.

With the noise, concentric waves of air started on their way around the globe. A day and a half after the explosion, the first of them hit London from the west. Then a second wave rushed over the city from the east. Four times the eastbound wave swept over London—and over Berlin, St. Petersburg and Valencia as well—and three times it swept back. The stratospheric seesaw continued for more than ten days before the blast had spent its force.

Far more violent was the effect of the eruption on the sea. In Anjer, on the west coast of Java, a retired sea captain suddenly noticed a new island that had bobbed up in the strait. The next moment he was running for his life. The island was a wall of water, 50 feet high, advancing across the narrows at incredible speed, battering down the wharves, engulfing Anjer, racing uphill, smashing everything in its path. The wave flung a log at him, and he went down. When he regained consciousness he was sitting on the top of a tree half a mile inland, stripped of every shred of clothing but otherwise unharmed.

He was one of the few who saw the wave and lived to describe its fury. Anjer had vanished. The wave, rising to a height of a hundred feet, wiped out scores of villages and killed thousands of people. On the coast of Sumatra, the wave tore the warship *Beroun* from her moorings and drove her, anchor dragging, two miles inland, leaving her stranded in the jungle, 30 feet above sea level.

The wave raced across the entire width of the Indian Ocean; when it reached Cape Town, 5100 miles away, it was still over a foot high. It rounded the Cape of Good Hope, turned northward into the Atlantic, along the coast of Africa, and at last spent itself in the English Channel.

Whole districts of Indonesia were buried under ashes; the jungles were choked, the rice paddies changed into deserts. The sky was so filled with ashes that for a time lamps were needed all day in Batavia.

But what covered the land and the sea was only a small part of the volcano. Most of Krakatoa's solid rock had been pulverized and blasted to a height of 150,000 feet. Clouds of volcanic dust hung suspended in the stratosphere for months. Air currents carried them across oceans and continents. All over the world, the rays of the sun were filtered through a veil spun in the depths of Sunda Strait. In Paris, New York, Cairo and London, the setting sun appeared blue, leaden, green and copper-colored, and at night the Earth was steeped in the light of a green moon and green stars.

The phenomenon lasted into the spring of 1884; then the colors faded, and Krakatoa's magnificent shroud disappeared. The final chapter in its history seemed to be over. Krakatoa was utterly dead. Nothing was left of it but a few square miles of rock buried under a mountain of ashes. All plants and insects and birds and mammals had been dissolved in a fiery cloud.

Then a miracle happened—the miracle of the rebirth of life. Four months after the eruption, a botanist found an almost microscopic spider, gallantly spinning its web where nothing was to be caught. It had apparently drifted in on the wind.

And then in a few years came the grasses and shrubs, the worms, ants, snakes and birds. They arrived by air—seeds dropped by birds on their flight over the barren land; small caterpillars carried by the wind; beetles and butterflies winging their way over from Java and Sumatra. They arrived by water—eggs of worms and reptiles flung ashore with flotsam; snails and scorpions riding the waves on decayed tree trunks; pythons and crocodiles swimming across the narrows. Parasites clung to their bodies.

Plants and animals came over by accident, but there was nothing accidental about the sequence in which they established themselves. It was a rigid chronological pattern telescoping millennia into months. Some forms of life had to be there first for others to live.

For a while some forms prospered through the absence of enemies and competitors. Around 1910, Krakatoa was overrun by swarms of ants; ten years later, when there were plenty of birds and reptiles, the ants had all but disappeared. By 1919 the first small clusters of trees had taken root, and by 1924 they had grown into a continuous forest. A few years later, climbing plants were already choking the trees to death and transforming the new forest into a tropical jungle with orchids, butterflies, snakes, birds and bats.

Krakatoa became a naturalist's paradise, and the Dutch made it a nature reserve and allowed no one but accredited scientists to set foot on the island. They worked out a complete inventory of life on Krakatoa. They counted the steadily growing number of new arrivals and observed how they lived with each other and fought each other. They even discovered several subspecies—birds and butterflies with peculiar characteristics not to be found anywhere else. Krakatoa was not only drawing on the forms of life around it; it was creating a life of its own.

Then, one day, the scientists discovered another sort of life on Krakatoa. The old volcano was alive.

Deep down under its rocky foundation a pocket of lava was seeking an outlet for its energies. The bottom of the inland sea was heaving and buckling again. A submarine cone was building up; on January 26, 1928, it broke the surface and showed its top, a flat, ugly island a few hundred feet across, which the waves washed away a few days later.

A year passed. Then suddenly a geyser began to spout steam and ashes. Sulfurous fumes drifted over the ocean. Again the sea was covered with dead fish floating belly up.

The new geyser is still there. It is a portion of the ancient crater rim with mud deposited on its top and a flue in its center—a safety valve for the stupendous pressure generated by the lava pocket underneath. The natives call the geyser "Anak Krakatoa," or "Child of Krakatoa." No name could be more ominous.

THE EARTH RANG LIKE A BELL

Earl Ubell

It was March 27, 1964. Many miles deep under Alaska, a huge slab of rock bent under the pressure of a shifting Earth. At 5:36 p.m., the slab snapped with the energy of a hundred hydrogen bombs.

The recoil played snap-the-whip with the whole state of Alaska, spreading panic and killing 115 persons. Releasing more energy than the disastrous 1906 San Francisco shock, that Good Friday quake excited the great Pacific Ocean, roiling huge waves down the West Coast and out into the Pacific to terrorize Hawaii and Japan.

In the midst of devastation, the quake performed a little-noticed service. Before this quake, scientists, with the aid of electronic computers, had drawn up the most accurate three-dimensional anatomical chart ever made of this planet, from the center of its iron-nickel core up through 4000 miles of rock to the surface, where we and a thin film of life cling precariously. The Good Friday quake verified this chart and may help reveal new details of the deep structure of the Earth, and even how the world began.

That huge temblor, like a clapper in a bell, set the Earth—all six billion trillion tons of rock—ringing. For earthquake waves behave in many respects like sound waves: They echo, bend and "sing" at different pitches. But instead of air it is rock vibrating. And so our planet sang a hundred different "tunes," heard not by human ears but by seismographs.

If you had viewed the whole globe at that time from some vantage point in space, you would have seen it jiggle like a spoonful of jelly. It took an hour for one shape, or mode, to form; others appeared and disappeared in minutes. In one mode the world looked like a football, in another it developed girlish dimples. Instruments picked up at least 80 different modes of vibration. Of course, you would have needed supersight to see these changes of shape. For the Earth actually moved up and down less than an inch at any particular spot, although the movement spread like a gentle ripple over hundreds of miles. Our planet continued to tremble for at least three weeks.

Only in the last few years has any progress been made in what scientists call free-oscillations research. But it was back in 1880 that A. E. H. Love, a British mathematician, made the first surmise. His mathematical formulas told him that a really big earthquake should jiggle the whole Earth, make it ring as if it were a plucked guitar string.

When you strike a guitar string, you start an up-and-down movement of the string—a wave—going out in two directions. As each wave hits the end of the string it bounces back to meet its twin in the center. The waves then combine to vibrate the string at a fundamental frequency, its pitch or note. This pitch depends on the string's tightness and thickness, and the material of which it is composed.

According to Love's theory, when a slab of rock breaks, as in an earthquake, it strikes the rocks around it and waves travel out in all directions, some scooting along the surface and others plunging deep into the Earth's interior. Eventually they meet their fellows coming around the other side and through the planet's body. They combine, as on the guitar string, and soon the whole Earth pulses in a fundamental frequency or pitch plus all the overtones—that is, in free oscillation.

The spread of the waves depends on the composition and density of the rock through which they go. In general, the harder the rock, the faster the wave. Some career along at 1000 miles in three minutes—as fast as an Earth satellite.

Love's idea lay sleeping until the middle of this century, when Dr. Hugo Benioff of the California Institute of Technology invented an instrument to pick up the very low notes of Earth's sound waves. On Novem-

Picture an egg with a paper-thin shell enclosing swirling, superheated white. The Earth is such an egg, with its thin, brittle crust being rubbed continuously by the hot, plastic rock of the mantle. No wonder half a million times a year the Earth's crust fractures seriously enough to send shock waves in every direction. By measuring the force and arrival times of these waves at 1200 seismograph stations around the world, scientists can locate unreported quakes, such as those occurring under the ocean floor, and can speculate about the composition of the Earth's interior. Greatly simplified, their reasoning goes as follows: Waves that have traveled through the outer core are delayed; liquids slow down waves; therefore the outer core is liquid. But waves detected directly opposite the focus of an earthquake are delayed less; therefore they must have passed through a solid inner core.

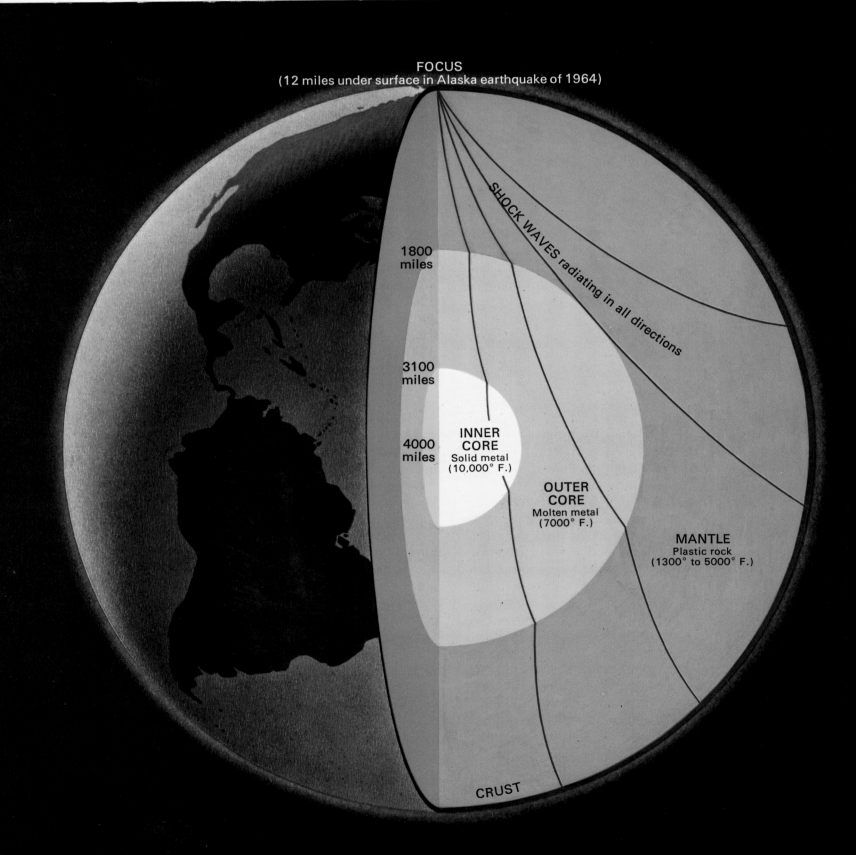

FOCUS
(12 miles under surface in Alaska earthquake of 1964)

SHOCK WAVES radiating in all directions

1800 miles

3100 miles

4000 miles

INNER CORE
Solid metal
(10,000° F.)

OUTER CORE
Molten metal
(7000° F.)

MANTLE
Plastic rock
(1300° to 5000° F.)

CRUST

ber 4, 1952, a huge quake struck the Kamchatka Peninsula of eastern Siberia, and Dr. Benioff's instruments picked up a wave that took *57 minutes* to go from crest to crest. He suspected that wave to be not a direct shock wave but a free oscillation of the planet.

With this clue, Dr. Chaim L. Pekeris, a geophysicist and mathematician at the Weizmann Institute of Science in Israel, put a computer to work on the problem in 1959. The computer clacked out the fundamental numbers by which scientists could recognize in the earthquake records of the future a ringing Earth, if ever it rang. Dr. Pekeris wrote out the "melodies" to look for in the seismic wiggles.

On the morning of May 21, 1960, the great fault off the coast of Chile slipped, and the shock of this sudden movement shook the landscape for hundreds of miles. This time the seismologists were ready. Instruments, including Dr. Benioff's device, had been planted above and below ground thousands of miles apart, in California and New Jersey. They "felt" the Earth moving up and down or sideways as the waves marched by, and measured these movements in hundredths of an inch. Later, when the seismologists looked at the wiggling lines on their paper records, one glance convinced them that the Earth had indeed shivered in harmony. They saw 40 different notes, and the notes were very close to what Dr. Pekeris' computer had told him to expect.

From then on, the world's geologists recognized the importance of a ringing Earth. Since the pitch of any free oscillations, like those of a guitar string or bell, depends on size, shape and material structure, and since seismologists know the size and shape of the Earth, they realized that they could work backward to determine the Earth's structure. In the last few years this program has succeeded brilliantly.

From analysis of more obvious earthquake waves, gathered over half a century, seismologists already had evolved a rough picture of the makeup of the Earth. The traditional model of our planet revealed it to be layered like an onion, in five major zones. On top lies a thin, soft peel, the crust—only 25 to 40 miles deep and containing all the oceans, continents, mountains and most of the earthquakes. Below this crust are the upper mantle, lower mantle, outer core and inner core.

Dr. Don Anderson of Caltech, and other scientists at Columbia University, have found *layers within layers* of that onion. Just below the crust stands the first sub-layer of the upper mantle, about 30 miles thick and composed of solidified rock. The temperature there may be 2000°F., not far from the melting point of the rock.

Just below that, the free-oscillations computations

have uncovered a peculiar zone of rock extending downward for about 140 miles. Although this band is under more pressure than the one above it, it is not so rigid. Dr. Anderson calls it plastic.

"This zone apparently can move up and down somewhat," he says. "This may explain why the deglaciated Scandinavian peninsula, having lost the heavy weight of its ice overburden, is now rising three inches a century."

This zone, according to one theory, may also be the birthplace of volcanoes. Magma—hot flowing rock—originating here flows up through breaks in the upper mantle and then up through the crust.

At the lower edge of the plastic zone the rock suddenly becomes more dense and relatively rigid again. The atoms of the rock have moved closer together under the tremendous pressure above and take up less volume. (The same thing happens to graphite when it becomes diamond under pressure.)

For the next 200 miles, the mantle gradually becomes denser. At 400 miles below the Earth's surface the density of the rock is twice that of granite. Here is the lower boundary of the 370-mile-thick upper mantle. Below this point the lower mantle extends for 1400 miles with a gradual increase of density. Looking again to the ringing-Earth computations, Dr. Anderson has detected a much closer molecular packing in the lower mantle than was previously supposed.

Below the mantle lies the core. Seismology formerly distinguished two zones in the core: a hard ball (inner core) 1800 miles in diameter, and a coverlet of liquid 1300 miles thick (outer core).

The liquid outer core, composed of iron, nickel and silicon (a component of sand and glass), is more than three times as dense as granite. The pressure there may be over a billion pounds per square foot, a force that has crushed the atoms together. Some geologists believe that this core liquid behaves as a dynamo, creating electric currents which in turn generate magnetism as if the Earth were a coil of wire.

The solid ball at the center is denser still. A cubic foot of it weighs nearly half a ton. Geologists think it is similar to the iron-nickel alloy of meteorites. At the moment, scientists are analyzing the free oscillations of the Earth to learn more about the core.

In addition to Earth structure, geophysicists are examining the free oscillations for clues about the origin of quakes in an effort to learn how to predict the big, dangerous ones. If geologists could measure the strain of the rock at various earthquake-prone locations in the crust, they might be able to predict when a huge slab of bending or sliding rock was about to snap, and an alarm could be sounded. A panel of the

Presidential Office of Science and Technology has been studying this possibility, under the chairmanship of Dr. Frank Press of Caltech.

Ringing-Earth analysis is still a new approach, but it has already paid off in many ways. Having just discovered that the Earth can play a tune, the scientists are now learning how to sing along with it.

THOSE AWESOME EXPLOSIONS: EARTHQUAKES

Ira Wolfert

A geophysicist I know, who had been living with earthquakes on charts for years, finally experienced one personally in Mexico one summer. He says it felt as if the whole world had become a rug that had been given a good strong double shake and then dropped. "The people, the buildings, the mountains—we were nothing more than dust in the rug," he said.

It was all over in about 30 seconds. But it's amazing how much a man can live through in the amount of time he might ordinarily devote to a yawn.

My friend was about to leave his house when, without warning, a force equivalent to 100 atomic bombs of the Hiroshima model broke loose in the Earth's subterranean rock and began racing toward him under the landscape. There had been a crunching shock, the kind you get when wood gripped in a vise splits. The pressure had been accumulating in the rock for years. Then it had become more than the rock could contain and now it was loose, a powerful and terrible bursting smothered by stupendous weight.

Along the split, or fault as it is called by scientists, there was slipping of the rock. As a result, riding out in all directions from the fracture were vibrations, or elastic waves such as a bomb blast would send out if it occurred in solid rock, not air.

The rock shuddered, its particles jarring back and forth like a train of cars jolted from behind. The jolt traveled miles before dwindling down to a gentle shoving. That was the first effect, the "P" (for primary) wave. Then came the "S" (for secondary) wave, which travels about half as fast. It doesn't jolt; it twists. A subterranean mass of rock had been wrung out like a wet sock. When the S wave passed, the rock untwisted itself and lay twanging and quivering, retching back into place.

Sometimes if it's quiet, you can hear earthquake waves coming—like a train roaring over a trestle, or

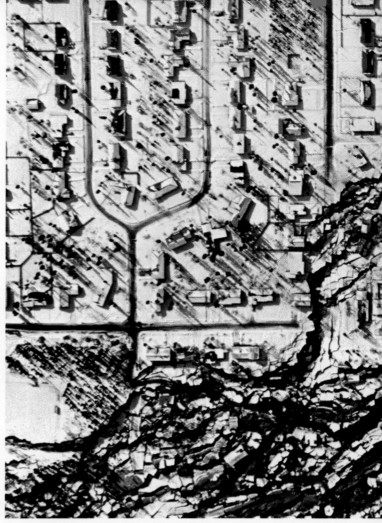

An earthquake made Anchorage, Alaska, a portrait of sheer disaster in 1964.

Yawning fissures in Anchorage's snow-clad earth bespeak the terrible energies unleashed by the Alaska quake.
The rubble pile at upper right is what remains of a newly built, but fortunately still unoccupied, apartment house.

with the snappings and cracklings of a brushfire. There's no outrunning it—just dive and duck. For the P wave travels at five miles a second, more than eight times faster than a high-velocity bullet. The S wave travels at two and three quarters miles a second.

My friend was in midstride, nearing his front door, when the jolt hit. His front foot landed on the floor somewhere behind him. He toppled and clutched at the wall and was flung away, as if sideswiped by a moving train. That was how he knew it was an earthquake, not something he had stumbled over.

He remembered what various authorities on earthquakes have said: "Get under something that will protect you from falling debris and count to 40." He tried to get under the door lintel, but the floor had become one of those witching-wave floors found in fun parks. Then there was a lull. The P wave had passed. He lunged across the floor, threw himself face down under the lintel and gripped the door jamb.

Above the thudding of his heart he could hear church bells ringing, set in motion by the quake. He began to count. Suddenly an incredibly long washboard was being pulled out from under him at terrific speed. The S wave had arrived. Just as suddenly, it was gone, leaving a spatter of plaster on the floor and the big hall chandelier swinging like a pendulum.

It was a relatively minor quake, though 52 people were killed. My friend's chief reaction, as a scientist, was: "How much we have to learn!"

An earthquake is perhaps the most deeply buried page in the book of nature's secrets. Only one thing known to man can explore it for him—earthquake waves. And now he's learning to translate what the waves say into a language he can understand. The most valuable maps of hidden treasure now known are drawn by seismologists for oil companies by setting off explosives and getting the seismic waves to tell what they've seen on their travels. This is one of the wonders of our day.

An earthquake was once believed to be a reminder to the wicked of God's wrath. If it is a reminder of anything, it is of the utter, dazing cunning of creation. We live our lives out on board a spaceship, one more superbly engineered than any in science fiction.

Father Joseph Lynch, famous seismologist of New York's Fordham University, says that earthquakes are one of the Earth's safety measures. The Earth is in perpetual motion, not only through space but within itself. It suffers wear and tear, yields and breaks under strain. This happens an average of 2700 times every day—little breaks releasing a force equaling about 50 pounds of dynamite, big ones mounting up awesomely. We feel a big break as an earthquake, the repair job that follows—when the rock settles back into shape—as aftershocks.

Only so much energy can accumulate in rock before the rock will break. However, that amount is at present unknown. When there's a fault that has suffered a previous fracture, the break is likely to come before prodigious energy has piled up. For a really big quake to occur, one scientist says, there must be an area of rock at least 50 miles in diameter, with every part of that area strained to the breaking point simultaneously.

The largest recorded quake registers 8.9 on the magnitude scale devised by Drs. Charles Richter and Beno Gutenberg of the California Institute of Technology. There has been only one such quake since 1904, when scientists first began to measure accurately the energy in an earthquake. It struck Colombia and Ecuador in January 1906, the most terrible of all earthquake years scientifically recorded. In April of that year, the famous San Francisco earthquake struck—8.3 on the scale. In August, the rock burst in Chile with a magnitude of 8.6, and the following month in New Guinea with a magnitude of 8.4. During the last decade disastrous earthquakes have struck in Colombia, Turkey and other areas of the world. In May 1960 an earthquake with a magnitude of 8.5 rocked Chile, and on March 27, 1964, an equally violent earthquake struck Alaska, destroying downtown Anchorage.

How is the energy generated that powers these shocks called "earthquakes"? One theory may give a partial answer. There are tides in the solid Earth, which Dr. Albert A. Michelson, famous University of Chicago physicist, measured. Every 12 hours, all the water, mountains, cities and people on half the globe rise one foot into the air, then sink one foot down in the next 12 hours when the Moon is pulling on the opposite side of the world. This action creates enormous subterranean pressures.

As the Earth rotates, its motion also creates a tremendous internal force. In addition, the Earth's surface is continually cooling; and as it contracts it clamps more tightly around the interior. All these forces are among the causes of earthquakes.

Japan is by far the greatest sufferer from earthquakes. (The ghastly Yokohama-Tokyo disaster of 1923 killed some 142,000.) But no place is immune. The interior of continents is generally regarded by geologists as stable, yet one of the greatest quakes in our history hit New Madrid, Missouri, in 1811. Felt as far north as Massachusetts, it destroyed a forest and created 20-mile-long Reelfoot Lake in Tennessee. "The ground rose and fell in successive furls like the ruffled waters of a lake," reported the naturalist John James Audubon. Then came the aftershocks, lasting the better part of a year, strong enough to make people seasick.

Earthquakes in the ocean bed occur almost daily. But you can't twist something out of shape when, like water, it has no shape to begin with. That's why liners passing over earthquakes have encountered only a single upward jolt like that caused by a bump in the road. But when a submarine earthquake is of some magnitude, the convulsive movements in the depths can create a tidal wave, which scientists prefer to call by its Japanese name, "tsunami," since it has nothing to do with the tides. Springing from the ocean bed above the focus of an earthquake, it can stretch scores of miles and race through the sea at speeds up to 500 m.p.h., pushing the ocean water before it.

As the tsunami approaches land, the first sign is likely to be a sharp swell, hardly different from an ordinary wave. Then there is an enormous, draining withdrawal. The ocean floor gapes open, exposing a litter of stranded fish far beyond the furthest ebb of low tide. Finally the gigantic wave, which may reach a height of 200 feet, comes crashing in. In 1946 one of these waves drowned 173 persons in Hilo, Hawaii.

This tsunami made history when a throng of oceanographers observing the Bikini atomic bomb test were caught in its path. Never before had a tidal wave been the object of such intense, on-the-spot observation. Out of it came a lifesaving warning system developed by the U. S. Coast and Geodetic Survey. Earthquake reports are sent from seismographic stations to Honolulu. There the position of each quake is plotted, and the arrival time of tsunamis is estimated.

Today about 1000 seismograph observatories are scattered around the world, watching the shock waves and translating what they say into a universal language of numbers and mathematical symbols. Big shocks are reported by urgent cable to Washington, where the information is collated and analyzed for the reporting observatories. In Strasbourg the Bureau Central Séismologique International and in England the International Seismological Center follow up with a more detailed report of the world view of the same quake.

It will be some time before scientists can tell us as much about the somber and awful storms in the subterranean rocks as they can about the more visible storms in the atmosphere. But every day they are learning anew what an awe-inspiring, humbling marvel this Earth of ours is.

FOOTPRINTS OF THE GREAT ICE

Ralph K. Andrist

A narrow band of low, gentle hills extends across the United States from Cape Cod to the Rocky Mountains. There is nothing to catch the casual eye, but the geologist recognizes this ridge as a "terminal moraine"—the line where North America's last continental glacier ended its long advance about 11,000 years ago and began to melt back.

The glacier was the last cataclysmic event that helped shape the face of the continent. The ice buried Manhattan and stopped with an advanced lobe resting on Staten Island. Its line bent north in Pennsylvania because the mountains held it back somewhat. It reached almost to the Ohio River in Indiana and Ohio, tended in an irregular line northwestward almost to the Canadian border in North Dakota, then ran straight westward to the mountains. The western mountains were too high to be overrun, but they proliferated a rich crop of mountain glaciers that joined into an almost solid icecap connecting with the continental glacier to the east.

Both coming and going, the ice reshaped the land. Consider two of the many rivers it rerouted. The streams that now make up the headwaters of the Ohio once flowed into Lake Erie; when ice dammed the old courses, the water was forced to flow south and west around the glacier front until it found its way to a tributary of the Mississippi, and so formed part of the Ohio River system. In the West, the upper Missouri flowed north into Canada until the ice blocked that outlet and made it find a new channel that also led to the Mississippi.

Contrary to popular belief, the ice did not form around the North Pole and then flow southward. It formed in a number of centers—Canada, Greenland, Northern Europe, Siberia—more or less simultaneously, and spread from each of those places. Nor was the glacial epoch a period of unusual cold; the essential for glacier formation is only that more snow fall during the winter than melts in summer.

There have been times when the winter snow outlasted the summer sun for thousands of years, piling up inch by inch, foot by foot, packing into ice, until it was probably two miles thick at the center and hundreds of miles across. It was a burden so massive that it pushed the rock foundations of the land down into the molten magma on which they float. (In many places the land is still slowly springing back.

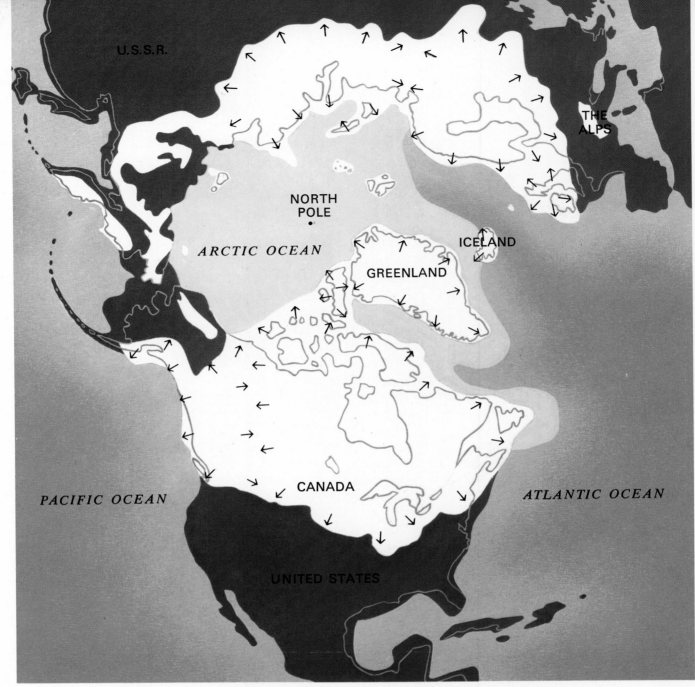

Several times in the past million years, a mile-deep blanket of ice has advanced and retreated over much of Europe and North America, eroding mountains, hollowing out lakes, changing the course of rivers. This map shows the combined extent of glaciation in all ice ages. Arrows give direction of ice flow; unglaciated areas are green; frozen areas are blue; the lines show present coastlines. During maximum glaciation enough water was locked up as ice to lower ocean levels over 300 feet, so that land areas were larger than they are now. Even today, an area equal to South America's is buried under ice, mainly in Greenland and Antarctica. If these glaciers melted, the sea level would rise at least 200 feet, inundating coasts around the world.

Eventually the bottom of Hudson Bay, where the ice first started to accumulate and disappeared last, may reemerge as dry land—provided another glacier does not come first.)

The ice moved forward when the enormous pressure of its own weight began to force the great mass outward at the edges. As the snow kept accumulating, the glacier kept pushing, grinding rocks to pebbles and pebbles to clay and sand, moving incredible quantities of rock and earth over the surface of the land.

The glacier reached its limit when weakening for-

ward movement was just balanced by the rate at which the ice front was melting back, a period of equilibrium that probably lasted for hundreds of years. During this time great quantities of the debris embedded in the ice were exposed and dropped at the melting front of the mass.

In the East the glacier stopped with its leading edge a number of miles beyond the present coastline. Much of the tremendous burden it dropped still abides, though considerably worn away by the sea; its largest portions are Long Island, Block Island, Martha's Vineyard, Nantucket and Cape Cod. Here is much of the earth that once clothed New England hillsides.

A mile-deep ice mass does not fade away in a summer or two: It took more than 4000 years for the glacier to melt from the present site of Hartford, Connecticut, to that of St. Johnsbury, Vermont, a sluggish average of only about one mile in 22 years. (During this period the Connecticut River valley was a lake.) Sometimes the ice melted back without interruption and dropped its load of debris in an even layer. At other times the ice front would pause, and occasionally a new forward surge would override and scatter earlier deposits.

The last continental glacier, called the Wisconsin, was the latest of four that came and went during the Pleistocene epoch. (Geologists have named the glaciations for the areas where their traces have been most clearly identified. The four are known in the United States as the Nebraskan, the Kansan, the Illinoian and the Wisconsin.)

In some of the earlier glaciations, the ice pushed as far south as Louisville, St. Louis and Topeka. Between times there were long periods when the climate grew mild and much of the work of the glaciers was erased by a hundred thousand or more years of erosion from other causes.

The most spectacular monument to the action of the ice is the Great Lakes. All four glaciers played a part in producing them, each one scooping the basins a bit deeper until the Earth's largest body of fresh water was formed. As it melted back, the ice not only filled the lake basins but also formed an enormous dam across the lowlands to the north. The overbrimming water had only one place to go: It burst through to the south in several mighty torrents. One of these was the great river that tore a channel from Lake Erie to the Hudson River. The Mohawk River still flows in the eastern part of the valley; the Erie Canal was dug in the old glacial watercourse.

Another overflow channel left Lake Erie where Toledo now stands, and ran into the Ohio. The Maumee and Wabash rivers now follow the same valley. Still another outlet ran across the site of Chicago and, via the present courses of the Des Plaines and Illinois rivers, to the Mississippi.

There are countless glacier-created lakes from the Dakotas to Maine and north into Canada. Minnesota alone has many more than enough to justify its slogan, "Land of Ten Thousand Lakes," while in Canada they are virtually uncountable. But the greatest of the glacial lakes, Lake Agassiz, is long since gone. At its largest extent it filled the valley of

the Red River of the North in Minnesota and North Dakota and covered most of Manitoba—an inland body of water larger than all the present Great Lakes combined. It formed when the retreating glacier left the area clear, while blocking the normal northward drainage of the Red River. Finally the glacier withdrew so far that the water could rush out into Hudson Bay.

The only remnants of Lake Agassiz are Lake Winnipeg and some swamps and smaller lakes, but its ancient bed is easy to identify. When the lake lay over the land, the silt brought into it by wind and water slowly settled, year after year, century after century, until the lake bottom was covered dozens of feet deep and every irregularity was hidden. When the water went at last, it revealed a plain as flat as a floor stretching to the horizon in every direction. It is a land monotonous to some, but it is a joy to the farmers who work its deep, rich, stoneless soil.

Most of the large ice-age mammals of North America, such as the woolly mammoth, disappeared at the end of the ice age. Scientists are not certain whether their extinction was caused by the overhunting of early man or by climatic changes that occurred as the glaciers retreated. Big mammals that escaped this fate included the woodland bison, the mountain sheep and the musk ox.

Another particularly interesting if less imposing survivor is the White Mountain butterfly. This insect's ancestors probably moved south ahead of the glaciers and then followed the ice back north as it melted. But some individuals managed to survive on the bleak summits of a few northeastern mountains long after the glaciers retreated. Today descendants of these ice-age butterflies can still be seen flitting about certain alpine meadows in New Hampshire's White Mountains and on the tundralike plateau of Maine's Mt. Katahdin. Their only close relatives are far to the north in polar lands around the globe.

Since the Northern Hemisphere has had four separate glaciations in recent geological times, the inevitable question is whether we can expect a fifth. The answer appears to be "Yes." Indeed, according to one scientific theory, the next glacial era may be breathing down our necks.

The beginning will be undramatic. Winter snowfalls will increase so that, at the end of summer, snow will still linger in the tundra lands of northern Canada, probably nothing more than a few patches of slush in the shade of rocks and moss hummocks. The next autumn the patches will be a little larger and deeper when the freeze-up comes.

Only a few Eskimos and scientists will notice.

Part Four

Worlds Without End

Chapter One

Sun, Moon and Planets

*We stand on the threshold of a great new age of exploration as one of mankind's
oldest dreams is fast becoming a reality. Freed at last from the shackles of
gravity, men and machines from Earth are setting forth to explore neighboring worlds
in our solar system. Yesterday's science fiction is today's accomplished fact.*

THE THING THAT HIT US FROM OUTER SPACE

Wolfgang Langewiesche

On the Arizona plains near Grand Canyon, just south of the Painted Desert, there's another wonder to be seen: the Meteor Crater, where we got hit by a *thing* that came from space.

You can't miss it. This is a privately owned natural wonder, strongly advertised on signboards along U.S. 66. "Bigger than the atom bomb!" they say.

A six-mile access road runs from U.S. 66 over the dry empty plain. You get to a parking lot; get funneled past souvenir counters to the "Pay Here" gate of a little museum. One wall of the building is all glass, and there, outside, it is: a hole in the ground, almost a mile across, 570 feet deep—deep enough to hide the Washington Monument!

A thing came from space, hit here, and made the hole in one second. The thing was nickel-iron, and it was huge: about as big as an ocean liner.

It did not simply drop; it *flew* in. It came out of the northern sky in nearly level flight, more orbiting than falling. Then it dipped down.

Some think the thing hit as one solid mass of iron. Others think it may have traveled through space as a cluster of iron boulders, flying in close formation. Certainly it pushed ahead of itself a mass of white-hot glowing air, a "plasma" several thousand degrees hot, more brilliant than the sun. And when it hit, it *hit*. The hole it made, through layer upon layer of solid rock, was originally more than 1000 feet deep. Some hunks of the iron probably went 1500 feet into the earth. It happened perhaps 20,000 years ago. Since then, the hole has partly filled up with loose rock fallen from the steep walls.

Look at the big hole for a minute and one thing strikes you: Where's all the rock that used to fill this hollow? Where is the alleged huge mass of iron?

When the iron mass hit (at several thousand miles per hour) and was instantly stopped, it just as instantly got hot all through; so hot much of it may have vaporized, the way a high-speed bullet does when it hits armor plate. It turned into an iron *steam,* you might say. It did not merely squash the rocks down or push them aside; it was a bomb, it exploded.

By atom-bomb standards, it was a 5.5-megaton bomb. There was certainly a mushroom cloud. It consisted in part of vaporized iron, and as it cooled off there fell from it an iron rain. Drops of this have been found by dragging magnets over the desert. A glass jar full of it is in one of the museum showcases. It looks like caviar. Hunks of the meteorite iron, some weighing half a ton, have also been found.

And some of the iron did go on into the ground and stay there. That is how the crater came to be private enterprise. In 1902 a mining engineer from Philadelphia, Daniel Moreau Barringer, heard that there was this amazing hole, and that the country around it was strewn with rock and meteorites. At that time, meteor craters were unknown on Earth; any crater was considered volcanic. But Barringer jumped to the correct conclusion that this one at least *was* meteoric. He dug holes just outside the crater and found meteorite chunks of iron containing 7 percent nickel. Convinced, he filed mining claims on the land and spent much of his life and fortune trying to lift its treasure.

Barringer started by sinking shafts from the bottom of the crater. Water and quicksand stopped him. He drilled. The drill found solid rock, but no iron. Up to that time he had assumed that the object had fallen straight down from the sky; "orbiting" was not thought of in those days. But now he reasoned: If the meteorite had come in slantwise, then its iron would be lodged not under the crater but under the rim. In 1919 he had another hole drilled, down from the rim. The drill found meteorite fragments; but at 1376 feet it got stuck in a cluster of

A mass of iron 200 feet in diameter and weighing at least 1 million tons is said to have punched this enormous meteor crater into the desert near Canyon Diablo in northeast Arizona. Some 30 tons of meteoric iron have been unearthed within a six-mile radius of the crater. The largest single piece, with a heat-blackened crust and silvery interior, weighs 1400 pounds and is now displayed in a museum at the crater's north rim.

meteorites and could not be moved. In 1928 he found a company that sank a shaft one half mile south of the crater. It was stopped by underground water. Barringer, deeply depressed, died in 1929.

With what remained of the money his sons had geophysical surveys conducted. They showed something down there that was magnetic, electrically conductive, extra heavy. They drilled two more holes; the drills were blocked by iron too hard to drill, too big to push aside. They had to stop; but they did not give up completely.

There is certainly a mass of iron down there, solid metal, at least 100,000 tons, more likely millions of tons. It is valuable because of its nickel, but so far it has been impossible to mine. Even if a shaft did reach the treasure, the hunks would be difficult to cut up and hoist. The Barringer family now leases the crater as a tourist sight.

More and more people come to see the wonder, because here, plain to the inexperienced eye, is evidence that star-stuff visits us on Earth. As you stand there and gawk, you begin to marvel. What does it mean? To find out, you have to turn to the meteor men. You might call them early spacemen. Long before astronauts and before missiles like the Mariner II began to stick their noses into stardust, these men studied space with the eyes and ears of telescope and radio. Their findings are scattered through the pages of *Scientific American* from 1950 to the present. When you piece together what the learned men have written, you begin to understand meteor impact.

Prof. Fletcher G. Watson of Harvard University

tells us that each day at least a billion meteors strike the Earth's atmosphere. Most of them, he says, are no bigger than a pinhead and burn up in the air. Their material—about five tons a day—is scattered over the planet as dust. Only four or five meteors a day are large enough to pass through the atmosphere and fall on the Earth. Most of them are never found.

Otto Struve, formerly of the Institute of Advanced Study at Princeton, New Jersey, describes the biggest meteor strike so far witnessed by man. It happened in 1947, in Siberia, on a sunny winter morning.

"Hundreds of people got a direct look," he tells us. "Against the blue sky they saw a ball of light as brilliant as the sun and about the size of the full moon. It traveled swiftly toward the south, shedding showers of sparks. Its wake was a bright-colored streak which quickly turned into a thick black trail. Within four or five seconds the object had disappeared. The strange track hung in the sky for many hours; with darkness it glowed like northern lights.

"Distant witnesses saw, rising from the spot where the thing had fallen, a gigantic brownish pillar. The column must have reached a height of 20 miles.

"Investigators found on the rocky slopes of the Sikhote-Alin Mountains more than 100 holes, some of them 20 feet deep, 75 feet across at the top, scattered over an area of one square mile. For miles around the ground was strewn with meteoric iron."

The thing that hit here, Struve explains, was a small asteroid, or minor planet. It must have weighed about 1000 tons and had a diameter of some 30 feet. After it entered the atmosphere, it broke up. Compared to the thing that hit Arizona, it was a pebble.

Now that we know that such things really happen, we begin to see lots of craters. It's like ants—once you've seen one, you see two more. There are now over 50 known and acknowledged meteor craters located in Australia, Arabia, Africa, Europe, Argentina, Siberia and North America.

The real land of craters is eastern Canada. One reason is that the Canadian shield is mostly a granite surface, extremely rigid; even very old craters have not yet been covered over or deformed. Another reason is that the Canadian Air Force has mapped the country; many "fossil" craters show up only in the air view.

Robert S. Dietz, an oceanographer formerly at the Navy Electronics Laboratory located in California, says there must be many more impact sites than we now know. The Moon is covered with meteor craters. The Earth must have taken at least the same bombardment from space. Where are the craters? His answer: Don't look only for craters, because on the

Earth raised rims weather away. The low places fill with sand and mud. The rocks bend and heave.

But one effect lasts: A meteor hit sends a shock wave into the earth, and this does things to rock that nothing else will do. It cracks rock into "shatter cones," shaped like ice-cream cones, in size from a fraction of an inch up to many feet. A shatter cone, when struck with a hammer, breaks up into smaller shatter cones. By way of proof, shatter cones have been produced experimentally by shooting into rocks a "shaped charge"—a front-directed explosive charge in a projectile which makes it capable of piercing armor. Shatter cones now reveal many old meteor hits.

Shatter cones have solved, according to Dietz, the puzzle of the Vredefort Ring in South Africa. This is not a crater. On the contrary, it is a raised dome of granite, 26 miles in diameter. That, in turn, is surrounded by a further circular pattern of rock folds 130 miles in diameter. Most geologists have doubted that this was a meteor hit, because there was neither a crater nor hunks of iron. But Dietz urged a South African geologist to look for shatter cones. Sure enough they were there.

Dietz is convinced that a small asteroid, a mile or so in diameter, plunged deep into the Earth here. It opened a crater 10 miles deep and 26 miles wide. The explosion peeled back rock layers like petals of a flower. If the Barringer thing was a five-megaton bomb, this one was 1,500,000 megatons! The whole world must have wobbled. It was very long ago. Since then, Dietz thinks, the granite deep down has reacted to the removal of all that weight. It has slowly, slowly welled up, filled the crater and bulged into a dome.

John H. Reynolds of the department of physics of the University of California, Berkeley, describes the detective work done on meteorites. Everything about them gets studied: chemistry, atomic structure, metallurgy, flight path, etc. Everything is a clue. *Item*: The nickel-iron shows signs of having cooled and solidified from the molten stage very slowly—this means it must come from within the interior of a fairly large planet. *Item:* The crystalline structure of the metal shows signs of sudden release of pressure. This means that the planet exploded. *Item:* The metal contains small amounts of helium 4. This isotope forms simply by lapse of time, and thus it indicates the time when that planet formed. Scientists have even investigated meteorites—the ones that are rock, not iron—for signs of life. So far, no clear-cut "Yes"; but no clearcut "No," either. A "Maybe."

Reynolds says that the age of the meteorite material is about the same as the age of the Earth. The chemical elements of the rest of the solar system are the same as those of the Earth. It appears that the planets of our solar system all crystallized at about the same time—4.6 billion years ago; and that not very long before that the chemical elements themselves formed "from primordial matter."

It's scientifically stated and rather big-scale on the time-and-distance factor, but it still sounds not very different from Genesis.

SPACE FLIGHT AND THE SPIRIT OF MAN

Arthur C. Clarke

In his book, *A Study of History*, Arnold Toynbee emphasizes "challenge and response" as the force shaping the rise and fall of civilizations. It seems to me that the opening of the space age presents a classic example of challenge and response.

My mind is inevitably drawn to the great voyages of discovery of the 15th and 16th centuries. These voyages liberated men's minds from the long trance of the Middle Ages and fueled the fires of the Renaissance. Perhaps something similar will happen with space flight. As Sir James Frazer wrote: "Intellectual progress, which reveals itself in the growth of art and science, receives an immense impetus from conquest and empire." Interplanetary travel is now the only form of "conquest and empire" compatible with civilization. Without it, the human mind, compelled to circle forever in its planetary goldfish bowl, must eventually stagnate.

Though the world is now undeniably space-conscious to an extent that would have seemed unbelievable only a few years ago, it is not yet space-*minded*. And, unfortunately, altogether too many educators, intellectuals and other molders of public opinion still regard space as a terrifying vacuum instead of a frontier with infinite possibilities.

The possible advantages of space can be best appreciated if we turn our backs upon it and return, in imagination, to the sea. Here is the perfect environment for life—the place where it originally evolved. In the sea, an all-pervading fluid medium carries oxygen and food directly to each organism. The same medium neutralizes gravity, ensures against temper-

A two-stage Saturn I blasts off on an exploratory space flight. Unmanned Apollo satellites and Pegasus meteoroid detection satellites have been orbited by this rocket, whose successor, Saturn V, is designed to carry America's Apollo space team to the Moon.

On June 3, 1965, Maj. Edward White climbed out of a satellite orbiting 100 miles above the Earth and became the first American to walk in space. A Soviet cosmonaut, Alexei Leonov, had stepped into space less than three months earlier. However, unlike White, who carried a compressed-air guidance gun, Leonov was not self-propelled.

ature extremes and prevents damage by too-intense solar radiation, which must have been lethal at the Earth's surface before the ozone layer was formed.

It seems incredible that life ever left the sea, for in some ways the dry land is almost as dangerous as space. Because we are accustomed to it, we forget the price we have had to pay in our daily battle against gravity. We seldom stop to think that we are still creatures of the sea, able to leave it only because we wear the water-filled space suits of our skins.

Yet until life invaded and conquered the land, it was trapped in an evolutionary cul-de-sac. The relative opacity of water and its resistance to movement were perhaps the chief factors limiting the progress of marine creatures. They had little incentive to develop keen vision or manual dexterity. The road to further development in the sea is also blocked by another impassable barrier. The difference between man and animals lies basically in the possession of fire. A marine culture could never escape from the Stone Age and discover the use of metals.

Perhaps we would have been happier had we re-

mained in the sea, but no philosopher has ever suggested that we took the wrong road. The world beneath the waves is beautiful but hopelessly limited. No fish can see the stars; we will never be content until we have reached them.

It cannot be *proved,* of course, that expansion into space will produce a quantum jump in our development as great as that which took place when our ancestors left the sea. We cannot predict the new forces, powers and discoveries that will be disclosed to us when we reach the other planets or can set up laboratories in space. They are as much beyond our vision today as fire or electricity would be beyond the imagination of a fish. Yet no one can doubt that the increasing flow of knowledge and sense impressions and the wholly new types of experience and emotion that will result from space travel will have a profoundly stimulating effect upon the human psyche.

Alarm has been expressed at the danger of "sensory deprivation" in space. Astronauts on long journeys, it has been suggested, will suffer the symptoms that afflict men who are cut off from their environment by being shut up in totally dark, soundproof rooms.

I would reverse this argument: Our entire culture will suffer from sensory deprivation if we do *not* go out into space. There is striking evidence for this. As soon as we were able to rise above the atmosphere, a new and surprising universe was opened up, far richer and more complex than had ever been suspected from ground observations.

But the facts of science, priceless though they are, tell only part of the story. Across the seas of space lie the new raw materials of the imagination, without which all forms of art must eventually sicken and die. Strangeness, wonder, mystery, adventure, magic —these things, which not long ago seemed lost forever, will soon return to the world. And with them, perhaps, will come again an age of sagas and epics such as Homer never knew.

Though we may welcome this, we may not enjoy it, for it is never easy to live in an age of transition. We must prepare ourselves for painful shocks that will involve our philosophical and religious beliefs. We take it for granted now that our planet is a tiny world in a remote corner of an infinite universe and have forgotten how this discovery shattered the calm certainties of medieval faith. Space will present us with facts that are even more disconcerting.

There can be little reasonable doubt that we shall ultimately come into contact with races more intelligent than our own. That contact may be the most devastating event in the history of mankind. The rash assertion that "God made Man in His own image" is ticking like a time bomb at the foundations of many faiths.

Many will find these thoughts unpalatable; the truth may be yet harder. Perhaps if we knew all that lay ahead of us on the road to space—a hundred or a thousand or a million years in the future—no man alive would have the courage to take the first step. But that first step has already been taken.

The eyes of all the ages are upon us now, as we create the myths of the future at Cape Kennedy and Kapustin Yar. No other generation has been given such powers and such responsibilities. The impartial agents of our destiny stand on their launching pads, awaiting our commands. They can take us to that greater Renaissance or they can make us one with the dinosaurs.

The choice is ours, it must be made soon, and it is irrevocable. If our wisdom fails to match our science, we will have no second chance. For there will be none to carry our dreams across another dark age, when the dust of all our cities incarnadines the sunsets of the world.

THE VIOLENT SUN

Herbert Friedman

At 2:37 p.m. on November 12, 1960, astronomers detected a brilliant explosion on the face of the Sun. Six hours later, a gigantic cloud of solar hydrogen gas, ten million miles across and still trailing halfway back to the Sun, 93 million miles away, collided with Earth at a speed of 4000 miles a second.

Though inaudible and invisible, the collision started a violent chain of disturbances on and around the Earth, an electric and magnetic storm of mammoth proportions. Compass needles wavered erratically. For hours all long-distance radio communications were blacked out. Teletypes printed gibberish. Overhead, sheets of flaming-red northern lights flashed in the night sky, bright enough to be seen through overcast and clouds. Electric lights flickered in farmhouses as if a thunderstorm raged, yet the air and sky were clear and silent.

For more than a week, such chaotic conditions continued. They were clearly the results of our Sun on the rampage. Yet let me assure you that such a storm amounts to no more than a tiny ripple in the usual steady flow of solar energy.

The Sun's power staggers the imagination. In one *second*, this star of ours (the Sun is, after all, just one of an estimated 100 *billion* stars in the Milky Way) radiates more energy than man has used since the beginning of civilization! The Sun delivers to us in a few days as much heat and light as would be produced by burning the Earth's entire oil and coal reserves and all the wood of its forests. Yet Earth receives only one half of one billionth of the Sun's radiant energy!

What makes the Sun shine so brilliantly? The answer now accepted as correct: atomic energy. The nuclei, or cores, of hydrogen atoms collide and unite —to form helium nuclei. As the union is accomplished, bursts of energy are given off.

Until very recently, man's study of the Sun was seriously hampered by the Earth's murky, shimmering atmosphere, which distorts light beams and blots out the Sun's X rays and much of its ultraviolet and infrared radiation. But in 1945 rockets became available to carry telescopes and spectrographs above the atmosphere. Now satellites point instruments steadily at the Sun. Huge radar transmitters bounce beams off the swollen outer atmosphere of the Sun and probe its structure and movement. Meanwhile, with the op-

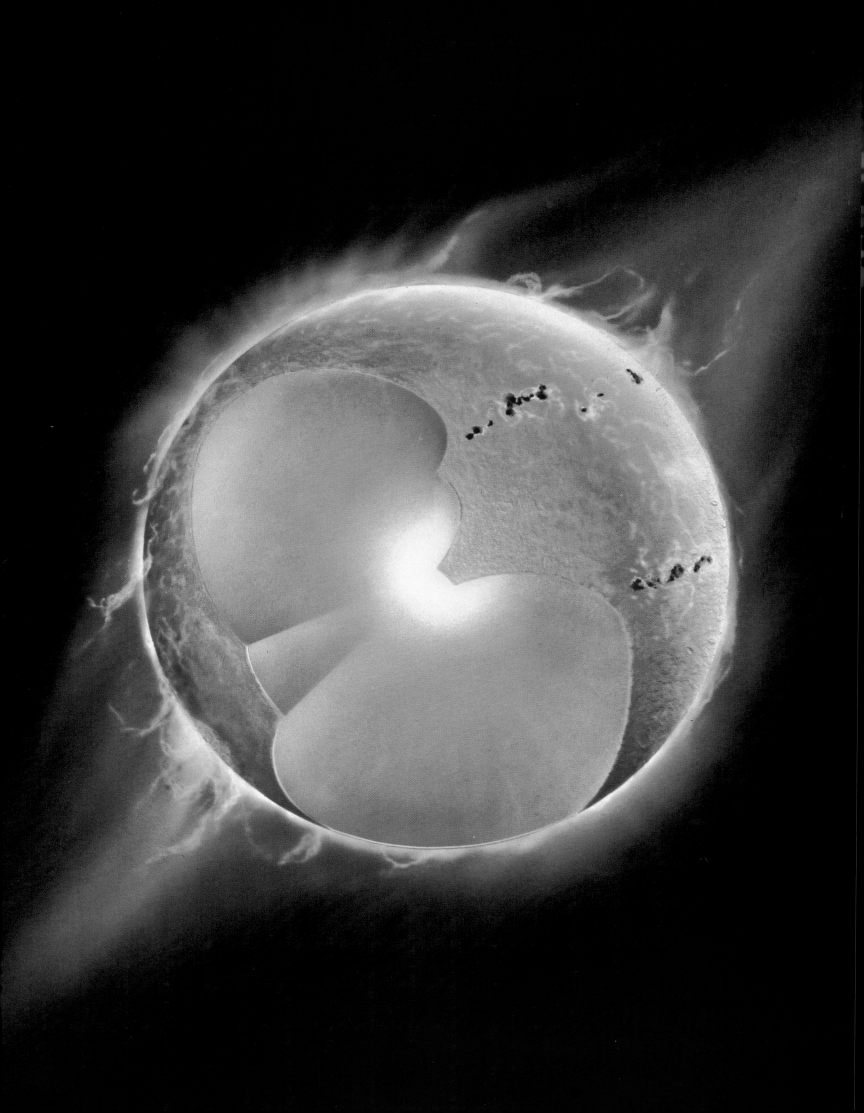

tical spectroscope, we can analyze light arriving from 93 million miles away and tell what the Sun is made of just as accurately as if we had a sample.

Using triangulation with other celestial objects, astronomers have gauged the size of the Sun very accurately. Its diameter of 864,000 miles compares with Earth's 7197. It could hold 1,300,000 earths!

The spectrum shows that the Sun consists principally of hydrogen. Hydrogen atoms are roughly ten times as abundant there as helium, the next most abundant element, and 1000 times as abundant as carbon, nitrogen or oxygen, which are so common on Earth. Except for the overabundance of hydrogen and helium, the chemical composition of the solar atmosphere is much the same as that of Earth's crust.

Although the density at the center of the Sun must be about 11.4 times that of lead, the Sun remains gaseous everywhere. That is, the atoms are free to move about, unlike those in a solid, which are fixed in a regular pattern. Spots on the Sun show us that it rotates from east to west, and in a very peculiar way: Different parts spin at various speeds. A spot close to the equator, for example, completes a rotation in 25 days; the polar zone may take 34 days. Most of the changing features observed on the surface of the Sun must be related to this contortion.

When astronomers examine the Sun with a solar telescope, its edge appears sharp, as if it marked a definite surface. This apparent surface is in fact a transparent, though highly luminous, layer of gas about 200 miles thick, called the photosphere. From it comes most of the light we get. Outside the photosphere lie two other layers—a region of flamelike outbursts of gas, called the chromosphere, and an almost endless outer atmosphere called the corona. All that we know of the Sun's interior is deduced from observation of these three external layers.

We have good reason to believe that at the Sun's center, close to half a million miles deep, pressure reaches 100 billion atmospheres. To produce such pressure, we know that gas must be heated to about 16,000,000° C. Sir James Jeans, in *The Universe Around Us*, calculates that a pinhead of material at the temperature of the Sun's core would emit heat to kill a man 100 miles away.

In this nuclear furnace most of the fantastically hot, dense gas is invisible, since nearly all its radiation

This cutaway view of the Sun reveals several interior layers surrounding a superhot core. Covering the interior is the visible surface, or photosphere; outside it are the transparent chromosphere, with its flamelike "spicules," and the flaring corona. The red specks are sunspots.

is X rays produced by nuclear reactions and the collisions of fast-racing nuclei and electrons. The path of an X ray as it escapes from the core resembles the zigzagging track of the steel ball in a pinball machine. Even though the rays travel at the speed of light—186,300 miles per second—the devious trip to the Sun's surface takes about 20,000 years. During that period the X rays gradually change. Each time one is deflected, the frequency of its vibration is reduced slightly and its wavelength is increased. In time, the X rays turn into ultraviolet and visible light.

Most of what we know of the Sun's outer atmosphere comes from studies of solar eclipses. During an eclipse in 1842, astronomers noted the very faint outer atmosphere of the Sun. As the Moon blocked out the brilliant disk, a pearly-white corona with delicate streams and curved arches stood revealed. Close to the black edge of the Moon, a reddish ring encircled the Sun, suggesting the name "chromosphere."

The spectrum of the chromosphere and corona reveals a very interesting paradox. The core temperature of 16,000,000° C. drops steadily to about 5700° at the Sun's surface. But in the solar *atmosphere* the temperature begins to rise again, eventually climbing to several million degrees.

Pictures of the rim show thousands of tongues of gas, called "spicules," springing fountainlike above the Sun's surface. They surge up and fall back in five to ten minutes, rising as high as 6000 miles. At any instant as many as 100,000 spicules may be in action. Also, huge streamers of bright gas, called "prominences," often loop as high as 100,000 miles into the corona, then dip back to the photosphere.

But these dramatic activities of a quiet Sun pale into insignificance beside the explosive phenomenon known as a solar flare. A large flare can erupt in an hour's time with the force of a billion hydrogen bombs. It was such a flare that disrupted earthly communications in November 1960.

Nevertheless, the Sun is a very ordinary star—a yellow dwarf, midway between the largest and the smallest, and between the hottest blue stars and the coolest red stars. To Earth-based observers, it is brighter than any other star, though Rigel, for example, is 15,000 times more luminous. And 36 million suns could be fitted into Antares, a red super-giant!

In time, the Sun's core will deplete its hydrogen: Some theoretical calculations indicate that the proportion has decreased from two thirds to one third in the past five billion years. With the core spent, the thermonuclear reactions will spread to outer portions where unused hydrogen still exists. As the reaction zone moves closer to the surface of the Sun, the tremendous nuclear heat at its core will also move outward, forcing the Sun to expand. The Sun will then become a giant red star like Antares. It will blow up to a monstrous ball of extremely rarefied, red-hot gas large enough to engulf the four nearest planets—Mercury, Venus, the Earth and Mars.

When will the Sun reach this stage? We have no cause for immediate concern—it may take another five billion years!

Finally, when all its hydrogen has been converted to helium, the Sun will cool and shrink, ultimately becoming a white dwarf, no bigger than the Earth but weighing several tons per cubic inch.

Meanwhile, the Sun is our bridge to the stars. It is the only star whose surface and atmosphere we can study in fine detail. With our magnificent new tools to observe the Sun, the coming years should bring a revolution in our understanding of Earth's bright and mighty companion in the heavens—and the myriad stars beyond.

THE FIRST U.S. "SOFT" LANDING ON THE MOON

Lee A. DuBridge

At 17 minutes and 36 seconds after 2 a.m. E.D.T. on June 2, 1966, an ungainly-looking object, over ten feet tall, landed gently on the surface of the Moon and proceeded to write a brilliant new chapter in space-age history. The object was Surveyor I, built and launched under the auspices of the National Aeronautics and Space Administration with the Caltech Jet Propulsion Laboratory (JPL) as project manager.

Within moments of its textbook-perfect landing, Surveyor I reported that it was undamaged, that the landing was a soft one, and that the solar cells, batteries, radio, camera and television transmitter were ready to go to work. A radio command beamed to the Moon by a huge antenna at Goldstone Lake in the Mojave Desert started the first picture-taking sequence. During the next 12 days, a total of 10,338 pictures of breathtaking clarity were received.

Then darkness descended on the landing site and Surveyor I settled down to endure the frigid temperatures of the long Moon night. The Moon's surface had been very hot (250° F.) during the day. But 52 hours after the sun set, the temperature of the spacecraft's exposed solar panel had dropped to −293°. The shielded battery compartment—in which heat was being generated—dropped to 0°. Then the

transmitter was shut off, for without solar power the battery voltage was dropping rapidly.

Miraculously, two weeks later, when the Sun rose again, it was found that the batteries, though weak, could still be partially charged by solar power. In the 14-day period before another Moon night descended, 812 more pictures were transmitted. Finally, its job well done, Surveyor was put to rest. But it was still not quite dead: 86 days later, in October, it responded again to commands and sent signals to Earth. It was heard from again in November and then for the last time in January 1967.

Surveyor's brilliant success was all the sweeter because the project had traveled a rough road since it was initiated in 1960. Its booster vehicle, the hydrogen-fueled Atlas Centaur, had been delayed by extraordinary technical problems. Surveyor had to be redesigned lighter—and redesigned again. The final weight of the spacecraft itself at takeoff was 2194 pounds, which included the elaborate stabilizing equipment required for a soft landing. The cost of the spacecraft alone was about $10 million, though over $250 million was spent developing it.

No one had expected perfect performance on the first trial. It was to be a long journey; there were hundreds of electronic components that could fail; if the spacecraft landed too hard, or if it did not come in quite vertically, it could be damaged or destroyed; the hot, airless surface of the Moon was a hostile environment; no similar space venture had ever been tried. Several Ranger vehicles had crash-landed on the Moon, as had Lunik IX, which was so constructed that the camera survived and took a few pictures. But Surveyor, designed to receive and execute 197 types of radio commands (as compared to Ranger's 12), was of a new order of complexity.

However, the launching from Cape Kennedy, at 10:41 a.m. May 30, was flawless. The Centaur performed perfectly, hurling Surveyor I into an excellent course that would have brought it to within 250 miles of the target point on the Moon's Sea of Storms. But that was not good enough. Sixteen hours after launch, a mid-course correction maneuver brought the actual landing point to within seven miles of the target. This—after a journey of some 240,000 miles in 63½ hours—can be compared to hitting the eye of a flying duck with a rifle from a moving and rotating platform at a range of 150 yards!

The guidance maneuver involved swinging the spacecraft around to bring the retro-rockets into position, firing them for a predetermined number of seconds, and then reorienting the craft into its "cruise mode." (On September 21, 1966, while Surveyor II was

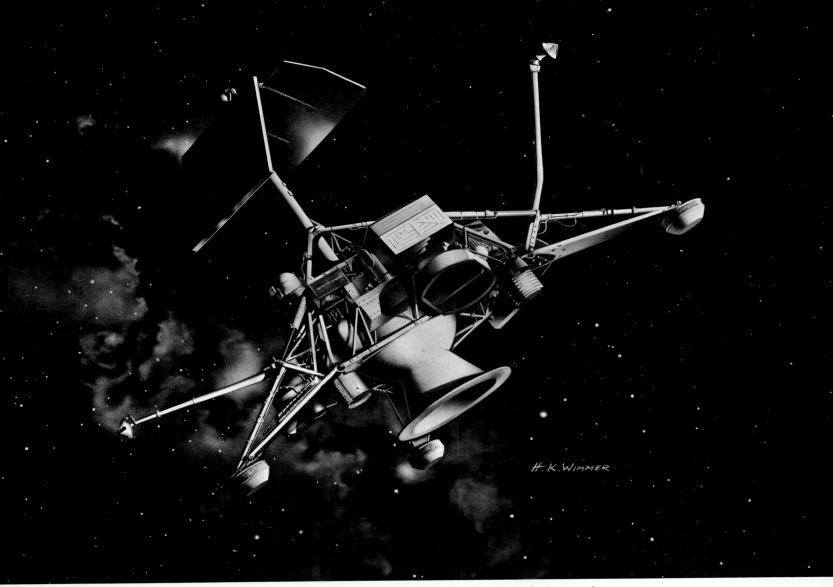

Outlandish in appearance but efficient in operation, Surveyor I transmitted more than 11,000 pictures of the rubble-strewn lunar landscape back to Earth. Surveyor's main retro-rocket, fired through the funnel-shaped structure at the bottom of the craft, slowed its descent enough so it could land intact on the Moon's surface.

making a similar maneuver, one of its three vernier rockets malfunctioned. The craft began to tumble and went out of control. It crashed onto the surface of the Moon September 22.) During the flight it was kept oriented toward the Sun to receive maximum power for the solar cells. The bright star Canopus in the southern sky had been chosen as a second guide point to prevent Surveyor from spinning or rolling. A photocell had to find this star, identify it and then "freeze" on it—firing tiny gas jets automatically to control the roll position. All of this was achieved.

The most complex and most critical portion of the flight was the soft-landing sequence—the first in history. As Surveyor I approached the Moon, 30 minutes before touchdown, it was rotated into position to point its radars and its retro-rockets along the line of flight. At about 60 miles from the lunar surface, an altitude-marking radar, mounted in the rocket nozzle, triggered the main solid-fuel retro-rocket.

At this point the crew at the JPL control center in Pasadena could only sit back and listen tensely as a

Photographs transmitted back to Earth several hours before the Moon's sunset show the shadow Surveyor I cast on the lunar surface. Here and on the next page, photographs of small areas were pieced together by NASA scientists to form photo-mosaics of larger areas.

programmed sequence took place and was reported back. No longer, during this operation, could new commands be sent: Time was too short for intervention by human beings 240,000 miles away. At that distance a radio signal would take $1^1/_3$ seconds to reach the spacecraft, an equal time for the reply to return—and in those $2^2/_3$ seconds the craft would travel more than 40 miles!

But at exactly the right distance from the Moon ($46^3/_4$ miles) the retro-rocket ignited and the spacecraft, traveling at nearly 6000 m.p.h., began to slow down. The voice of Surveyor Control, in the person of Dr. Albert Hibbs, announced calmly, "Speed now 4900 miles per hour . . . 3000 miles per hour . . . 1000 miles per hour. . . ." Then, 39 seconds after ignition, the retro-rocket burned out and was jettisoned.

Surveyor was now traveling at 267 m.p.h. A second,

"Doppler" radar system took control, with four beams measuring speed, distance and orientation of the craft relative to the Moon's surface. The designers had to take a chance it was the *top* surface of the Moon that would be the radar reflector—not a hard layer buried beneath a few feet of nonreflecting dust. The gamble paid off.

The Doppler radar fired Surveyor's vernier rockets at an altitude of 25,000 feet above the Moon, then delicately throttled them as necessary to slow the craft further and keep it on a vertical path. The speed began to drop again—"200 miles an hour, 100 miles an hour. . . ." And then, faster than Al Hibbs could announce it, it came down to about three m.p.h. at 12 *feet* above the surface. The vernier rockets were turned off to prevent stirring up a cloud of dust that might coat the camera lens and other sen-

Low, rounded hills similar in shape to many in the eastern United States form the horizon northeast of Surveyor VII's landing site. In the foreground, some 18 feet from the camera, is a rock-filled crater about 5 feet wide. Toward the upper left, almost 400 yards from the camera, is a rock about 20 feet across. Opposite the rock, in the left-hand corner (2100 feet away), is a crater approximately 200 feet in diameter.

sitive components. After this last 12 feet of free fall, Surveyor landed on the Moon—a perfect three-point vertical landing, more gentle than most parachutists hitting the Earth. Like a car hitting a bump, it bounced up 2½ inches off the surface, settled down, oscillated gently five or six times—and then was still.

"Touchdown!" An enthusiastic cheer went up from hundreds of onlookers at JPL. Visiting NASA officials and Congressmen rushed up to congratulate Dr. William Pickering, laboratory director.

Now the engineers were again in charge. They made preliminary tests, then pointed the camera at Surveyor's own feet. When the first picture came on the screen, there was another loud cheer. The picture revealed that the craft's landing pads were intact, resting firmly on top of the lunar soil in a shallow (one-inch) depression caused by the landing impact.

More superb-quality pictures followed, showing other parts of the spacecraft and portions of the nearby lunar surface. As fast as prints could be run off, we pored over these first close-up, high-resolution pictures of the lunar surface. "It looks just like ordinary *dirt*," the scientists exclaimed.

And so it did. You could find the same sort of stuff in the rock-stewn vacant lot next door—fine dirt, coarse gravel, rocks of all sizes. A desertlike stretch of lunar "rubble" extended to the horizon, a mile or more away. A row of large rocks appeared a few hundred yards distant. Scores of small craters pockmarked the otherwise flat surface. And over the northern horizon a range of low hills was spotted.

And how hard was the surface?

As each foot-pad hit, it splashed out a little dirt —as though you kicked your toe in the soil in your garden. But the landing pads did not sink in; they were fully visible. The weight resting on each pad was about 33 pounds—100 pounds in all. (Surveyor weighed some 600 pounds Earth-weight as it rested on the Moon without the main retro-rocket.) So a man *could* walk on the Moon! He would not sink into dust up to his knees—or to his neck. One of the great unknowns was at last answered.

What kind of camera was it that sent back these extraordinary pictures? Some of them show tiny grains of dirt only 1/50 of an inch in diameter. Others show fine details of the structure of nearby rocks. Assembled into a mosaic they reveal a striking panorama of the lunar scene.

At first sight the camera was nothing spectacular. It had a zoom lens that could focus on either nearby or distant objects. It could take narrow- or wide-angle photos. Exposure time could be varied from about 1/6 second to infinity (time exposure). All

of these could be adjusted at will by commands from Pasadena. The image was focused on a vidicon tube, and 600-line pictures (a standard TV picture has 550 lines) were transmitted back to Earth at the rate of one picture in 3.6 seconds.

The camera axis was nearly vertical, shooting up into a mirror that could be tilted up and down or rotated through 360 degrees. Three color filters enabled the camera to take separate black and white negatives that were reconstructed in the laboratory to make color prints. The entire visible lunar surface, it turns out, is a neutral gray color.

The camera was the only "scientific instrument" that Surveyor I could carry (within its weight limit) and many scientists bemoaned this fact. But later Surveyors have carried other instruments—this was an engineering test flight. And it was a brilliant achievement. A great number of questions were successfully answered, and the road to even more complex lunar missions—including a manned landing —was opened.

SO YOU'RE GOING TO MARS?

Arthur C. Clarke

So you're going to Mars? That's still quite an adventure—though I suppose that in another ten years no one will think twice about it. It's hard to remember that the first ships reached Mars only half a century ago, and that our colony on the planet is less than 30 years old.

I suppose you've read all the tourist literature from the Department of Extraterrestrial Affairs. But there's a lot you won't learn just by reading, so here are some pointers. I won't say my information is right up-to-date—things change so rapidly, and it's a year since I got back from Mars myself—but on the whole you'll find it reliable.

The cost of your passage varies considerably according to the relative position of Mars and Earth, and, oddly enough, the shortest trips are the most expensive, since they involve the greatest changes of speed as you hop from one orbit to the other. In space, speed, not distance, is what costs money. The cheapest round trip comes to about $30,000, and most of your fellow passengers will be engineers, scientists or administrators with a job to do on Mars.

I take it you passed the medical examination. The physical strain involved in space flight is negligible, but you'll be spending at least two months on the trip, and it would be a pity if your teeth or appendix started to misbehave.

You're probably wondering how you can possibly manage on your weight allowance. It can be done. Don't take any suits. Inside a spaceship there's no weather: All you'll want is an ultra-lightweight tropical kit. When you get to Mars, you'll buy what you need there, and dump it when you leave. Take a camera by all means. There's a chance of some unforgettable shots as you leave Earth and when you approach Mars. You can sell a good camera on Mars for five times its price here, and save yourself the cost of freighting it home.

The ferry rocket will probably leave from the New Guinea field, two miles above sea level on top of the Orange Range. Why there? It's on the equator, so a ship gets the full 1000-mile-an-hour boost of the Earth's spin as it takes off, and there's the whole width of the Pacific for jettisoned fuel tanks to fall into. And if you've ever *heard* a spaceship taking off, you'll understand why the launching sites have to be a few hundred miles from civilization.

There's really nothing to the blast-off, as long as you're in good health. You just lie down on the acceleration couch, put in your earplugs and relax. About a minute will pass before you'll feel the full strain of the opposition between the Earth's gravitational pull and the rocket's thrust. You *will* notice the noise immediately. Still, it only lasts five minutes; then you'll be up in orbit and the motors will cut out.

There are no viewing ports on the ferry rockets. It takes about 30 minutes to reach the satellite space station, make the necessary steering corrections and match its speed. You'll know when that happens from the rather alarming *clang* as the air locks make contact. Then you can undo your safety belt and see what it's like being weightless. But hang on to the guide rope while passing through the air lock, and don't try to go flying around like a bird—you may injure yourself.

At Space Station One, which is where the ferries and the liners meet to transfer their cargoes, you'll spend all your time in the observation lounge; everyone does, no matter how many times he has been out in space. I won't attempt to describe that incredible view. In the 120 minutes the station takes to complete its orbit, you'll see the Earth wax from a thin crescent to a gigantic multicolored disk, then shrink again to a black shield eclipsing the stars. As you pass over the night side, you'll see the lights of cities, like patches of phosphorescence. And the stars! You'll realize that you've never really seen them before.

You'll go aboard the liner when you've had your final medical check, and the steward will show you to the tiny, shelf-size cabin where you'll sleep for the next few months. If you're on one of the larger liners, there'll be about 100 passengers and a crew of 20—a self-contained community floating in vacuum millions of miles from anywhere, kept alive in a bubble of plastic and metal.

It won't take you long to get used to the ship's gadgets. Handling liquids is the main skill to acquire. Oddly enough, taking a shower is quite simple; you do it in a sort of plastic cocoon, and a circulating air current carries the water out at the bottom. At first the absence of gravity may make sleeping difficult— you'll miss your accustomed weight. But the bunk covers have spring tensioning to prevent you from drifting out.

The breakaway of the liner from its satellite orbit is gentle. The ship will uncouple from the space station and drift a few miles away. When the atomic drive goes on you'll notice only the faintest of vibrations, and the liner's acceleration will be very gradual. But after a week it will have built up a colossal speed. Then the motors are cut and you carry on under momentum. You'll seem to be hanging motionless— no more aware of your speed than you are of the Earth's moving at 66,000 miles an hour around the Sun right now.

During your weeks in space there will be radio and TV contact with Earth and Mars, so you'll be able to keep in touch with things—if, in fact, you want to. The ship will have a good library of microbooks. On my first trip, I spent a lot of time learning my way around the stars and looking at clusters and nebulae through a small telescope. Having the stars all around you is an experience you'll never forget.

One of the big moments comes when you realize that Mars has begun to show a visible disk. The first feature you'll be able to see with the naked eye will be one of the polar caps, glittering like a tiny star on the edge of the planet. A few days later the dark areas—the so-called seas—will begin to appear and, in the week before landing, you'll get to know the planet's geography pretty well.

After the short braking period you'll drop down on Phobos, Mars' inner moon, which acts as a natural space station about 4000 miles above the planet's surface. When the ship has settled down into the landing cradle, the air lock will be coupled up and you'll go through a connecting tube into the port. Then you go inside the centrifuge—a little cabin on a rotating arm—and it will spin you up to half a gravity, or rather more than the weight Mars will give you. This is so you can practice using your legs again.

Here is an artist's view of the Martian landscape as it might look to a man standing at the rim of a large crater. Prominent details—the low hills, the intense blue of the sky and the gentle slope of the crater—are based on data obtained from telescopic photographs and photos transmitted by the spacecraft Mariner IV, which passed within 5700 miles of the planet. Dust storms like the one blowing up on the left are believed to be common on Mars.

There are two ferry rockets in service from Phobos to Mars, each carrying 20 passengers. The descent takes about three hours. The ferries enter the atmosphere at over 5000 miles an hour, and go halfway around Mars before they lose enough speed to land like ordinary aircraft. You'll land at Port Lowell, the largest settlement. The population is more than 20,000 now, I believe. Port Lowell has practically everything you find in a city on Earth. From the air, the inflated plastic domes look like a cluster of bubbles, a very pretty sight when the sun catches them.

The port, like all the major settlements, lies in the dark belt of vegetation that roughly follows the equator and occupies about half the southern hemisphere. The northern hemisphere is almost all desert—the red oxides that give the planet its ruddy color. Some of these desert regions are beautiful; they're far older than anything on the surface of our Earth, because there's been little weathering on Mars to wear down the rocks, at least since the seas dried up, more than 500 million years ago.

Outside the domes, the natural Martian atmosphere is much less dense than that at the top of Mt. Everest, and it contains practically no oxygen. So when you go out you'll have to wear a helmet, or travel in one of those pressurized jeeps they call "sand fleas." Thanks to the low gravity, enough oxygen for 12 hours' normal working can be carried quite easily. Don't attempt to imitate any of the second-generation colonists you may see walking around without oxygen gear. They can't breathe the Martian atmosphere any more than you can, but like the old-time native pearl divers they can make one lungful last for several minutes.

The other great obstacle to life on Mars is the low temperature. The highest ever recorded was in the 80's, but that's exceptional. In the long winters and during the night in summer *or* winter, it never rises above freezing. I believe the record low is −190° ! For the sort of excursions you'll be doing, there is a simple, light thermosuit that traps body heat.

The two methods of transport outside the cities are sand fleas for short ranges (with a full charge of power cells, they're good for a couple of thousand miles) and aircraft for longer distances. Although Mars seems small compared with the Earth, its land area is almost as great because so much of our planet is covered with oceans. Vast regions of Mars have never been properly explored, particularly around the poles. Those stubborn people who still believe that there was once an indigenous Martian civilization pin their hopes on these great blanks. Every so often you hear rumors of some wonderful archeological find in the wastelands—but nothing ever comes of it.

Martians or no, you'll be fascinated by the plant life, and by the queer animals that manage to live without oxygen, migrating each year from hemisphere to hemisphere, across the ancient seabeds, to avoid the ferocious winter. The fight for survival on Mars has been fierce, and evolution has produced some pretty odd results. Don't go investigating any Martian life forms unless you have a guide, or you may get some unpleasant surprises.

Well, that's all I've got to say, except to wish you a pleasant trip. Oh, there *is* one other thing. My boy collects stamps, and I rather let him down when I was on Mars. So, if you could drop me a few letters while you're there, I'd be much obliged!

Beyond Our Solar System

The myriad stars in the Milky Way and in the billions of other galaxies will be perhaps forever beyond our physical reach. But with optical instruments and radio telescopes we can study the messages they send us, and astronomers are now formulating tentative answers to some of man's age-old questions about the cosmos.

OUT OF THIS WORLD

Wayne Amos

I've found a new way to get out of this world. All I have to do is go out in my backyard, peek into a black tube, and suddenly I am out in space, exploring the rings of Saturn, following four diamond-like moons around Jupiter or tracing the mountains and "seas" of our own Moon.

And I'm not alone. Amateur astronomy is a new craze that's growing like Jack's beanstalk, whetted by all the talk about space travel. Secretaries of amateur astronomy clubs estimate there are now at least 100,000 amateurs poking telescopes into the skies. My telescope cost only $29.75. It works on the same principle as the world's largest reflecting telescope on Mt. Palomar.

All the amateur astronomers I have talked with say that their new awareness of the vastness of the universe and of the astonishing beauty of the heavenly bodies has made them more humble, more tolerant—and happier. They confess to a healthy loss of vanity and a more comfortable feeling toward the world. An astronomer at the Hayden Planetarium in New York told me that he doesn't know of any atheists among professional astronomers—they are all forced to believe in an infinite power.

I know what they mean. These adventures into space are incredibly moving. One evening recently an old friend came over just as I was about to go out in the yard, and I dragged him along. The Moon was a silver shaving—perfect for observing through a telescope. When it is full it is too bright. In crescent, when the Sun lights it from the side, the details come out sharply.

As I focused my telescope, the Moon's craters and mountains came out in bold relief. Again I thrilled to see the tremendous ball hanging in space, with no means of support except its centrifugal force outward balanced by the pull of gravity from the Earth. It seems to be standing still, but actually it is whirling around the Earth at the rate of 2304 miles an hour.

When I turned the view over to my guest, he gasped and said, "I can almost reach out and touch it!"

This was exactly the way I felt the first time I saw the Moon in a telescope. It changes suddenly from a lovely two-dimensional light to what it really is—a three-dimensional sphere. You feel you can almost hold it in your hands.

My favorite planet is Jupiter, a glowing pearl with six or seven dark stripes around it. Near it—where you see nothing but dark sky with the naked eye—are usually four of Jupiter's 12 moons, all looking like little diamonds. They go around Jupiter at different speeds. The fastest makes it in two days, the slowest in 17. When we first looked we could see only three moons, but when we turned back to it an hour later a fourth had appeared from behind the planet.

Stars are glowing suns that give out a light of their own. They are inconceivably far away. If you think of our Sun as the size of a dot over a letter "i," the next nearest sun is the dot over another letter "i" ten miles away. The planets are much closer—right in the backyard by comparison. Like the Earth, they move around our Sun; they do not glow like the stars but reflect the light from the Sun.

When you really get to know stars you can become a member of a nationwide team of amateurs who are actively helping the professional astronomers. Amateurs send in reports about meteors, the Moon, the northern lights, and about stars that vary in brightness. Thousands of stars grow bright, then dim, then bright again, in periods of time varying from a few hours to several months. Scientists still don't know exactly why.

There's always the chance, too, that an amateur may make an important discovery. In Delphos, Ohio, Leslie Peltier discovered seven comets, and several have been named after him. Nearly all of the newly

The great spiral galaxy in the constellation of Andromeda is some 2 million light-years away. As one of the nearest and brightest of our galactic neighbors, it is easily seen by amateur astronomers with small telescopes. The galaxy is a nearly circular disk, but its inclination gives it an oval appearance when viewed from Earth.

discovered stars have been found by amateurs, for the reason that they sweep the skies, while professionals concentrate on particular points.

Clyde Tombaugh, the discoverer of the planet Pluto, began as an amateur in Kansas. Russel Porter of Springfield, Vermont, an amateur astronomer and telescope maker, became so proficient that he was called in as a consultant during the grinding and polishing of the 200-inch telescope on Mt. Palomar.

One of the fascinating things in the sky and one that frightens me a little, too, is the faint glow in the constellation of Andromeda. In the glass it leaps out as a luminous glow that seems to come from behind the farthest stars. It is actually the glow from another galaxy—one with millions of stars like our own Milky Way system—and it is about two million light-years away from us.

But the really staggering thing is that professional astronomers say the universe probably contains billions of such galaxies.

DOES THE STAR OF BETHLEHEM STILL SHINE?

Arthur C. Clarke

What was the Star of Nativity that blazed from the Milky Way with awesome brilliance and guided the Wise Men to Bethlehem—assuming that it was a natural phenomenon and not a miraculous apparition? The Bible gives us few clues; all we can do is consider some possibilities.

One early theory suggests that Venus was this Star, and at least one massive book has been written to prove it. Every 19 months our sister planet appears in the morning sky, rising shortly before the Sun: one of the most beautiful sights in all the heavens, a blazing beacon, many times brighter than Sirius, the most brilliant of our nighttime stars.

But to all the peoples of the Eastern world, Venus has always been one of the most familiar objects in the sky; even today she serves as a kind of alarm clock to Arab nomads, a warning to start moving before the Sun begins to blast the desert with its heat. To the Magi, who knew the movements of the planets, there could have been nothing remarkable about Venus.

Four other planets are easily visible to the naked eye, and two may sometimes appear to pass very close to one another. Such occurrences are called conjunctions. On October 4, 1953, for example, Mars and Venus appeared to be fused into a single bright star.

Such a spectacle is rare enough to be striking, and the great 16th-century astronomer, Johannes Kepler, devoted much time to proving that the Star of Bethlehem was a conjunction of Jupiter and Saturn. More correct astronomical calculations since then, however, have shown that this conjunction was not a very close one. Furthermore, the Biblical account indicates that the Star was visible for several weeks; the conjunction of two planets lasts only hours.

Is there any other astronomical phenomenon that fits the Biblical text, yet is sufficiently startling to surprise men familiar with the movements of the heavenly bodies?

A comet may be millions of times larger than the entire Earth and shine in the night sky for weeks on end, like a searchlight shining across the stars. Attempts have been made, without success, to discover whether any of the known comets were visible around the date of the birth of Christ. But the number of comets whose paths and periods we do know is small compared with the colossal number that must exist.

Picture a comet in that Oriental dawn: a band of light like a great arrow aimed at the East. As the Sun rises, the comet fades into invisibility—but the next morning it is in almost the same place, still directing the Magi. It might be visible for weeks before it disappears once more into the depths of space.

But there is another theory, one that many astronomers today would probably accept. It makes other explanations look commonplace indeed, for it leads us to one of the most astonishing and terrifying events yet discovered in the realm of nature.

There are some stars, the so-called novae, or new stars, that suddenly turn themselves into celestial atomic bombs. Such a star may explode so violently that it leaps a hundred-thousandfold in brilliance within a few hours. One night it may be invisible to the naked eye; the next, it may dominate the sky.

Novae are routine occurrences of the universe. Many are observed every year, though few are near enough to be visible except through telescopes. On an average of once every 200 years, however, a star in our galaxy becomes a *supernova*; its brilliance may increase by a thousand million times in the course of a few hours. The last time such an event was witnessed was in A.D. 1604; another supernova in 1572 was so brilliant that it was visible in broad daylight; and Chinese astronomers recorded one in 1054. It is quite possible that the Star of Bethlehem was such a supernova. If so, we can draw some rather remarkable conclusions.

We'll assume that since Supernova Bethlehem could be seen by day, it must have been as brilliant as Venus. Astronomical reasoning suggests that a supernova of this brightness would be 3000 light-years away. That means its light had been traveling for 3000 years. By the most conservative estimate, this great new star must have shone over thousands of other worlds before its light reached Earth.

If such a supernova appeared to the Magi of old, its light is still flooding out through space. It has left Earth far behind in the 20 centuries that have elapsed since men saw it for the first and last time. To any beings who may be seeing it now as a new star in their skies, it will still be more brilliant than any other star in their entire heavens, for its brightness will have decreased only 50 percent in its extra 2000 years of travel.

Thus at this very moment, the Star of Bethlehem may still be shining in the skies of countless distant worlds. And it will continue to do so for thousands of years to come, as its radiance ebbs out toward the frontiers of the universe.

THE GREATEST EXPLOSION OF THEM ALL

Earl Ubell

Recently astronomers have come closer than ever to deciding which of two theories best answers the ultimate question: How did our universe begin?

New evidence from cosmic light and radio waves arriving on Earth from distant starry worlds has tilted the balance between scientists of two camps: those who believe we exist in an eternal, infinite, never-changing universe, and those who believe the universe was born in a cataclysmic explosion some 10 to 20 billion years ago.

An increasing number of astronomers see growing evidence for the "big-bang" theory:

• Four years ago, a metallic horn-shaped antenna pointed at the sky from a New Jersey hill detected peculiar radiation that may be a remnant of a white-hot ball of matter and energy—the cosmic egg from which the universe may have been hatched.

• For several years the 200-inch telescope atop Mt. Palomar, California, has been collecting data on strange objects called quasars. Brighter than 100 million suns, they stand like beacons on the shore of the universe, billions upon trillions of miles from us. The quasars appear to be receding so fast it could mean an exploding universe.

• An English radio antenna has picked up the burble and squeak of worlds we cannot see. The distribution of those radio sources indicates to some astronomers a scattering by a massive explosive force.

The big-bang proponents believe that originally a primal blob of glowing hydrogen shot its fragments far out into space, where they are still traveling at thousands of miles a second. Those speeding wisps of hydrogen, now condensed into star-studded galaxies, make up our expanding universe.

That big bang, however, may be just one of an eternal succession of explosions. Some astronomers anticipate that the speeding galaxies will slow down and then start moving back toward one another. Ultimately, they will fall into that primitive ball, only to explode once more and repeat the cycle endlessly.

The new evidence for the big bang has made life difficult for the advocates of the second leading theory, called the steady-state theory. These astronomers think that the universe has the quality of a field of grass, where individual blades that die are replaced by new shoots.

The protagonists of this idea agree that the universe is expanding. The sight of galaxies flying apart comes from undeniable telescope observation. However, they believe this results not from an explosion but from some mysterious repulsive force. The steady-state men suggest that new galaxies are continually formed out of hydrogen gas in intergalactic space, thereby filling in the space left by the hurtling galaxies. The hydrogen is created out of nothingness.

Prof. Fred Hoyle of Cambridge University, England, leader of the steady-state faction, has modified his theory to fit the recent data. He now says that a limited region of the universe behaves like the big bang. Beyond lies the unchanging infinity.

Man has always gazed at the star-spangled night sky and wondered how it came to be. Today astronomers can form theories, and then test them against the observation and measurement of heavenly bodies. Both the big-bang and steady-state theories have consequences that can be observed. But it should be remembered that no astronomer believes that any current cosmology adequately describes the universe.

The big-bang theory was born in 1922, when Dr. Alexander Friedman, a Russian mathematician, found an alternative approach to the field equations of Einstein's general relativity theory and went on to predict the possibility of an expanding universe. By 1928 Dr. H. P. Robertson, later of California Institute of Technology, identified the first telescopic evidence to support that theory. The light from the galaxies, redder than expected, indicated that they were retreating at great speed.

Dr. Edwin P. Hubble of the Mt. Wilson Observatory also measured the distance to the flying galaxies. The closest galaxy to our own, the Magellanic Clouds, stands some 200,000 light-years from us. That means that a light ray traveling at 186,000 miles a second from that crowd of 100 million stars takes 200,000 years to get to us.

Dr. Hubble was amazed to find that the farthest galaxies were traveling the fastest. About the same time a Belgian astronomer-priest, Abbé Georges Lemaître, suggested the modern form of the big-bang theory, which fitted the Robertson-Hubble observations: As in any explosion, the farthest pieces were flying fastest.

Immediately, questions flooded the astronomical world: How long ago did the bang occur? How were the stars and galaxies formed? How were the many elements created?

It has taken 40 years to get a hint of the answers. The hint had to wait for the completion of the giant 200-inch telescope on Mt. Palomar in California after World War II, the development of the atomic-

energy theory and the invention of radio telescopes.

The problem of the creation of the elements nearly destroyed the big-bang theory. If the cosmic egg were composed only of hydrogen, how were the heavy elements produced? As the astronomers learned more nuclear physics, they realized that the burst of matter occurred too quickly to create any element heavier than helium.

Then in 1938 scientists discovered that stars burn hydrogen—converting it to helium and extracting energy in the process. That occurs in the heart of the star at 20 million°C. After a while the hydrogen at the core is exhausted and is replaced by helium. In 1955 a Caltech team of scientists showed that the stars could convert that helium into all the elements—in effect, the stars are the bake ovens of the elements.

Next the cosmological detectives tried to ascertain the age of the universe. It had to be older than the Earth, which radioactive rock measurements had revealed to be at least 4.6 billion years old. Dr. Sandage has figured out that the oldest stars in our galaxy must have been born 12 billion years ago. He calculated that age by determining how long it takes stars to burn up their hydrogen and convert it into helium. Independently Dr. William A. Fowler of Caltech calculated the age of the synthesis of the uranium and thorium found on the Earth. He knew these elements had been originally manufactured in stars that had exploded long ago and sent their fragments through the galaxy to become part of the material from which our solar system was formed. The age: 12 billion years.

A third measurement made by Dr. Sandage indicates an eight-billion-year age for the universe. The discrepancies bother the big-bang scientists, but they anticipate that they will be resolved.

The big excitement in the last few years has been over discoveries that test the more subtle consequences of the two major theories. In this respect, it is easier to disprove the steady-state theory than the big-bang. If astronomers can prove, for example, that the universe was expanding faster in the past than it is today, the steady-state theory will fall. To get at past history, astronomers merely look out to greater distances. Since it takes time for light to travel, when they look at galaxies a billion light-years away they see the universe as it existed a billion years ago. Therefore they are interested in measuring the speed of recession of

Radio telescopes like this 140-foot "dish" at Green Bank, West Virginia, receive radio waves produced— no one knows just how—by the Sun, Moon and about 3000 stars, galaxies and unidentified objects.

the most distant galaxies. If those galaxies are flying faster than they should, as predicted by the steady-state proponents, that will kill the theory.

By 1960 Dr. Rudolph Minkowski, then at Mt. Wilson and Mt. Palomar, had discovered a galaxy, 3C 295, retreating from us at 70,000 miles a second. It was the most distant galaxy known—perhaps four billion light-years away. With that measurement, plus a few others, astronomers believed that they detected a departure from the steady-state prediction.

But the real break came several years ago. In February 1963 Dr. Maarten Schmidt of Mt. Palomar found a quasi-stellar radio source, or quasar, that put out 50 times as much light as an ordinary galaxy.

Dr. Schmidt was able to detect that quasar because radio astronomers had located spots in the heaven from which radio waves came in torrents. Photographing with the 200-inch telescope in just those locations, Dr. Schmidt picked up the quasar.

His significant contribution was the discovery that this and other previously detected quasars were charging through space as fast as, or faster than, the fastest known galaxies. He has found one quasar, 3C 9, clipping along at 80 percent of the velocity of light. Dr. Schmidt does not know exactly how far away 3C 9 is, because astronomers do not know the true nature of the subtle curvature of space.

In an effort to determine the curvature, astronomers have so far taken complex measurements of 22 quasars. Dr. Sandage believes it will take about 100 quasars to get a good answer. However, he has discovered other quasarlike objects, called blue stellar objects, that may help get the answer faster.

In an approach to the problem of the origin of the universe, Prof. Martin Ryle, working in the '50's with the radio telescope at Cambridge, mapped the locations of thousands of objects—galaxies and quasars— that are sources of radio waves. Graphs of these radio sources according to location and radio output do not support the steady-state theory.

Not long ago it was announced that a metal horn at the Bell Telephone Laboratories in New Jersey had been receiving a strange radio signal from outer space for a year. The Bell Lab men discovered that the radio waves were coming from all over the sky. Unbeknownst to them, Drs. Robert H. Dicke and James Peebles, both at Princeton University, had predicted the existence of those strange radio signals. Since the universe was once hotter and denser, they reasoned that it should be filled with radiation that eventually cooled as the universe evolved and expanded. Drs. Dicke and Peebles said that ancient radiation would be detected today as lower-energy radio waves.

Another horn set up at Princeton University by Dr. Dicke's research group has also found such radiation. The steady-state theory has thus received still another powerful blow. It apparently has no way to account for such radiation.

Although the big-bang theory seems to be winning, there are still unanswered questions. How far away are the quasars? What caused the explosion? How does the distribution of hydrogen and helium fit into the explosion calculations?

Uncommitted to the debate are such critics as Dr. Philip Morrison of the Massachusetts Institute of Technology. He declares that astronomers know far too little to make a choice among theories of the universe and that no theory is adequate at the moment. "We have been wrong too many times in the past," he says. "We do not have enough measurements of distant galaxies to say anything definite. We're in the kindergarten stage of cosmology."

Perhaps. But astronomers are hopeful that they will soon graduate to the first grade.

OUTER SPACE— WHAT IS OUT THERE?

Arthur C. Clarke

Every informed person knows that the conquest of interplanetary space, first by instrumented rockets and later by manned vehicles, has begun. The shadow of these events lies across our age, stirring the thoughts of all men who have ever stared at the night sky and wondered what part our species is destined to play in the unfolding drama of the universe. Some of the great questions which seemed forever beyond hope of solution may soon be answered.

Whether intelligent life exists outside Earth is, perhaps, unique among these problems in its intellectual and emotional appeal. The only type of life that we can imagine without losing ourselves in biological fantasies must be planet-based, and until a short time ago planets were regarded as the results of cosmic accidents that could occur only a very few times.

Today we are fairly confident that many, if not most, stars have planets revolving around them. This was given considerable support by the detection in 1942 of a hitherto unknown body in the double-star system 61 Cygni, one of our neighbors. It would be a remarkable coincidence, if planets were indeed rare, to find a specimen practically on our doorstep. Any figure is, at the present stage of our semi-ignorance, pure guesswork; but we may not be far wrong if we guess that one star in a hundred has at least one planet where life could theoretically exist.

Vanished with the belief in the uniqueness of our solar system is the idea that life on Earth is some freak or special creation. Until about 15 years ago it could be maintained that living things could not possibly arise from "dead" inorganic matter by the operation of purely natural forces. The complexity of even the simplest single-celled organism was so enormous that to expect atoms of carbon, hydrogen, oxygen and the rest to form one by spontaneous aggregation was much too improbable.

We now surmise that life can evolve from nonliving matter in the circumstances that must exist upon many primitive, newly formed planets. Stanley Miller's experiment at the University of Chicago in 1953, in which a complex organic soup was produced by the action of electrical discharges upon simple solutions of water vapor, ammonia, methane and hydrogen, suggests how the first steps in the evolution of life may have taken place.

That both planets and living creatures are common throughout the universe must, therefore, be taken as highly probable. This implies the existence of a billion life-bearing worlds in our galaxy—the whirlpool of stars of which our Sun is an undistinguished out-of-town member, lying in one of the remoter spiral arms.

Should you feel like trying to visualize what this means, empty a bucketful of sand on a table. Now imagine that every one of those billion-odd grains of

This painting shows our galaxy, some 6 billion billion miles across, as it would look from an imaginary planet 400,000 light-years away. The Sun is in an arm about two thirds of the way out from the hub to the rim. On the left are two satellite galaxies, the Magellanic Clouds; at right are larger, more distant neighboring galaxies.

sand is itself a world, perhaps teeming with life and bearing rational creatures who measure their history not in thousands but in millions of years. You have thus a faint picture of our galaxy. If you wish to visualize the whole universe, the operation must be repeated, with each grain of sand representing a galaxy.

There is a temptation, when brainwashed by such numbers, to argue that these astronomical vistas are of no practical importance, since we can never have direct knowledge of more than a small portion of the universe. However, we can no longer pretend that the universe isn't there, for we have already started to explore it.

At the moment astronomical evidence does not suggest that we shall encounter intelligence in the solar system. But the discovery of any form of life, however humble, would greatly affect our outlook upon the universe. Even a few lichens on Mars would prove that life is not a rare phenomenon that happens to have occurred upon the planet Earth. And with that settled, it would be illogical to deny the existence of higher forms elsewhere. Until we have reason to believe the contrary, however, it would be safest to assume that *Homo sapiens* is the only intelligent creature to have evolved in the solar system. To find our equals or our superiors we must go farther afield.

This, to put it mildly, presents problems. Though we have begun to challenge interplanetary distances, the gulfs separating us from the stars are a million times greater, and light itself takes years to span them.

Physical transportation is not necessary, however. With today's electronic techniques stretched to the utmost, we could just about get a readable Morse signal to the nearest star. And if we can tackle interstellar communication only a little more than 50 years after we invented radio, it is not unreasonable to assume that there may be transmitters within a few light-years of us far more powerful than any we have.

We may hope, therefore, to establish the existence of extraterrestrial intelligences before many more decades—or, at most, centuries—have passed. If anyone is doubtful of this, I would remind him of the unfortunate error of Auguste Comte, who rashly proclaimed our eternal ignorance concerning the composition of the stars. The speed and thoroughness with which the spectroscope refuted him is a good reminder that there are no apparently fundamental limits to knowledge.

We might also remember that our species has come into existence only in the last seven thousandth of Earth's history, and that the entire span of human civilization extends over barely more than a millionth of that time. Such extreme youth on any cosmic time scale makes it seem likely that the majority of rational extraterrestrial creatures must be superior to us by many millions of years of development.

Part Five

Invitation to Wonder

Chapter One

Some Riddles

Men will study the marvels and mysteries of life as long as they have the will to know, the capacity for wonder. How did life begin? What makes it change? Why do some forms of life die out while others thrive? Can we create life in the laboratory? Each answer gives rise to new, even more perplexing questions.

CLOSING IN ON THE LOCH NESS MONSTER

David Scott

It was the biggest slug I'd ever seen, five inches of black creepy-crawly. I'd nearly stepped on it as I climbed over a hill above Loch Ness, Scotland's longest and second-deepest lake. "They grow big here," my companion observed. "And our quarry may be the granddaddy of them all—a giant sea slug."

My guide was Clem Skelton, resident technician of a group that is hunting the celebrated Loch Ness Monster. A free-lance film director and a dedicated believer in "Nessie," Skelton has seen the aquatic what-is-it six times, once at midnight—"a huge hump surrounded by boiling foam"—from only 15 yards. According to the monster hunters, the landlocked lake is inhabited by a colony of the creatures—rather than a single one long-lived enough to give rise to more than 30 years' reported sightings.

Loch Ness's storied monster has long been regarded as a myth and generally ignored. Until early in 1966, that is. Then a Royal Air Force photo-intelligence unit studied a 16-mm. film of the "monster" taken in 1960. These photo experts were from the Joint Air Reconnaissance Intelligence Center (JARIC), the crack outfit that analyzes long-range aerial photographs and detected Germany's secret buzz-bomb bases during World War II. They concluded that Loch Ness hold some enormous object, probably alive.

The film was made by Tim Dinsdale, an aeronautical engineer who now advises the group on the trail of Nessie. On the last day of a six-day vigil at Loch Ness in April 1960, he was driving slowly along a cliffside road 300 feet above the glassy black water when he spotted a reddish-brown humpbacked object floating about 1600 yards away.

As he hurriedly stopped his car and grabbed his camera, the thing began moving toward the far shore. Dinsdale filmed what he was sure was the back of a huge semi-submerged animal. The creature swam away in a slow zigzag course, disappeared below the surface, and turned left along the opposite shore, throwing up a tremendous wash of foam. In 40 feet of film, Dinsdale captured the evidence.

Later that year Dinsdale's film of the monster was shown on BBC television, and subsequently on TV programs all over the world. Letters poured in, and previously silent witnesses offered new corroborative testimony. But there the matter rested. Zoologists would not be moved by something that cut across the natural order of things. Officialdom was apathetic about financing a scientific investigation.

So it remained for a small group of amateur naturalists—whose moving spirit was David James, a publisher and at that time a Member of Parliament—to set up a body called the Loch Ness Phenomena Investigation Bureau. In 1964 the group turned over Dinsdale's film to the photoreconnaissance experts, saying simply, "Here's a film—tell us what's on it." The resulting report is a 2000-word document, couched in guarded military phraseology.

It states that 20-times enlargements of frames were used for examination, and tells how distance-estimating scales were established along and across the line of sight. It says that the object rose three feet above the waterline, moved at ten m.p.h., and was *not* a surface craft or submarine, "which leaves the conclusion that it is probably an animate object. The normal body 'rounding' in nature would suggest that there is at least two feet of it under the water. It may be deduced that a cross section through the object would not be less than six feet wide and five feet high." The pooh-poohed Loch Ness Monster had suddenly become respectable.

A drawing and a model of the gigantic mystery creature, based on the few existing photos and on more than 100 eyewitness reports, present a strange-

Two humps rise above the surface near the Loch Ness shore. The wake behind them seems to indicate that a partially submerged creature is moving.

These unretouched photographs are said to show the giant reptile, worm or sea slug known as the Loch Ness monster. Here, what appears to be the monster's head and part of its body projects above water.

Three humps are visible above water in the middle of the lake. Another appearance by the monster? Skeptics say the humps might simply be a family of otters gamboling through the water single file.

looking animal. To some it resembles a plesiosaur—a fish-eating, egg-laying reptile from the age of dinosaurs. This giant, adapted for life in the open sea, grew to 30 feet in length. It had a barrel-shaped body, four paddlelike limbs, a long slender neck and a tiny head with a large mouth and pointed teeth. Since it supposedly became extinct 70 million years ago, living ones in Loch Ness would be a sensational find—but one not without precedent. The coelacanth, a primitive fish, was believed extinct for almost as long, until a living specimen was caught off Africa in 1938.

Some naturalists say Nessie could be an enormous and unknown variety of sea slug—a type of mollusk. Like its little brother in the radish patch, which can elongate its body to enter worm burrows in search of food, such a creature could shape its bulk into the one, two, three or more humps seen by different wit-

nesses. Other authorities think it's a marine bristle worm. Among the highest forms of worm life, these have appendages called false feet, and a well-developed head with jaws; the body could convolute to form the humps visible on the water. Most agree Nessie is neither a whale nor a shark.

How did it get into Loch Ness? From the sea, all say. Until the end of the last ice age, Loch Ness was an arm of the sea. Then the ice on the craggy rocks melted—and the Earth's crust rose and isolated it.

The murky depths of the lake, well stocked with fish, could provide an ideal sanctuary for a colony of monsters. With their basic needs satisfied, they could make themselves at home and breed. Gradual adaptation to a freshwater environment would have been quite possible.

Today the surface of Loch Ness is 52 feet above sea level. Wedged between beautiful pine-clad hills that rise to more than 2200 feet, Loch Ness is about 23 miles long and one to 1½ miles wide. It is one of the deepest lakes in Europe. It has a maximum depth of 754 feet, and more than half goes down 700 feet. The water never freezes; it remains at near-constant temperatures throughout the year—a steady 42 degrees at the flat, muddy bottom. Marine life is plentiful—salmon up to 30 pounds, 15- to 20-pound trout, eels, pike. It adds up to a haven for the giant.

While legends of the monster go back centuries, the first credible reports of our times began in 1933. In that year, a road from Inverness to Fort Augustus was blasted out of rock along the lake. Perhaps the shock waves disturbed the creatures, for many sightings were reported in the following months.

At Fort Augustus, I met one of the earliest and most reliable witnesses—Alex Campbell, water bailiff of Loch Ness, who works for the local Fishery Board. His first view of Nessie was in May 1934.

"A flat reptilian head on a swanlike neck towered six feet over the water," he told me. "A humped black body stretched a full 30 feet behind. The head flicked nervously from side to side as a couple of herring trawlers approached, then ducked under the water and disappeared." Since then, Campbell has seen the animal many times.

Tim Dinsdale sifts the reports of 100 eyewitnesses in his book, *Loch Ness Monster*. They make astonishing reading: "Three humps churning through the water leaving a foaming trail. . . . Head about the same width as neck, mouth 12 to 18 inches wide. . . . Looked like an elephant's back, four feet high, 12 feet long. . . . Wake like from a torpedo."

Except for the number of humps, the descriptions are remarkably consistent. The creatures, probably several of them, have been seen in all parts of the lake. About all that is known of their behavior is their apparent fear of noise—they submerge at the sound of a motorboat.

Currently the quest is spearheaded by the enthusiasts of the Loch Ness Phenomena Investigation Bureau, whose directors include Dr. Roy P. Mackal, associate professor of biochemistry at the University of Chicago. A crew of 15, recruited for a week or two at a time, mans the observation posts. The main camera battery overlooks the lake near Achnahannet. Five additional crews are stationed at other vantage points around the lake on calm, sunny days, so that 80 percent of its surface is within view of the cameras.

Results in 1966 included a few long-range photos showing little detail, and 32 accepted sightings by expedition members and others in the area. But 1967 proved much more productive. After receiving a grant from Field Enterprises Educational Corporation, LNPIB obtained a number of high-quality 35-mm. motion-picture sequences and submitted them to the Royal Air Force photo-intelligence unit for independent analysis and interpretation.

LNPIB plans for the summer of 1968 included launching at the monster a retrievable biopsy dart developed by Dr. Mackal, the use of an infrared "sniperscope" for nighttime observation, and curtain sonar that would blanket an area of the lake with a continuous signal to alert the watchers of the monster's approach.

In such ways, says the LNPIB, it should finally be possible to identify the species, find out how many individuals there are, learn their habits, and protect and preserve them. Scientists could then study their physiology and origins. It would be a dramatic new chapter in natural history.

THE CASE OF THE VANISHING DINOSAURS

J.D.Ratcliff

It was one of the most violent combats ever recorded on earth. Before the sneak attack the enemy lurked in the steaming vegetation, watching with small, hungry eyes. He was something out of a nightmare. Reared on powerful hind legs, this terrifying carnivorous killer towered 20 feet in the air. His short forelegs had sharp, powerful claws for tearing; in his great jaw were teeth as long as steak knives. With a roar, he crashed through the underbrush toward his prey.

Apparently flight was the only hope for the victim, a ponderous 90-foot lizard that had been grazing on reeds and marsh grasses in the shallow, tropical inland sea. Even though its 30 tons outweighed the attacker three to one, it desperately tried to splash its way toward deeper water and safety, leaving footprints the size of washtubs. But the three-toed enemy followed, gaining because it was fleeter, faster.

It is easy to guess the result—but we cannot be sure. That battle of the dinosaurs took place 100 million years ago. The event can only be brought to life from fossilized tracks found near the Paluxy River in central Texas—the great round tracks of the grazing animal and the clawed prints of the pursuing meat-eater.

Rooting through fossilized boneyards, paleontologists have been able to reconstruct animals that vanished tens of millions of years ago. Tooth marks on skeletons reveal battles. Jaws and teeth provide information on the type of foods eaten. Bone deformities tell of diseases. Each year we learn more about the creatures that prowled the earth when the world was young.

The age of the great reptiles, in the Mesozoic era, began approximately 200 million years ago and lasted some 130 million years. The more than 200 genera of dinosaurs that ruled life then were, by a wide margin, the most extraordinary creatures ever to exist. We think of them as cumbersome, dim-witted animals who blundered their way to extinction. Yet the dinosaurs (Greek for "terrible lizards") were able to dominate the earth for something like 100 million years. Man, by contrast, has been here less than one two-hundredth as long.

Dinosaurs were remarkably varied. Some were no larger than chickens; others weighed 85 tons. Some looked a bit like the ostrich, others like the rhinoceros, the turtle or the kangaroo. Some were ponderous and slow-moving; others were agile enough to jump into the air and catch birds.

Stegosaurus was a peaceful vegetarian that resembled a monstrous anteater. Living in exposed upland regions, he needed protection against fierce meat-eaters. He developed into a reptilian tank, with armor-plated hide, a double ridge of projecting plates along his spine, a short but powerful tail equipped with four long daggers. By thrashing his tail, he must have done enormous damage to predators.

Brontosaurus ("thunder lizard"), the enormous four-footed reptile with the long neck and great trailing tail, is the giant most of us think of as a dinosaur. A vegetarian, he was big enough to nibble leaves from the top of a 30-foot tree. His small head and four peg teeth were useless for fighting; he could only lash his tail. For safety, he spent most of his time in the water, which not only gave protection but helped support his vast body. In moments of

The largest dinosaur, mighty Brontosaurus, *weighed approximately 35 tons and grew to be about 70 feet long. This huge reptile lived 140 million years ago, and was especially common on the plains of Utah, Colorado and Wyoming. Much of the area is now very dry, but at that time it was swampy lowland and provided an ideal environment for* Brontosaurus, *whose legs were barely able to support its heavy body on dry land.*

This confrontation might have taken place in Wyoming 140 million years ago. Stegosaurus (far right) *was a formidably armed plant-eater about 20 feet long.* Allosaurus (left), *which stood on two legs, was a spike-toothed flesh-eater about 30 feet long.* Camptosaurus (far left) *was a small, horny-beaked plant-eater. Flying reptiles were contemporary with these ground-dwellers, as were some feathered creatures considered the first birds.*

peril he could submerge almost completely, breathing through nostrils atop his head. Skeletal remains of *Brontosaurus* are plentiful in what is now Utah, Montana, Wyoming and Colorado.

The big lizard's brain was tiny, one one-hundredth of his body weight: On a comparable scale, man's brain would be no larger than a pea. But *Brontosaurus* had a great swelling in his spinal cord near his hips. This undoubtedly served as a kind of second brain governing reflex actions in the hind limbs and tail—causing the tail, for example, to switch automatically if hurt. Dr. Glenn Jepsen, professor of vertebrate paleontology at Princeton University, estimates that without this plexus it would have taken two seconds for a nerve impulse to travel from tail to brain—"time enough for him to be 'de-tailed' by an enemy before he was even aware of it."

Tyrannosaurus ("tyrant lizard") was the most fearsome brute that ever trod the earth. Stretching as much as 47 feet from head to tail, he towered 19 or 20 feet when standing erect, weighed perhaps ten

tons and had four-foot jaws and six-inch teeth. He was a battler who had to kill to survive.

What was the world like in that Mesozoic era? The greater part of the globe was relatively flat, featureless—the Himalayas, Alps and Rockies hadn't yet pushed their way upward. Vast shallow inland seas, which came and went, covered a large portion of today's land areas. At one time or another everything west of the Mississippi River was under water.

With no mountains to give regional climate, weather conditions were much the same worldwide—except for the polar regions, which were far less extensive than today. There was a mild cooling in winter and a slight warming in summer, but there were no seasons as we know them. Almost the entire earth had a tropical or subtropical climate.

Vegetation consisted of giant ferns, reeds and conifers such as pine, hemlock, spruce. Broad-leaved trees —maples, oaks, elms—and flowering plants were not to develop until near the end of the age of dinosaurs. The Mesozoic landscape was drab by today's stand-

the temperature of their environment. They had to live in a narrow temperature range: At 100° F. they would die, and at a point well above freezing they would become too torpid for movement.

If overheated, they were much too large to burrow into the ground as small reptiles do. And on chilly days they became sluggish and couldn't exercise enough to produce heat or consume sufficient food for large energy expenditures. Such considerations suggest why dinosaurs grew so large. Great tonnages of tissue cool less rapidly and heat up more slowly when exposed to the sun. Thus, size in itself may have been a temperature regulator.

No one knows the average life-span of a dinosaur, but most paleontologists think that the giant reptiles must have been long-lived—perhaps between 100 and 200 years. Study of dinosaur skeletons indicates that bone strata were laid down much like tree rings.

Did dinosaurs have voices? A few years ago Dr. Edwin H. Colbert of New York City's Museum of Natural History and a colleague, John Ostrom, simultaneously discovered dinosaur stapes, the middle-ear bone essential to hearing. If dinosaurs could hear, presumably they also had voices, probably ranging from pips to squeaks to roars.

The greatest riddle about the dinosaurs is why they vanished from the earth they had dominated so long. Almost certainly they did not suddenly become extinct, but gradually disappeared over a period of several million years. Whatever disaster struck them down was global in extent; they had disappeared completely by the end of the Mesozoic period.

There are dozens of theories. One is that the earth warmed up. Sex glands of male reptiles are extremely sensitive to heat; too great a temperature rise leads to sterility. Another explanation is the exact reverse: that the earth cooled off. Since during cool periods dinosaurs would become torpid, like frogs in winter, they would eventually starve if the cold persisted.

Possibly, as broad-leaved plants and grasses evolved and pumped growing amounts of oxygen into the air, dinosaurs could not stand the higher oxygen levels. This would have stimulated their bodies to burn food at a faster rate; they simply could not eat enough to stay alive. Another guess is that, as the small furry animals began to evolve in increasing numbers, they raided dinosaur nests for eggs, finally eating them out of existence.

Working in universities and museums, fossil hunters have done a remarkable job in piecing together the life histories of the terrible lizards. But, Professor Jepsen predicts, "the most exciting discoveries about dinosaurs are yet to be made."

ards; dark greens and dark browns predominated.

Besides the dinosaurs, there were other bizarre creatures—snakes 50 feet long, deadly giant crocodiles with six-foot jaws. Fantastic flying reptiles called pterosaurs, with a 20-foot wingspread (greater than that of a small plane), soared in the air. Having legs too small and weak to get a running start and launch themselves, they probably lived on cliffs and simply fell out into the air.

While most insects had already developed, it wasn't until the middle to latter part of the dinosaur's reign that reptilian scales evolved into feathers and birds made their appearance. It is difficult to think of the robin as one of the dinosaur's closest surviving relatives, but it is a fact. Warm-blooded mammals didn't appear until the dinosaur had been around for perhaps 50 million years. So long as he ruled the earth, mammals remained small—primitive shrews, opossums, hedgehogs.

Probably cold-blooded and having no internal mechanism to control body heat, dinosaurs assumed

CAN SCIENCE PRODUCE LIFE?

Rutherford Platt

When Planet Earth was born it slowly cooled to form a crust of black volcanic rock. Then, in time, masses of silicon mixed with mineral elements were squeezed to the surface by the pressures of internal fires and crystallized as big islands of granite that formed the foundations of continents. The whole crust heaved and buckled, cloudbursts drenched the rocks and sterile water collected in wide depressions to form the Earth's first seas. Countless volcanoes and fissures continuously gushed methane, steam, ammonia and perhaps carbon dioxide, to give the earth its first atmosphere. That "air" contained the four chief elements of life—carbon, oxygen, hydrogen and nitrogen. But they were in the form of gases deadly to present-day life. Moreover, the atmosphere was flooded with ultraviolet radiation and stabbed by incessant lightning.

How, in this elemental turmoil, did life on Earth begin? Many have tried to supply the answer. Among the first was Anaxagoras of Greece, who in the fifth century B.C. declared that life comes down to earth in raindrops, in the form of spermata (little seeds). Came the 20th century, and the origin of life was still a mystery.

Then in 1924 the Russian scientist A. I. Oparin stated that life might have arisen out of inanimate matter in a prolonged process of "preorganic evolution." He showed how, in theory, atoms of carbon, oxygen, hydrogen and nitrogen could have formed molecules basic to life, even under the raw, inhospitable conditions of the primordial Earth—and how self-reproducing clusters of these molecules might have adhered together and then evolved toward more complex forms.

Three years later the English biochemist J. B. S. Haldane wrote that although such substances would be destroyed by microorganisms, "before the origin of life they must have accumulated till the primitive oceans reached the consistency of hot, dilute soup." And when the surface of this soup was radiated by ultraviolet light, inorganic compounds would have been converted into organic molecules—molecules containing carbon. At one time scientists believed that such molecules could be produced only by living things.

By the 1950's the scene was shifting from the theorist's armchair to the laboratory, where scientists were striving to demonstrate that the molecular constituents of life *could* have emerged under primordial conditions.

Dr. Oparin had reasoned in the late thirties that methane, ammonia and hydrogen were probable constituents of the primordial atmosphere. What would happen if these lifeless substances were placed in a flask and then stabbed repeatedly by electric flashes to represent lightning? In 1953, Stanley L. Miller, collaborating with the atomic scientist Dr. Harold C. Urey, attempted such an experiment. To their surprise and delight, they found that amino acids had indeed been formed.

Amino acids are the building blocks of protein and hence of all life. They are also believed to have been involved in the first stage of the evolution toward life. The theory is this:

The colossal retort of the primordial earth must have yielded myriads of molecules as ephemeral as bubbles. But, because of their peculiar molecular structure, the molecules of amino acids are especially stable. The four elements of life—carbon, oxygen, hydrogen and nitrogen—are assembled in every amino-acid molecule into two opposing groups so well matched in their electrical charges that they are stabilized like wrestlers locked in equal combat. Thus the tenacious amino acids could have survived in the chaos to become an early link between no-life and life.

In experiments that followed, a surprising fact turned up. The basic molecules of life could also have been produced by many other forces in those fierce, elemental times, including X rays, cosmic rays, ultraviolet light and volcanic heat.

After the creation of amino acids, two even larger problems remained. Giant protein molecules, discovered everywhere in living things, are made of long chains of amino acids. How did the amino acids get hooked up into these long chains? And then, how did these twisted protein giants turn into living cells?

Giant proteins are fantastically elegant structures—"the noblest piece of architecture produced by nature" in the opinion of biologists. One molecule of the vital protein of blood, hemoglobin, for example, has 8954 atoms fitted together in a dazzling pattern. The problem is that all the complicated proteins in life around us—those that make flesh, blood, bone, hair, eggs, milk, seeds, feathers—are created by *living cells*. Those living cells in turn are made of protein. How could protein be created in the first place, when there were no living cells?

One line of reasoning, first put forward by Dr. Oparin in 1938, is that there could be conditions occurring in nature in which amino acids might themselves furnish the answer. And so they did—quickly and beautifully—when the stage was set for them by Dr. Sidney W. Fox, now of the Institute of Molecular Evolution of the University of Miami. The "miracle" occurred when amino acids were permitted to dry out. The thinking was that solutions of amino acids, billions of years ago, had puddled in warm, dry spots. What would happen to such solutions today if the water was allowed to evaporate? The scientists who watched this experiment saw a marvelous event.

As the wet spot on the warm test tube dried, its amino acids formed long, submicroscopic, threadlike structures. These chains, some with hundreds of little molecules joined end to end, were named proteinoids. The sum of their electric energies endowed them with power to bend and fold!

There are about 20 kinds of amino acids common to the proteins of life, and the precise order in which these are lined up in the chains spells what their protein creates—flesh or bone, hair or feather. The scientists have been able to manufacture all these amino acids under presumed primordial conditions. Dr. Kaoru Harada synthesized 14 in a single experiment.

So the answer to one question is found. Amino acids *by themselves* can produce primitive proteinlike material under certain conditions—no need for a cell to help them. Still, the final question remains. How could these proteins form a living cell, with its millions of atoms and molecules carefully arranged in a precise pattern?

The primitive proteins came long before living cells appeared. The precisely ordered proteins of present-day plants and animals would have acquired their amino-acid arrangement in the course of many millions of years of evolution. Dr. Melvin Calvin estimates that molecular life must have evolved for two billion years *before* the first living cell appeared.

We have already begun to duplicate this great leap, to make a whole living cell in the laboratory. A most striking experiment, which has produced crude, cell-like spheres that maintain their identity and are capable of dividing themselves, has taken us a giant step along the pathway toward understanding the origin of life.

Again, the experiment was run by Dr. Fox. To reconfirm his laboratory findings, he climbed up the broad slope of a cinder cone in Hawaii, looking for spots where conditions might have permitted primitive proteins to form in the pre-life world. He was surprised to discover that large areas of the cone were oven-hot just beneath the surface. Might not this warm, primitive earth have been the womb for the

molecules of life—where they could bake and boil, before being washed through the loose lava by a cloudburst and so into the sea? What would this have done to the elemental amino acids?

Dr. Fox took hunks of lava back to the laboratory and placed on them amino acids coined from methane, ammonia and water. With everything sterilized to avoid contamination, he baked this concoction for hours in a glass oven at 338°F., the temperature he found four inches under the surface of the cinder cone. When the materials cooled, a brown sticky residue was left clinging to the lava. He then deluged the lava with sterile water, and a brown soupy liquid resulted.

This unpromising stuff turned out to be very exciting. As seen through an ordinary optical microscope, a wonderful galaxy of spheres swarmed across the field of vision. The amino acids had first united to make proteinoids—and then these had combined to form little spheres! Dr. Fox named these fascinating strangers "microspheres." They looked like, in many ways behaved like, and were the same size as certain simple bacteria, and they clung together in chains as do the one-celled blue-green algae. Bacteria and blue-green algae are two of the most elementary forms of life that exist on earth.

Although these spheres were not true cells, they did possess many cellular properties. They had stability: They kept their shapes indefinitely. They stained in the same way as the present-day protein in cells, an important chemical test. But the real significance of these microspheres was that scientists did not *synthesize* them piece by piece; they simply set up the right *conditions*—and microspheres produced themselves.

The core of a living cell is DNA, the "magic molecule" that holds the inheritance code and governs all the activities of the cell. In December 1967 Dr. Arthur Kornberg announced that his team of biologists at Stanford University, California, had synthesized DNA in a test tube after 11 years of patient and precise experiment. They had isolated the pattern of a DNA code from a virus, after determining its characteristics by watching the behavior of the virus. Then they copied it in the test tube using enzymes from living cells and—astonishingly—the artificial DNA worked just as well as the one which nature had made.

To combine laboratory-made units such as microspheres and DNA made outside a living cell is only an imaginary concept at this writing. But science is taking such giant strides in penetrating the mysteries of the living cell that Colin S. Pittendrigh, professor of biology at Princeton University, said in December 1967 that "laboratories will be creating a living cell within ten years."

Protecting Our Precious Heritage

Each living thing, however humble, is a unique, irreplaceable product of millions of years of nature's handiwork. Through carelessness, greed or indifference, man has caused several hundred animal and plant species to become extinct. More will inevitably follow unless we take action now. Tomorrow will be too late.

THE BUFFALO IS BACK!

Bill Surface

A buffalo bull stood facing the wind. Suddenly he smelled men and horses. Snorting fiercely, he led a herd of some 100 buffalo thundering across South Dakota's Great Plains. But cowboys, using the old Indian trick of hiding behind a butte, intercepted and "cut" the herd into several sections, then drove one group up a path. There 28 were shot.

A vignette from the Old West? Not at all. The year in which this hunt took place was 1967, not 1867. The scene, occurring with increasing frequency across the West and Midwest, is only one illustration of the phenomenal comeback made by the American buffalo in recent years.

Today about 14,000 buffalo live on 220 ranges and parks and on about 450 private ranches from California to Rhode Island. Indeed, so many ranchers currently raise buffalo for profit that this magnificent beast regularly appears at state fairs, select markets—and on menus. Recently Roy Houck, who keeps 1450 buffalo on his Standing Butte Ranch, near Fort Pierre, South Dakota, shipped 28,000 pounds of buffalo meat to Chicago for food chains and restaurants, which now sell hamburgers *and* buffaloburgers, and to metropolitan gourmet markets. Similarly, buffalo hides are so marketable that some furriers are predicting a fashion trend toward durable, lightweight buffalo coats.

The really significant fact about today's buffalo, however, is that he exists at all. Once so many millions of bison (the buffalo's correct name) roamed North America that as late as 1867 Kansas–Pacific trains often had to wait hours for a herd to cross the tracks. But man's scandalous slaughter of the buffalo for meat, pelts and "sport" nearly exterminated the species. By 1887 hunters for New York City's American Museum of Natural History were unable to find a single buffalo during a three-month expedition. By 1900 only 20 wild buffalo remained in the United States—hidden in remote reaches of Yellowstone National Park. Alarmingly all but four of these were killed by poachers before naturalists, using most of the 521 buffalo then held in captivity, stocked preserves in the western United States and in northwestern Canada.

We are forever indebted to these conservationists. But much credit for the bison's comeback is due to his own remarkable hardiness. Virtually nothing except a well-aimed bullet or arrow can stop this seemingly awkward beast. Oddly proportioned, he stands about six feet at the peak of his hump, measures nine feet from his bearded chin to his little flaglike tail. So much of his weight is in his enormous woolly head, hump and comically short forequarters that he seems about to tip over. Yet he is so agile that he can stop instantly, whirl and outfight a grizzly bear by spearing it with his short, curved horns. Or he can gallop as fast as 35 m.p.h. over rough terrain.

Pursued over a long distance, the bison shifts into a lumbering pace and can still appear fresh 12 miles later—while a relay team of three horses is left haggard. He can outmaneuver a Siberian husky in powdery snow, outswim dogs and climb steep slopes nearly as well as mountain sheep. Still, when possible the bison uses the firmest, most direct path, just as he did a century ago when engineers planning America's railroad routes often were unable to improve upon his trails.

Perhaps the bison's most valuable asset is his inbred herd instinct. When a small herd is threatened, bison usually huddle much like a football team, leave "baby-sitters" with the calves, then charge cavalry-style. If one buffalo is ill or injured, the herd sometimes forms a protective circle against predators.

Other self-preservation traits were dramatized a year ago at Standing Butte when a week-long blizzard buried all food under drifts up to 30 feet high. Nearly

100 of Houck's 1900 cattle died. All 1450 buffalo not only survived, but reacted wisely afterward. When the snow thawed, the half-starved cattle overate, and another 100 died. The buffalo ate sparingly, then gradually increased consumption until their digestion was normal. Not one became ill.

Though obviously intelligent, buffalo can be downright irascible around humans. Relying on keen hearing and smell to offset their nearsightedness, they may move off peacefully when a man approaches on horseback. But recently, when a cowhand galloped a bit too swiftly across the bow of a "docile" beast, he suddenly found himself and his horse riding on top of the buffalo's horns. "It's plain suicide to run around a buffalo in close quarters," said Julian Howard, manager of the 59,000-acre Wichita Mountains Wildlife Refuge in Oklahoma.

No matter how gentle the buffalo appears, he simply cannot be trusted. "Men who know the buffalo best trust him the least," old buffalo hands say. As a warning against befriending any buffalo, new employes at bison ranges are told about old-timers Dick Rock and A. H. Cole, who raised buffalo from calves, then trained, rode and exhibited them. Ultimately, Rock's favorite buffalo, for no apparent reason, gored him to death and wouldn't give up the body until shot. Cole turned his back just once on a six-year-old "pet"—and was fatally gored.

Horns lowered, two bull bison square off in a head-on shoving match. During the summer mating season, bulls paw the earth, bellow angrily and batter each other for the right to possess any cow in breeding condition.

The bison shows extraordinary traits right from birth. After a nine-month gestation period, usually ending in late spring, the buffalo cow (followed by several "godmothers") goes into a thicket and gives birth to a 50-pound, reddish-tan calf. Within five minutes, the shiny little creature rises, suckles and may even run. Easily tamed, he will follow a man like a puppy, though a month later he is so suspicious of the same man that he is apt to attack.

In five or six weeks the buffalo calf begins to graze, and within a year he is weaned. Full growth—about 1300 pounds for a cow, 2000 pounds or more for a large bull—is reached in seven or eight years. By then the buffalo has developed two hoary, semi-curved horns. He has two extra ribs, giving him 14 on each side to 13 for his cattle relatives. His coat has turned dark brown, only to shed each spring and hang in ragged patches everywhere except on his head, hump and forequarters. To relieve the itch caused by shedding and the stings of insects, the monster massages himself by rolling on the ground. By October, he has a woolly new coat that will repel the severest temperatures.

The bison's rugged self-sufficiency is the prime reason why farmers began raising him; herds now graze in many U.S. states and in western Canada. Though nearly twice as large as a domestic cow, bisons can live on one-third less grazing land, eat grass that cattle won't touch and prudently ration themselves if faced with a food shortage. Moreover, bison meat, which sells well in western markets, tastes like beef.

Rounding up buffalo, though, is a far cry from herding cattle. Last November, for instance, eight cowboys and their horses at the Wichita Mountains refuge rounded up 1200 buffalo, herd by herd, some scattered as far as ten miles from the pens. It was a month-long job! As manager Howard stressed, "We can make the buffalo go anyplace *he* wants to go."

To make the buffalo want to go toward the corrals, the cowboys rode up from three directions, causing *most* of each herd to move toward the "unguarded" area. About 25 stubborn beasts didn't want to go anywhere. Since the cowboys have learned that an infantry division can't budge these critters, they were bypassed—and later counted from a helicopter—while the "cooperative" buffalo were encouraged to move into a series of ten fenced pastures that gradually narrowed into corrals.

After the young were vaccinated and branded, most of this group were freed to live out their 20-to-30-year life-span just as their ancestors did in Indian days. Forty-seven two-year-olds were either sold for $235 each to ranchers and breeders or given to nonprofit institutions, while 150 surplus bulls and cows were butchered and sold to individuals who had applied in advance. Although the refuge was created to perpetuate the bison, its manager must continue to get rid of about 200 buffalo each year. "The range can only graze a thousand head," said Howard. "So our problem, in effect, is having too many buffalo."

Similar fall roundups, necessitated by overpopulation, are held at Fort Niobrara National Wildlife Refuge in Nebraska, National Bison Range in Montana, Sully's Hill National Game Preserve and Theodore Roosevelt National Memorial Park in North Dakota, and Custer State Park in South Dakota. In Canada, there is an annual roundup at Alberta's Elk Island National Park, which has a herd of 800 buffalo. As long as the "king of the range" causes "problems" like this, we can be assured that the buffalo will always roam.

BRINGING BACK THE CHESTNUT TREE

J. C. Furnas

One black day in 1904, H. W. Merkel, forester for the New York Zoological Society's Bronx Zoo, spotted trouble in his chestnut trees—tops dying back, bark going yellowish and cracking into messy "cankers." Dr. W. A. Murrill, an expert from the New York Botanical Garden, focused his microscope and found a previously unknown fungus, *Endothia parasitica*, a blight destined to be more destructive to the chestnut than any epidemic disease has ever been to human beings.

At the time, the American chestnut (*Castanea dentata*) was king of hardwoods from Maine to Tennessee, from Illinois to the Carolinas. Forest-grown trees often exceeded 100 feet in height, mast-straight, six feet in breast-high diameter. Donald Culross Peattie has described the view from an Appalachian mountaintop of the unbroken chestnut forest below gloriously "waving with creamy-white blossoms in the crowns of ancient trees, so that it looked like a sea with white combers plowing across. . . ."

Planted as a shade tree, the chestnut grew faster than oak, yet was just as stately—a shadow-rich dome of glossy, sawtoothed leaves, with white blossoms each spring. In usefulness it surpassed all the oaks, maples, tulip poplars and hickory trees.

The chestnut tree's tannin, as rich in the wood as in the bark, was important enough in leather tanning to make felling and chipping chestnut a small industry in the Carolina uplands. The timber, though not as strong as oak, took glue better, making it a fine veneer base. Highly decay-resistant, it was widely used in house frames, mine props, fence posts and rails, railroad ties, utility poles. And every fall showers of big, sweet, shiny-brown nuts pattered down from the prickly burrs: food for squirrels, game birds, deer, mice—and men. (Chestnuts used to bring $7 a bushel; they were in demand for roasting and as stuffing for turkeys.)

Now this lordly and valuable tree was under deadly attack. The blight, it turned out, was native to China. But the Oriental species of chestnut, having lived with the fungus as it evolved over thousands of years, had developed a high resistance. Relatively unharmed by the infectious organism themselves, they were nevertheless able to pass it on. The fungus probably crossed the Pacific on nursery-imported stock in the 1890's. In addition to the epidemic spreading out from New York City, the blight soon was found on trees of European and Oriental origin on Canada's Pacific coast and on Japanese chestnut trees in a North Carolina nursery.

How the fungus kills was soon plain. Spores of the organism, carried by the wind or on the feet of birds and insects, lodge in cracks or wounds in the chestnut's bark. There they sprout and grow into mats of fungus that clog the water and sap ducts of the inner bark layers. The fungus then works out to the surface in a visible canker that spreads until the trunk is girdled and death ensues. (The Dutch elm disease that now imperils American elms is a cousin fungus, although spread by insects.) One infected tree usually involves several others within a year, and these then spread the blight in geometric progression.

Experiments taught tree experts that the blight was unaffected by tree surgery, spraying or injection of chemicals. Moving some 25 miles a year, it was out of hand before its full ferocity was grasped. Pennsylvania hoped to stop it east of the Appalachians by cutting a wide belt clean of chestnut all across the state. But before cutting had progressed very far, the blight jumped the line.

Between 1913 and 1923 the sickness swept Virginia and invaded the southerly mountains. By the late 1930's the limits of the tree's natural range were reached, and the forward march of the scourge halted. Behind stood the ghastly spectacle of millions of great trees stark in death, gradually losing their bark to loom like pale-gray ghosts among the green woodlands. A few adult specimens were untouched, in plantings outside the natural range—in Missouri,

Healthy leaves and burrs often grow from the stumps of American chestnut trees blighted by fungus. These sprouts may live for a season or two, but usually die before becoming saplings because the stumps still carry the fungus and new sprouts have no more resistance to deadly blight than the parent trees.

Wisconsin, on the West Coast. But for all practical purposes, the American chestnut was finished.

Unable to halt the epidemic, scientists at once began to look for ways of helping the tree to come back. Theoretically, a lucky mutation of one of the very few tough individuals still surviving within the natural range area could found a blight-resistant variety. So the U.S. Forest Service sought out such survivors and cut scions from them to graft onto healthy Asian trees. Dr. Jesse D. Diller, formerly of the Northeastern Forest Experiment Station at Upper Darby, Pennsylvania, was able to confirm some 180 genuine survivors in the old range area. Scions cut from these were regularly sent to volunteer "cooperators" in 17 states for grafting and for crossbreeding.

To get the specific crossings they want, tree breeders use the same devices as breeders of hybrid corn: Paper bags protect the blooms, pollen is applied by hand, string-mesh bags shield the nuts from squirrels. Since trees are far taller than Iowa corn, the men must be part steeplejack, working on 30-foot A-ladders with legs wrapped tightly around the top rungs to leave their hands free to pollinate the blooms.

It is all very slow-paced. Tree breeding takes time, time, time. But there is a payoff. A chestnut-breeding project near New Haven, Connecticut, sponsored by the Connecticut Agricultural Experiment Station, has produced several combinations of Asian and American chestnuts and chinquapins—the genetic details are dizzying—gloriously fulfilling early promise. With their mast-straight growth, well above 40 feet, they are chestnut trees worthy of the old tradition. And they are free of the disease that tortures the vulnerable cousin trees around them.

Scientists have already made great strides in their

In this Currier and Ives print, as in Longfellow's famous poem, a village blacksmith plies his trade "under a spreading chestnut tree." The chestnut was once regarded as a typically American tree and a symbol of strength and durability. Yet, by the early part of this century, it had nearly vanished from the American landscape.

search for the blight-resistant chestnut tree. But more research must be done. The procedure for producing one resistant tree is still a long and very costly one. With present methods a tree must be 15 to 20 years old before experimenters can fully test its resistance to the blight. Dr. Richard Jaynes and his colleagues at the Connecticut Agricultural Experiment Station are searching for a way to spot the hardier trees when they are only about five years old, still in the seedling stage. By choosing the most resistant young seedlings this early, they could save the time and cost of raising both resistant and nonresistant seedlings and young trees for many years.

Researchers must also find a simpler and more economical way to propagate the trees, since most chestnut tree nuts do not "breed true," and a young plant that grows from a nut may not have the blight resistance of its parent tree. This problem, too, is being attacked, and perhaps eventually a true-breeding nut can be produced. Scientists are also experimenting with better methods of grafting, at present the only method of reproducing blight-resistant trees.

Dr. Jaynes is optimistic that these problems will be solved within the next few years. When that time arrives, and the chestnut tree becomes again a familiar sight throughout America, we shall be able to say proudly that we have indeed succeeded in bringing back the chestnut tree.

THE TRUMPETER RETURNS FROM OBLIVION

Robert Murphy

In the wilderness of southwestern Montana, 40 miles from the town of West Yellowstone, lies the wild and spacious Centennial Valley. Perched amid snowcapped peaks some 6600 feet above sea level, the valley contains great marshes, three shallow blue lakes and several sparkling streams.

It is a beautiful, untroubled spot. And it is here, at the Red Rock Lakes National Wildlife Refuge, that one of the rarest and most beautiful of our waterfowl, the wild trumpeter swan, lives and multiplies. At one time near extinction, the great bird has been delivered from final annihilation, and the story is one of the most heartwarming in the whole field of wildlife conservation.

Once the wild trumpeter swan—a huge, graceful, gleaming-white bird—ranged over much of the central part of the continent, from Alaska south to Missouri, wintering in vast numbers in the Ohio and Mis-

sissippi valleys, the lower Columbia River valley and along the Gulf of Mexico. Then man's guns began to exact their heavy toll. By the mid-1930's, with fewer than a hundred of these wild swans left, militant conservationists finally set out to save this heritage of our past.

Early in May 1966, my wife and I drove into the Red Rock Lakes Refuge to see these trumpeters. Eldon McLaury, the wildlife-management biologist, took us to the edge of a lake—and there I glimpsed my first pair of trumpeters, floating with the special grace that characterizes all swans. They weren't far from shore. Indeed, the fact that they like to swim along a shoreline is one of the characteristics that made the trumpeter so vulnerable to hunters. In contrast, the whistling swan, our other native and a close cousin of the trumpeter, gathers in flocks far out on large lakes.

Serene and untroubled by our presence, this pair of trumpeters swam slowly away with their long necks erect and their heads held high. The somewhat smaller whistling swan also carries itself this way; it is only the mute swan of Europe that curves its neck.

The largest of our waterfowl, trumpeters are five feet long, have a wingspread of seven feet or more and attain a weight of 35 pounds. So shining white is their plumage that in flight they can be seen at a great distance. They have black bills and feet, and a deep, resonant call, clear and trumpetlike, which can be heard a mile or more away. In fall and winter, gathered in flocks, they sometimes hold songfests that build in a crescendo and end in long wailing notes. Softened by distance, these vocalizations are one of the most stirring sounds in nature.

Despite their size, trumpeters are fast swimmers and strong, graceful fliers. They get into the air with a flapping run over the water's surface, fly with neck extended and feet tucked under their tail. When traveling any distance, they fly in angular lines and often at considerable heights. To alight on the water, they glide down majestically, spread their feet before them and "ski" to a halt on the broad webs.

Trumpeters are thought to mate for life, according to Winston E. Banko, who was for years refuge manager at Red Rock Lakes and wrote the authoritative *The Trumpeter Swan* for the U.S. Fish and Wildlife Service. Their huge nests, five or six feet across, are made of marsh plants and often sit on top of a muskrat house. The female, or pen, incubates a clutch of two to ten half-pound eggs for about 35 days, covering them with down and plants when she leaves the nest to feed. The male, or cob, stays on guard nearby.

Hatched in June, the baby trumpeters, or cygnets,

A pair of trumpeter swans fly over snow-covered Montana hills. Their unmistakable resonant bugling is rarely heard outside a few national parks and refuges. In recent years trumpeters have made a comeback and may someday return to other portions of their original range, which extended from the Carolinas to Alaska.

leave the nest for the water as soon as their gray down is dry. In October they are ready to fly. Their parents skim low over the water, several hundred feet ahead of them, calling encouragement. The cygnets follow excitedly, running over the water and beating their wings until at last they, too, are airborne.

In earlier years the trumpeter was able to withstand the drain on its numbers by natural enemies such as coyotes and eagles. But the pioneer settlers relished tender young swan as a change from deer and buffalo meat, and the fur trade soon learned the value of swan skins. Trumpeter down made the best quilts, feather beds and powder puffs; the quills, hard but elastic, were perfect for pens. Later, around the turn of the century, these spectacular birds were suddenly in great demand for zoos, parks and estates. The young, captured before they could fly, brought a princely $50 a pair, and were shipped all over the United States and across the Atlantic. The remaining few retreated to remote areas of the West.

Market hunting was outlawed in 1900, and the Migratory Bird Treaty made with Great Britain in 1918 ended all hunting of swans. But these measures were almost too late. Duck hunters, trophy seekers and poachers continued to shoot swans illegally, settlers encroached on their nesting grounds, and it was thought by many to be only a matter of years before their total extermination.

It was J. N. (Ding) Darling, a famous newspaper cartoonist, militant conservationist and first president of the National Wildlife Federation, who really saved the swans. For years, through his cartoons and speeches, he publicized the cause of wildlife conservation. Appointed chief of the U.S. Bureau of Biological Survey in 1934, he insisted—as other conservationists long had—that a sanctuary for the trumpeters must be established. The refuge at Red Rock Lakes finally became a reality in 1935.

At the time, the Biological Survey reported that there were only 73 trumpeters in the United States— 46 of them at Red Rock, a few additional pairs in Yellowstone Park and in Idaho. But rigorous protection turned the tide, and slowly the great birds began to multiply. In 1966 aerial surveys counted 878 wild trumpeters in the contiguous United States, 417 of them in Montana; about 1000 more live in western Canada and Alaska. Also, 84 live in captivity in the United States. Thus, in contrast with the passenger pigeon, which was exterminated, and the whooping crane, whose fate is still touch-and-go, the trumpeter swan is one of the few severely threatened bird species to be substantially re-established.

Somewhere along the way, while they were taking a beating from the hunters' guns and traps, a remarkable thing happened to the trumpeters. They quit migrating, and the swans today keep to their remote western fastnesses, summer and winter.

At Red Rock Lakes several warm springs remain open all winter. The refuge managers have been able to use them to provide open water for the swans even when the temperature plunges to 25 below. For, besides illegal shooting, the trumpeters face another danger when they leave their wilderness homes. They have an almost suicidal predilection for flying into the sides of barns or other man-made obstructions, or for hanging themselves on fences and telephone wires. "Give them half a chance," says one refuge executive, "and they'll kill themselves."

With the continued growth of the flocks of wild trumpeters, some are now being moved from Red Rock Lakes to other protected areas. Eventually it may be easier for the public to glimpse them. It is doubtful, however, if we will ever see great strings of trumpeters moving majestically across the sky, as in the days of the early settlers. It is a serious loss, for they are a truly magnificent sight, with wild voices that stir the blood. Yet we should be grateful, for it is better to have them where they are, in seclusion, than not to have them at all.

TO SAVE
THE BLUEBIRD

Robert Gannon

The early-spring wind gathered itself on the Illinois plains and whipped icy drops into our faces. But my companion and I hardly noticed; we were preoccupied with the plight of three baby bluebirds.

We had first seen that something was wrong a few minutes before, as Dr. T. E. Musselman, biologist and former president of Gem City Business College, was driving me along one of his bluebird-house routes on the outskirts of Quincy. One bird was flying frantically around her box—swooping toward the ground, darting in and out of the opening.

We stopped, walked to the birdhouse set atop an old stump and lifted the cover. Three tiny, naked bluebirds, mouths agape in fright, were straining to hold their heads above water. A fourth was drowned. The birdhouse drainage holes had become stopped up. Tenderly, Dr. Musselman cupped the shivering creatures in his big hand. "Put them under your shirt," he said. "I'll clean out this mess."

Next to my skin the babies gradually lost their iciness, slowly stopped their plaintive peeping. The doctor, meanwhile, unplugged the drainage holes, put in some fresh, dry bluegrass he kept in his car trunk, and formed a rough nest. Warm, dry and content, the tiny birds were transferred back to the house. The mother sped to her babies as we moved away.

About that same time in Roslin, Ontario, a young farmer found in one of his half-dozen birdhouses a bluebird mother and three miniature eggs, the first bluebird eggs he had seen in three years. And Stiles Thomas, a New Jersey insurance broker, was going the rounds of his bluebird housing project—105 separate domiciles that literally brought the bluebird back to Bergen County.

These people, and a thousand more across the United States and Canada, belong to a loose-knit group whose goal is to save the bluebird from extinction. Years ago it seemed that every corner fence post —from the western plains to the East Coast, from Mexico to Manitoba—contained a bluebird nest. Bluebirds once labored from dawn to dusk to rid farm and garden of ants, weevils and other garden pests. A hike through the fields wasn't really complete in those days if you saw no flashing bit of radiant blue, heard no warbling "tru-a-ly, tru-a-ly."

Today in many areas you may look for weeks before catching sight of this little thrush, whose traits have been immortalized by poets and songwriters, the bird whose song once told us of spring.

Why did the bluebird population drastically decrease? The answers generally boil down to three: indiscriminate mass insect spraying; icy winter temperatures in the South and late-spring snowstorms all over; and lack of nesting places.

Poisoning of bluebirds by insecticides has not been scientifically proved. But bluebirds feed largely on insects, and many ornithologists point out that if poisoned insects are eaten, toxin is passed on to the birds, and if they don't die, their eggs may be infertile.

Unusually rugged weather, even when coupled with mass poisoning, may be only a temporary setback. Unfortunately, the housing shortage is long-term. Stiles Thomas puts the problem plainly: "Bluebirds like to nest in hollow trees and fence posts and in old woodpecker holes. But man cuts down dead trees, fills up holes, prunes dead branches and replaces wood posts with metal." What nesting space is left is often usurped by nonmigrating house sparrows and starlings, which move in when the homeowners go south for the winter.

What can be done? In Decatur, Illinois, Frank Irwin saw bluebirds flying around a spot where winter

296

sleet had felled an old apple tree. Irwin quickly built a box in his basement and nailed it atop a fence post. Three weeks later, five baby bluebirds were cheeping hungrily within. Now Irwin, with aid from the Decatur Audubon Society, has birdhouses spread over the entire county.

This, say most experts, is the way people can help. Thousands of well-designed and well-placed nest boxes strung across the land may, with luck, turn the tables and bring back the dying species. This has already been done in many places. During the past 11 years, William L. Highhouse of Warren, Pennsylvania, has headed "Operation Bluebird" in Warren County. This group has placed more than 200 bluebird houses and has fledged more than 4000 bluebirds. Last spring, Highhouse and others participating in "Operation Bluebird" observed 170 pairs of bluebirds: There were 730 eggs, 650 young, 615 fledglings. Highhouse reports there are now "more than enough bluebirds in Warren County." This is a prime example of results that can be achieved by dedicated work.

New York 4-H clubs are engaged in an extensive bluebird housing project throughout the state. In 1967, under the general direction of Wayne T. Bell, Jr., of Cornell University's department of conservation, about 2000 bluebird nest boxes were placed by some 200 4-H'ers. More than double that number were put out last year. Bell stated: "The total bluebird population in New York is still at a critical stage, but it has shown good signs of holding at present levels, thanks primarily to youth groups such as 4-H and the many amateur naturalists who are also taking part in this concerted effort to bring the bluebird back in New York State."

About 45 years ago, Dr. Musselman of Quincy constructed a well-designed bluebird-house prototype. Tramping in the woods, he bumped against a rotten willow stump. It fell and split open. There, nestled in an old woodpecker home, were three bluebird babies. The doctor carefully measured the gourd-shaped cavity and entrance hole, then closed up the stump as best he could. Back home, he constructed 27 boxes patterned on the original. He placed them along fence rows on the city's outskirts, and the first year bluebirds came and nested in almost every one of the houses;

Perched on the branch of a blossoming apple tree, a male bluebird announces his territory. Bluebirds often set up housekeeping in orchards or along roadsides. The female builds a grass nest in a treehole or birdhouse. But after the young have been hatched, the male cares for them, while the female builds a new nest—or renovates the old one— in preparation for the arrival of another brood.

three quarters of them had fledglings by summer's end.

Through the years Musselman built and set out more and more houses. Ruddy-faced and energetic despite his advancing years, he still travels over the countryside in semiweekly trips, repairing, replacing and cleaning out more than 1000 houses with which he has lined the roads within a 100-mile radius of Quincy, Illinois.

OUR VANISHING TIDELANDS

Polly Redford

Along the Gulf Coast and most of our seaboard from Florida to Massachusetts, a long greenish-brown cushion lies between solid ground and open ocean. Without it, the land would be gnawed away by the sea. This cushion is made of soft materials, mostly sand and mud held together by huge mats of tough, resilient rushes and grasses. Endless amounts of water can be hurled upon it; each grain of sand, each blade of grass, acts as a tiny baffle catching and holding the water back. And twice a day, like a sponge, it slowly soaks up the flooding tide, impounding the water until it subsides.

No one word includes the whole of this spongy natural barrier; we speak instead of bays, basins, lagoons, sounds, creeks, deltas, sandbanks, marshes, mangroves, mud flats and oyster bars. But whether they are covered twice a day or only twice a year, it is the tides that shape them and give them life.

Tidelands, then, are all of that long, low, drowned country where fresh waters merge with salt. Most people, seeing only a monotony of mud and grass, sand and silence, think of them as desolate wastes, uninhabitable, therefore worthless. Besides, they are buggy. The bugs themselves are a sign of life. So are the millions of birds that live in the marshes, and the millions more that migrate from northern to southern tidelands every year. So, too, are the clams and crabs, the oysters and lobsters that are now such luxuries, and the myriad fish—salmon, sturgeon, shad, flounder, weakfish, pompano, snapper, striped bass, redfish, bluefish, tautog, anchovy, sand lance, herring, alewife, mackerel, menhaden, silversides, smelt and others—that are found there.

But even if tidelands were lifeless, we would need them as safety valves against major storms. Without them, storm tides pile higher and higher upon the shore, overflowing harbors, sucking away beaches and roads. And by meeting the ocean and impounding its overflow, they gather many of its riches, since the richest part of the Atlantic and the Gulf of Mexico is the shallow, sloping continental shelf that lies just seaward of our tidelands. Only recently have marine scientists learned how the wealth of the two is tied together; and only recently have the rest of us begun to realize that instead of fighting the sea, we have much more to gain by farming it.

Our continental shelf and tidelands combine to make our south and east coasts the largest, most productive in the world. In the swamps and marshes alone, biologists have discovered an annual growth of living matter equal to that of the most fertile farmlands. For tidelands trap the silt and organic matter that rivers wash down from the land, holding them to be fertilized again and again by new loads of minerals and salts carried in from the sea.

Among the shallow bays and creeks, the ebbing, flowing tide spreads all these ingredients out in the sun and blends them. What follows is an extraordinary bloom of life. It blooms in the surface water, where microscopic vegetables called phytoplankton grow in fantastic numbers; and on the bottom, where marine algae and grasses also draw substance from the water and energy from the sun; and in the marshes, where thick mats of decaying grasses make a compost of proteins, vitamins and carbohydrates.

And on the flats there's an algal scum, just enough to give the top of the mud the faintest tinge of green. Ten years ago someone thought of taking a section of mud and measuring the life there, only to find that one pound of mud may yield more food each year than many pounds of grass.

All this is only plant life, so-called primary production. It does not include protozoans, copepods, or the countless tiny wiggling things that only scientists can name; nor does it include the worms and oysters, shrimps and clams that filter this rich broth and add their own proteins to the mixture. These, in turn, are eaten by crustaceans and small fish, which themselves become food for larger fish and birds and mammals, whose wastes add still more proteins, vitamins, oils and amino acids to what is now called the ecosystem.

So much lives and grows and breeds in our tidelands that more than half of the saltwater fish and shellfish that we take are called "estuarine dependent," which means that they either spawn or hatch here, or spend some vital stage of their lives here, or feed upon the life that flows from here out over our continental shelf, where 90 percent of our offshore seafoods are harvested. Thus, tidelands represent the livelihood of about 100,000 American fishermen,

whose three-billion-pound catch paid them $250 million in 1965.

Still, we Americans go right on treating our tidelands as sewers and garbage dumps. We drain them, dredge them, fill them with rubble—and then enter these "improvements" on our tax rolls. Or we build massive piers, seawalls and dikes as fortresses to repel the tides. This may be fine for engineers and contractors, but not for taxpayers—or tidelands.

Fortunately, however, all along our coasts people are working to save what they can. At Cape May, New Jersey, a small but determined chapter of the Izaak Walton League is leading the fight for county action to preserve 35,000 acres of coastal marshes. On the Gulf Coast, the Nature Conservancy has bought 1600 acres of flats and mangroves in Rookery Bay and has an option on 1000 more. To protect Mobile Bay, the National Wildlife Federation joined with sportsmen, citizen groups and the state conservation department to push through a complete revision of fresh- and salt-water pollution laws. In Massachusetts, a coalition of conservation groups pushed through in 1965 the model Coastal Wetlands Act, which allows the state to restrict action damaging to coastal wetlands unless the landowner can prove that the restriction deprives him of practical use of that area. If he proves it, the state may either abandon the restriction or take the land by eminent domain.

But not all tidelands can become parks or preserves. We need other methods, a variety of them, to administer the nation's shoreline as an ecological unit. Several bills have been introduced in Congress which mark the beginning of an overall policy for these misunderstood, mismanaged areas.

To pass even limited tidelands legislation will take strong popular support—not just from people who understand the aesthetics of marshlands and their importance to game and conservation, but from those who understand their economic value. Some Americans, of course, find it profitable to keep tidelands just as they are—divided among hundreds of ineffectual, conflicting jurisdictions. But this is something the rest of us can no longer afford—not if we hope to have fish or birds or open space left on our shores. No nation, even the richest, is rich enough to throw so much away.

As viewed from the air, Cape Cod's Nauset Marsh is a lush green carpet of marsh grass pockmarked by salt pools and laced by tidal channels. Among the most fruitful lands on earth, salt marshes not only harbor rich wildlife communities but indirectly support offshore fisheries by discharging nutrients into coastal waters.

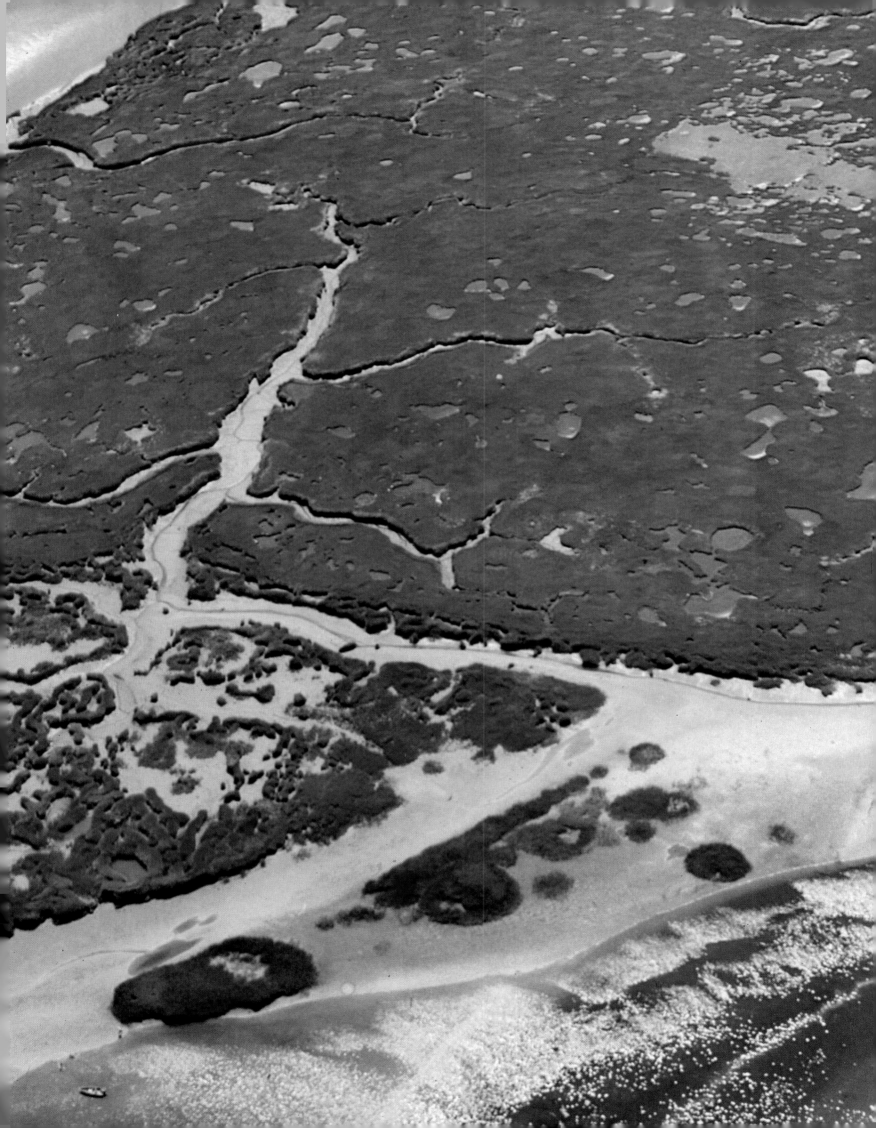

Chapter Three

Enjoying the World Around Us

*The small miracles of the natural world that are available in backyards, puddles,
roadsides and vacant lots can offer the same sort of excitement to us all
that scientists find in exploring such exotic areas as coral reefs and arctic tundra.
Curiosity and a willingness to watch and listen closely are the only essentials.*

BE A BACKYARD EXPLORER

Edwin Way Teale

For 20 years I have found fun and relaxation in exploring the strange world of the insects close to home. Our backyard on Long Island, less than 25 miles from New York City, is little different from other suburban yards. It is about 75 by 75 feet, has a grassplot, a maple tree, a few rosebushes, a rock garden. Yet it holds a menagerie of fabulous creatures, as does yours.

Stop and see what is taking place under leaves and in the grass. A close look will lead you into a wonderland in which your flower beds and grassplots become forests and jungles inhabited by creatures as strange as any found in Tasmania or Timbuctoo.

Like a streamlined armored car, a beetle looms up over the horizon line of a leaf. It is one of the strongest animals in the world—some beetles can support hundreds of times their weight. If an African elephant did as well it could carry a freight train on its back.

From the tip of a rose shoot, a frosty-gray robber fly, designed like a pursuit plane, darts aloft, snatches a gnat from the air and returns to its perch. It has seen its tiny victim through bulging compound eyes that contain as many lenses as the eyes of several hundred human beings. An ant runs this way and that; it is following a scent-trail of special secretions laid down by others of its kind.

Nearby, a curious swelling on a leaf forms the edible home of a baby gallfly. In depositing her eggs within the tissues of the leaf, its mother injected chemicals that caused the swelling, or gall. Snug within a dining room equipped with edible walls, the minute grub dwells in safety, protected from enemies from without and provided with ample food within.

As soon as you begin to look closer, new vistas open up. I remember the morning I first came upon a dew-spangled iris leaf from which a score of small, oval objects stuck up, perched like lollipops at the tops of threadlike stalks. These were the eggs of a gauzy-winged, golden-eyed lacewing fly. All over the country such eggs are laid wherever plant lice are found. From them hatch aphis lions—immature lacewings resembling minute lizards—that spend their days consuming immense numbers of plant lice. So ravenous are these six-legged lions that the first to hatch would devour all its brothers and sisters if the eggs were not on stalks to keep them out of reach.

I also recall vividly my first encounter with milkmaid ants. Clustered along a rose shoot were a hundred or more plant lice, rotund little creatures placidly sucking sap through hollow, needle-sharp beaks. So thick were they that they stood shoulder to shoulder like a flock of feeding sheep. Among the aphids half a dozen black carpenter ants were stretching out their antennae, gently stroking the backs of the smaller insects. This "milking" induces the aphids to give off droplets of a sweet fluid which the ants eat. Moreover, the ants guard the plant lice from insect enemies. They even take aphids into their nests in autumn, keep them safe during the winter, and place them "out to pasture" when spring arrives. Among insects found in Baltic amber, ants and aphids have been discovered imprisoned together. Thus ants have been tending and milking their insect cattle for at least 20 million years. Yet this activity, ages old, is one you can see on almost any summer day in almost any backyard garden.

Scattered among the plants of our backyard every spring, we find shining spots of snow-white foam. Each snow-speck, about the size of a pea, is the foam-castle of a baby froghopper. Sucking sap from plant stems, the tiny, 1/8-inch-long froghopper produces

*A female cecropia moth deposits her oval eggs on the
stem of a fern. The cecropia flies at night and thus
avoids many predators. When the light strikes its feathery
antennae, the insect drops to the ground and hides.*

These newly hatched lacewing fly larvae will climb down the hairlike stalks on which their eggs were laid.
If the eggs were laid in clusters, the firstborn might eat the other eggs. Usually the female lacewing lays her
eggs near an aphid colony, and the voracious little predators, also called aphis lions, start feeding at once.

the froth, blowing up each bubble with a unique bellows formed of overlapping plates beneath its body. Hidden within the foamy covering, the froghopper is invisible to its enemies and is protected from drying out in the heat of the sun. It lives within its bubble walls until it reaches maturity, develops wings and flies away.

Scientists have described nearly 1,000,000 different kinds of insects. Comparatively few are injurious. Many are beneficial. And all are interesting. You don't have to be a professional to enjoy watching them. The equipment you need to enter their world is simple and inexpensive. A guide, such as Frank E. Lutz's *Field Book of Insects*, will help identify the creatures you meet. A strong pocket magnifying glass will put you on intimate terms with the more minute Lilliputians. If photography is a hobby of yours, there is a whole new world to record on film.

Many of the things you see will puzzle you—they puzzle scientists. Two ants meet. They touch antennae. They twiddle their feelers. They tap each other. They move on. What have they been doing? Communicating by touch? Some insect students believe so. One European scientist even went so far, some years ago, as to compile an "Ant Dictionary" in which he listed his idea of what the many different antennae taps mean.

Carpenter ants are among several species of ants that
milk aphid "cows" by stroking them with antennae.
The aphids excrete a sweet liquid, which the ants drink.

You see winged ants, males and females, pouring from the ground on a mating and dispersal flight. Notice the weather afterward. I have never known ants to swarm in this way except when at least 24 hours or more of clear and settled weather have followed.

Ants, crickets and aphids are usually old settlers in a yard. Many other insects are transients, pausing to feed among the leaves and flowers. Wasplike parasites search for caterpillars—in some cases depositing eggs that have the ability to multiply themselves so that hundreds of individuals result from the placing of a single egg. Honeybees range among the blossoms.

Dragonflies—creatures that began life under water, breathing through gills like a fish—hawk over the yard, scooping flying insects out of the air in nets formed of their six bunched and spiny legs. And a yard may be visited by one of those gorgeous creatures of the night, the great American silk moths—the cecropia, the luna, the polyphemus. Our largest and most beautiful moths, they emerge from their cocoons, live and mate and die without once tasting food. All their eating is done in the caterpillar state.

The real globe-trotter among these transients is the familiar black-and-orange monarch butterfly. Some travel on four-inch wings all the way from Hudson Bay to Florida. Millions of these butterflies move southward all over the United States—yet not one among them has ever made the trip before. Instinct, the most mysterious compass of all, guides them on their journey.

During late summer and early fall, a number of insects "engage rooms for the night" within flowers that close during the hours of darkness. Once with my flashlight I came upon a large robber fly that had pushed its way into the heart of a rose after sundown. The petals closed loosely around it and thus it spent the night, snug and protected, until the rose opened in the warmth of the sunshine next day.

A flashlight, incidentally, is a passport to special adventures in backyard exploring. Its beam, running through the tangles of grass, spotlighting leaves and twigs, sweeping across spider webs, traveling among the ridges and valleys of tree bark, picking out katydids and other singers of the dark, reveals a little-seen world of activity. In the circle of its light, sow bugs creep like midget armadillos, daddy longlegs go bobbing past with twin eyes that peer to either side at the top of little turrets, and pale, tan-colored moths hover in the air with eyes that shine like rubies.

Among the bushes, the beam spotlights a beautiful and ghostly creature—the snowy tree cricket. Its mellow, rhythmical song fills the late-summer nights. As you listen to its pulsing rhythm, take out your watch.

Count the number of calls in one minute. Divide that number by four and add 40. Then look at the thermometer. The number you have obtained and the temperature will almost always be the same. So responsive is this insect musician to the rise and fall of the mercury that it has been nicknamed the temperature cricket.

In exploring at home there is always the chance that you will make a discovery. For years, no one knew how a certain spider snared its prey; no one had ever seen it make a web. Then, in his backyard, a boy solved the problem. He saw the spider hastily construct a web after dark and take it down before dawn.

On Staten Island, within sight of Manhattan's skyscrapers, the late William T. Davis became a world-famous authority on American cicadas. Many of his researches were carried on in his own yard. And that most celebrated of all stay-at-home explorers, Jean Henri Fabre of France—"the Homer of insects"—spent half a century setting down the things he saw within the small area surrounded by his garden walls. As a boy, Fabre dreamed of journeying to the Andes and the Amazon. Poverty kept him from ever seeing faraway places. But he was able to find a lifetime of excitement, interest and new discovery no farther away than his own dooryard.

THE LAKE I LIVED WITH

Jean George

One summer, while my husband was absorbed in a research project, I was alone with a lake. Higgins Lake, on the Lower Peninsula of Michigan, is big, five miles across; deep, over 100 feet in spots; gouged out long ago by the ice blades of the glacier. Hugged by cottages and wilderness, it is, except for minor differences, any large, deep lake in the temperate zone. Day after day I slid beneath its surface with snorkel and mask, and at the end I understood more about a lake.

Symbol of calm, a lake is serene only on its mirror surface. Underneath is a world of tumult and turbulence as restless as the sea. In the apparently still shallows of a lake is such agitation that life is there only because it can hang on.

I first became aware of the battle for survival in a lake after watching a water scorpion, an insect that employs many devices to wrench a living from the water. I was drifting in the shallows, getting accustomed to my snorkel, when one of these two-inch bugs

Its body covered by a silvery film of air, a backswimmer clings to an aquatic plant. Lighter than water, the insect must anchor itself to stay submerged when at rest. The air film acts as a breathing chamber, allowing oxygen from the water to pass in and carbon dioxide to pass out. Backswimmers can stay submerged for up to six hours.

alighted close inshore and, with oarlike strokes of its long legs, rode to the bottom. Then, to my amusement, he threw up the slickest snorkel in the water business. It was a two-inch tube attached to the insect's breathing apparatus—in his tail—and extended to surface and air.

With a supply of oxygen assured, the scorpion settled to the problem of obtaining food. He kicked; and a swirl of silt went up, then settled over him like a blanket. Within this disguise he unfolded two nasty-looking knife blades. (The front legs work like jackknives, folding into themselves.)

A school of minnows darted past. There was a puff of silt, a flash of a blade and one less minnow. A small landslide on the bottom of the lake marked the spot where the scorpion dug in and, I assume, ate his meal. This done, the snorkel went up, the eyes appeared out of the mud and he waited for another passerby.

As I drifted along the shore under the surface, I saw above me a whirligig beetle, that swirling, twirling water bug seen on every stream, pond and lake. He saw me beneath him and spun away. I stood up and followed him. This time he spotted me in the air, dived and disappeared. No matter how I approached him, he saw me. For the whirligig has four eyes: two to peer down into the water below, two to peer up into the air above, because his enemies attack from both quarters.

Water insects are not really aquatic like the fish, but all have evolved ways to live in the water. The larva of a species of leaf beetle hunts under water all day, though he has no gills, nor does he have a snorkel like the scorpion's. His secret? He bores into the stems of water plants and takes a breath of almost pure oxygen. And when it is time to spin a cocoon, the larva simply pokes a hole in a plant stem and spins a waterproof bag around the opening. The plant fills the bag with fresh air while the leaf-beetle pupa sleeps down in the depths of the lake.

The diving beetles also have solved the problem of breathing under water without gills. Half submerged, I watched one of these brownish-black beetles tip head down into the water, lift his wings, fold in a supply of air and spin to the bottom like a skin diver with an air tank. Using this captured air, the beetle rowed all over the bottom looking for food. When the air grew stale the beetle surfaced and got a new supply.

At times I pushed out a little deeper and hung over the weed beds. Here the contest for survival was more than how to breathe. Among the grasses lay the logs and among the logs the spawning fish. Some, like the sunfish, were tending a nest of eggs. Others, like the male black bass, were baby-sitting. But all were in the weed beds for one reason—to protect their eggs and young.

One day I found an old black bass tending a cluster

of wriggly fry, adroitly herding them close to a log where they could suck the invisible plankton from the water. I circled the old fellow as he fanned his family. Silt is a serious problem in a lake. Even a small amount can smother fish eggs and small fry. So the bass was "dusting" and aerating his young.

I moved too quickly. The bass took fright and fanned too hard. Three or four of the youngsters were blown into the weeds. They seemed lost. But the father, either by scent—for a fish can smell—or by listening with his hidden ears or the many spots on his body that "hear," sped into the grasses, found them and nudged them home.

Then I noticed a big crayfish lurking under the log, one eyestalk crooked on the nestful of fry. The old bass swirled his tail. A puff of silt blew over the crayfish, and it wiggled its eyestalk. This was its last move. With a noiseless gulp, the bass had a crayfish dinner.

Several days later, over the weed beds, I watched the family life of a catfish. Both catfish parents tend the young, the fry traveling before the parents in a black bewhiskered cluster.

Catfish are usually nocturnal, but this family was drifting toward me in the daylight. I looked to see what had awakened them to activity. The great submarine shape of a snapping turtle came over the edge of a log. The parents hustled the young along until the turtle could no longer see them, then halted beside a stump. As the fish lay still, the death shroud of the lake—the silt—began to drift down on the fry. The old cat did an astounding thing: He opened his big, grinning mouth and engulfed a number of his young. Presently he spewed them out—and they seemed clean and aerated and shiny. He took the others group by group into his mouth and repeated the procedure.

One day, when my son and I were rowing on the lake, a bluish-green mass came moving toward us, windblown. I dipped into it with a towel. Much of it

A school of young bullheads swim under the watchful eye of a parent. Bullheads are square-tailed catfish living on the muddy bottoms of lakes, ponds and rivers. The male is a solicitous father. He builds a nest for his mate, guards her eggs until they hatch and helps care for the fry until they grow big enough to fend for themselves.

ran out through the cloth, but a few pinhead curios remained.

"Lake plankton," I explained to my son. "It's the microscopic life of a lake, although some bits of it are easily seen. This one is a tiny member of the lobster family. Some are plants, others animals. There are mollusks and tiny shellfish, sponges and spiny worms. Lake plankton is all the lowly forms of life, moving as a single mass in the water, providing food for everything in the lake—fish, snail, mussel, insect—and for one another."

Autumn came to chill the lake, and we were less eager spectators to the battle within Higgins Lake. However, from the shore we could sense the vigorous life in the water. The autumn weather had created the

Many inhabitants of the lake sleep away the night, but some predators, such as carp, frogs, leeches and water scorpions, are most active after sunset.

"overturn," that time in a lake when the bottom comes to the top, because the top has cooled and displaced the lighter water below.

On the warm Indian-summer evening before our departure we built a fire and watched the moon rise and cut a path across the water. I said to the children, "There is little dawn or twilight inside a lake because of the manner in which the water bends the light. So I wonder if there is moonlight down there?"

We stepped into the water, leaving our clothes like shells on the shore, and swam on the moonpath. Far out, we went under the surface and looked around. There seemed to be *no* moonlight under the lake. To see it we had to look up, where it glittered and danced on top.

My children surfaced and I followed. In the dusk of the moonshine I saw them run ashore, water dripping from their sleek bodies—and for a fleeting moment I understood that enormous transition in the world's history, when life pulled out of the dark sea and came leaping and singing into the moonlight.

The roads home from Michigan took us past many a lake. As each new one appeared, the knowledge of our own Higgins Lake enlivened the lapping waters with life and problems, and no lake was ever again just water.

THE MAGIC OF A MIDSUMMER NIGHT

Jean George

The maddest, the most marvelous night of the year is the night that falls on August 6, midway between the summer solstice (June 21) and the first day of autumn. But for the insects, the birds and the beasts, it is the many warm nights in late July and August, when the sun sits not far below the horizon and keeps the natural world up and shouting.

Most of us, only vaguely aware of these shatter-pated nights, miss their vibrant impact. Believing that we cannot see in the dark (actually, after about 45 minutes of adjustment, the human eye can see almost as well as an owl's and a lot better than a rabbit's), most of us are content to sit outside on a hot summer evening, staring sightlessly before us, slapping mosquitoes, only to retire precisely when things are warming up. So it was with my husband and me until a scientist friend urged us to go out in the dark and "see" how exquisitely nature equips her creations for the night.

"One way to see better," he said, "is to pick out a single sound and follow it to its source. The creature you find will help you understand the night."

So one summer night we concentrated on an individual sound out of that tin-pan jazz session of a July evening. It was a zany cat-purring that emanated from our window sill. We turned a flashlight in the direction of the sound. It ceased, we waited; it commenced, we crept forward . . . until we reached the concert artist, a small gray-and-green tree frog. In the dark he had crept to our window to lash out his tongue at insects flying for the light. From the apple tree, and even from our mailbox, came the voices of his kinsmen.

We picked him up and uncovered the mystery of how this land frog can reach odd places where he does not have to compete with other frogs for food. His feet are sticky. He can hang by one adhesive toe or climb on any surface—especially when he moves in the dew-moisture of the night.

Another night we followed a sound to a cricket. By moving and waiting, moving and waiting, we finally sat down beside one while he lifted his wings to a 45-degree angle and rubbed the saw-blade edges swiftly back and forth for an earsplitting call that told female crickets how to find the lover in the dark.

One night our flashlights led us to, of all things, a noisy worm. Craig, our son, had picked a sound to trace, like live wires snapping in the grass. There on a log was the larva of a wood-boring beetle, which makes a noise to frighten enemies.

This tracing of sounds has led us to roosting birds, for the cacophony in the half-light of a summer night very often keeps the night-sleeping birds up, and they sing. We have even discovered that some sparrows argue in the dark, waking up from time to time, perhaps to scold a neighbor who has taken too much toehold.

To track down sounds is revealing, but to start them is electrifying. Two summers ago an expert on frogs told us that he often started his laboratory bullfrogs into song by singing in a deep voice, "There is a tavern in the town." Unlike most frogs, which sing only to find mates, the bullfrog (our largest frog) likes to sing for the sheer joy of it, and will often chime in.

One night our whole family slipped down to a pond. John began, "There is . . ." and the children and I joined him. We repeated the song a few times, and then in the reeds beside us belled out a deep "Be drowned, be drowned," the refrain of the bullfrog. Four beats later another frog chimed in, then another and another, until the entire pool was a din.

But it didn't last. The children burst into laughter, and the sensitive artists hushed.

You can make other sounds at night to bring forth nocturnal dwellers. A long, wavery whistle at the edge of a graveyard will almost invariably bring a male screech owl winging within several feet of you to discover who is singing on his property. You might even hear him snap his bill, the owl's warning alarm in the dark, designed to scare off raccoons, foxes, cats and people. The timid field mouse can be called from its burrow at the foot of grass clumps and rocks. Sit quietly for a few minutes, then noisily kiss the back of your hand. Even the lowly mouse has a sense of pride in his property, and this imitation of a mouse sound brings him wide-eyed into the night to challenge his foe.

Sometimes we set a kerosine lantern in the yard. To it come the mayflies, caddis flies, electric-light bugs, the many moths—all insects equipped to see and travel by night. Each summer our most exciting "catch" is the big splashy female cecropia moth, largest of all U.S. silkworms. This amazing creature has a special secret that only the night unlocks. She gives out a scent in the cool dampness of a summer night that the male cecropias detect and follow with the tips of their antennae, from the unbelievable distance of a mile or more away.

Only last summer we captured a female cecropia, her clay-colored wings decorated with white-and-red eyespots, and put her in a box with a handkerchief over the top, secured with a rubber band. Then we blew out the light and waited, counting the meteors that shower down from the midsummer sky. An hour —and 63 falling stars—later, we lighted the lantern and saw that the box and the bush near her were covered with almost two dozen of these beautiful creations.

Plants, too, have their night secrets. The moonflowers, some water lilies and desert cacti bloom in darkness, to be pollinated by moths and night flies in exchange for food. One plant specially equipped by nature for the darkness is the yellow evening primrose, found along most country roads throughout the land. It opens just at dusk, so swiftly that it can be seen—and heard! Many an exciting evening in my childhood, as the sun sank, I would sit down in a clump of these flowers to watch. Presently I would hear a noise like popping soap bubbles and, as I looked closer, I could see the swelling buds burst open. Before my eyes the petals wrenched free, then, shaking and twisting, spread wide.

In addition to special night equipment, nature has devised one more artifice to keep life humming:

The screech owl, whose cry is more a whinny than a screech, flies through the night on wings silenced by downy-tipped flight feathers. The owl snatches insects in mid-air and pounces upon mice, frogs or snakes in meadows below.

Almost all things move on a time schedule—so that they will not have to compete too strenuously for space and food. This schedule is based not on clock time but on light time. When the light intensity reaches a bird's or mammal's "threshold," he pops awake or goes to sleep, whichever the case may be.

We often watch the light-timing in the twilight tick the birds off to sleep, each at a different minute. In our area the wren is the first to leave the work of the day. Then, as night slips up (for it rises rather than falls), and the last rays of sun remain in the treetops, the crows gather and argue over roosting spots. For the next 20 minutes the night songs of the phoebes, the sparrows and the thrushes are called off like signatures as these species go to sleep. The sun sets, the robin chirps on for about an hour, the swallows dive and dip after the rising insects until they can no longer see.

When the light is almost gone, the deer arise and begin eating. They will browse until it becomes too dark, then bed down until the early light of morning awakens them again. One summer in Michigan we found that the deer were so attuned to their moment of light that, driving along a country road, we could clock them. At exactly 18 minutes after sundown they began grazing the woodland meadows.

At this moment of almost no light there arises from the depths of the forest the most beautiful bird voice of the day: the sad, pensive cry of the wood pewee. I hear this song and I stop; I am crying for all the things in life I have never quite fulfilled. The song ends. I lift my head and the midsummer night is upon me.

That last note inaugurates bat time. Into the night come these wonderful winged mammals, equipped with their radar and sonar. They gorge on insects awakening over ponds and streams and lakes until they are stuffed; then they may retire for a nap, awakening to stuff and gorge again until the morning light drives them home.

Around 11 on a summer night the darkness becomes thick enough for the nocturnal mammals to awaken, the raccoons, skunks, mink, beaver, flying squirrels. These get up in the deepest dark to hunt

and train their young, then retire around two or three o'clock in the morning.

One night, camped along a stream, we watched a raccoon catch fish in the dark by chasing them into puddles left by cattle hooves. Rolling suddenly upon us came one of the greatest thrills of a summer night —the throbbing thunderstorm. The raccoon took cover by climbing a tree, ears back—apparently scared. We looked about us in the lightning flashes. Above us in the rookery there were frightened comments when the light awoke the crows. The fish turned upstream and lay still. The insects, even the mosquitoes, crawled under leaves.

With the passing of the storm, John and I came out from our shelter to find it almost dawn, the world wet and dripping. The good smell of damp earth filled our lungs. And then, softly out of the lifting darkness, came again the voice of the wood pewee. I stood listening, filled with admiration. For the morning song, in the same beat and same minor key as the twilight song, seemed not to carry the same sadness. Now there was a subtle lilt, a glad anticipation of the dawn and the return of the glorious sun.

WHY BE BLIND TO BEAUTY?

Donald Culross Peattie

That day the ambulance brought me home from a sojourn at death's door, the park pigeons looked to me like angels, their wings flashing bright and dark and white again as they banked at unheard command. Office girls walking home wore halos where the spring sunlight glinted in their hair. Overhead the street elms arched, and it seemed to me that never before had I seen the miracle of trees—fountains of life gushing out of the earth to fall in a million droplets of greening buds. From the fields meadowlarks raised praise to heaven. And heaven, I saw, arched over all the world, in its depths an infinite smile.

I knew then that I had seen the world as it really is, fair as on the first day that the Lord rested. That April

The raccoon has superior night vision and generally waits until dark to patrol its broad territory. Its wanderings may include a camp site where it can upend a garbage can and feed on scraps, a stream where crayfish can be grabbed in the shallows or an orchard where fruit can be shaken from the branches.

310

This delicate lacework spangled with gems is really the web of an orb-weaving spider hung with morning dew. Its fragile appearance belies its strength: Its viscous threads are so strong that they can easily stop a grasshopper in full flight. Both male and female spiders spin webs, and each species has its own pattern.

view of the world had the clarity of a religious revelation. And all that I have ever learned assures me that it was the true one. For we have not only the five senses to bring us sensations but an intellect wherewith to make order of their messages, to select, compose, relate and project these into beauty. Every normal being is born with these powers. Given this radiant earth, given the lively senses and the human mind —why be blind to beauty?

Yet often the dust we raise in our daily living beclouds the bright reality around us. As if the whole earth weren't on view, by blue-eyed day and dark-haired night—the running of grass before the wind, the stab of jeweled light from a dragonfly, the new moon in the twilight sky shining slim as the nail-paring of a goddess.

All the senses can bring us knowledge of the treasures of earth. There are the boles of trees, smooth as birch, shaggy as hickory, to feel. If there are not lilacs to smell, there may be sagebrush. The more you listen, the more you hear—swamp peepers or hidden fledglings, the lisping of cottonwoods, the clapping hands of lake waters. As for taste, there's the juice of a summer in a nibbled timothy stalk, and a plunge in the sea leaves the salt of living on your lips. All this becomes beauty only through your own response to it.

For nature, smiling and indifferent, does not press her treasures upon you. She lets them fall into the out-held and open hand. Too many of us go to her tightly clutching our preoccupations. Often it takes a conscious effort to put out of mind the black news in the day's paper and gaze at the field before me, at the long furrows newly turned. How straight, after all, can run the purposes of man! The trees, as I walk on, say each their names to me. And there in the grass the blue, broken cup of a robin's egg tells me that, in a world of loss and grief, hope is forever born again.

The beauty of nature is not just in the joys of the senses. The Psalmist knew it when he lifted up his eyes to the hills. Hills, and valleys made for homes, and the stars over them—from these comes our help. For the deepest beauty of the natural world lies not in its sheen and color, but in its order and meaning. On this agree the scientist and the religious teacher. When you make room for beauty, you cast out ugliness.

I suppose that nowhere on this various globe is there natural splendor more wonderful than the Grand Canyon of the Colorado. To stand upon its brink is to behold a vast sweep of space and depth and sunset color so profound in beauty that the immense silence welling up from it is eloquent. "If I were an American," says J. B. Priestley, "I should make my remembrance of it the final test of men, art and pol-

icies. I should ask myself: Is this good enough to exist in the same country as the Canyon?"

All of us have our yardsticks of superlative beauty —the redwoods, the Maine coast, the Great Smokies. It's good to use them—to recall them, and how you felt when you looked at them, how sure of your values, how reassured of some ultimate, enduring goodness. These experiences leave us a great fund of comfort and strength, and we can add to it daily by looking for more.

Did you see that a spider in the night spun her orb web in the bush by your door? It's still hung with dew, its careful geometry flashing like jewels. All the fern forests of the Carboniferous Age are reproduced for you upon a frosted pane. Look for the ancient wonder of stones, the fantasies in beach-worn stones, the glister in brook stones, the time-sculptured strength of field stones with lichens on them like maps of elfin islands. And a whole pageant of color and sound and scent is opened to you by the passage of a summer thunderstorm—the blue-black of the cumulonimbus cloud split by the Lucifer lightning, the triumphant drums of the thunder, the onslaught of rain, the million-tongued answer of leaves, and the reborn scents of earth.

Enjoyment of beauty is habit-forming; the longer your addiction, the more you look for new sources, try new approaches. I love best to see things in the light of early morning, emerging fresh from the bath of night. When there is fog or snow, one's familiar walk is simplified and mystified; an artist touched it, eliminating trivial details, emphasizing essential lines.

This view of things is what makes so enduring the work of ancient Chinese painters. Before beginning a picture, a master of this school would gaze at his subject every day for a year, in all the moods of nature, till he could have drawn it without looking at it. What he then painted was not photographic realism, but the very soul and essence of tree, mountain, mist or blossom. You too look at the same scene every day from bedroom or kitchen or office window. If, like me, you cannot paint, you will find it exciting, at least, to close your eyes now and see what you can remember of this picture you know so well. You'll find that your memory leaves out much detail, and, like a Chinese brush, paints essence of oak, or silo, or skyscraper. Yet open your eyes now, and as the actual scene rushes upon you with brilliant impact, you discover new lights, new angles, new possibilities of composition.

Like art, science stands at your side, to show you that deeper beauty of significance in what you see. Follow up your curiosities about what you see on your walk—the bird, the leaf, the nest. Library shelves are

In late summer, green Russula *mushrooms sprout on the forest floor. Young russulas have rounded caps that gradually unfold like umbrellas as they mature. The taller mushroom on the left has reached the final stage of growth.*

bulging with popular, well-illustrated books on everything you wonder about. Perhaps you're one to notice toadstools; the fungi are an underworld in themselves. Though wild flowers wilt if you pick them, they stay fresh in your mind when you know their names. You look at a caterpillar with intelligent interest when you know that it will turn into the pale-green elegance of a luna moth. The very landscape, when you comprehend something about its underpinnings, tells a grand tale of upheavals, invasions by the sea, the march and retreat of the glaciers.

So, as the great interrelated pattern emerges through your understanding, you see its beauty ever more plainly, more lovingly. Saint Francis of Assisi worshiped God through nature, praising Him for sun and moon, fire and water, wind and weather, and flowers and grass. We cannot be saints, but we can try, at least, to reverence this natural world, to open our eyes to it, as in prayer we open our hearts. Beauty is of God's making; to see it is to know Him very near.

Related to mushrooms but different in shape, the purple Clavaria *fungus (above) branches like undersea coral. The shaggy ink cap mushroom (right) can grow up overnight and be gone by morning. As the cap opens, its white gills turn pink, then purplish, then brown; finally they dissolve into an inky black fluid that drips to the ground. The cap disappears within hours, leaving only a stem.*

Poisonous, but looking as innocent as an orange flecked with snow, a young fly agaric grows under a fern. As it matures, its cap will flatten. The color of this mushroom species varies from yellow through orange to scarlet.

EARTH IN ALL
HER GLORY

Donald Culross Peattie

As a child I spent months of happy isolation in a log-cabin inn with my mother on a mountaintop in the Appalachians. It was my habit to go out upon a point in the forested peak to see the sun set on the autumn foliage in the valley far below. And standing thus, with the valley sinking into purple shadow and the pine trunks about me still ruddy with departing light, I felt my tremendous solitude. But, though alone, I was not lonely. For I felt companioned by the nature about me, a presence mightier than any human fellowship can be, embracing me and enfolding me.

For the first time I understood that man is a part of nature. He is subject to her great laws, sharing in her sanctities, never without companionship in her, if he can discover the brotherhood to be found in trees, the fellowship in all that flies or runs or creeps. I was too small then to accept this fact in any way save as a high, happy emotion. But it has grown in me with increasing understanding, deep-rooted now as is a man's religious faith. Through the years, nature has given me not only a profession but a sanctuary, a philosophy, a way of life.

Not long after this sunset hour, a gentle old man, examining with me some flowers we had gathered together, explained that not only animals but plants have sex. All at once the plant and animal kingdoms were for me united in one grand kingdom of life and I was filled with inexpressible delight. This oneness of living things, made entrancing by their infinite variety, was for me a new way of loving nature and finding strength there; it remains so today.

It was when I first began to identify plants that this bewildering variety that is in nature all began to fall into place. For as I came to comprehend the great system of classification originated by Linnaeus, the "father of botany," I saw that all the dancing fields of flowers, the great stands of forest trees, the humming insects, the sunning lizards and running rabbits, had each an appointed place in the scheme of things, and that by studying the structure of each, and its relation to the others, one could find that place and name that flower or tree or creature with the exact name, in double Latin, which had been given it by some wiser scientist that I was.

So, with study, I came to realize the grand order in nature. Families and species stood ranked securely in a system that not all mankind's revolutions could upset. Underneath all the wild sweet growing, the free-winged flying and the careless flowering, there lay this tremendous, unshakable order on which I could always count. This gave me a sense of security in nature, which has steadily increased with my abil-

As fall advances down the Appalachians, the mountain slopes are transformed from varying shades of green to a brilliant tapestry of brown, purple, gold and crimson. In all the world there is no spectacle that can equal the broad-leaved forests of eastern North America dressed in autumnal splendor and basking in October sunshine.

ity to find my way around in this established natural order of things.

My philosophy has been based sometimes on study and experience in the field, sometimes on moments that stand out in memory as revelations. Of these have been the makings of a naturalist, who remem-bers each of them with great reverence and profound gratitude.

I know that in nature growth is sure, and up-ward. That at the heart of things is serenity. That in due season even the desert will flower, and that for all of us life is a gift to be revered as divine.

INDEX

Page numbers in italics indicate illustrations.

ILLUSTRATION CREDITS

"PART" PHOTOGRAPHS: 8, 9: (Barn owls) Matthew Vinciguerra. *120, 121:* (Oregon seascape) Ray Atkeson. *164, 165:* (Arctic pack ice) Fred Baldwin, National Audubon Society. *254, 255:* (Trifid nebula) Mount Wilson and Palomar Observatories, © copyright 1959 by California Institute of Technology and Carnegie Institution of Washington. *278, 279:* (Monterey sunset) David Muench. *ALL OTHER ILLUSTRATIONS: 11:* Thase Daniel. *13:* George Leavens, Photo Researchers. *14:* (top) Matthew Vinciguerra; (bottom) Edward S. Ross. *17:* John H. Blower, National Audubon Society. *18, 19:* Donald Wooldridge. *21:* Harry Engels. *24:* André Durenceau. *26:* (top) Joe Barnell, courtesy of The American Museum of Natural History; (bottom) F. Jalayer. *31:* (left, top and bottom) Edward S. Ross; (right, top and bottom) B. B. Jones. *32:* Edward S. Ross. *34:* Irvin L. Oakes, Photo Researchers. *37:* Stephen Collins. *38:* Edward R. Degginger. *40:* William Vandivert. *43:* Matthew Vinciguerra. *44:* (left) N. Smythe; (right) B. B. Jones. *45:* (left) Kelly Motherspaugh; (right, top and bottom) N. Smythe. *46:* (top) N. Smythe; (bottom) Stephen Collins. *47:* (top) Larry West, Full Moon Studio; (bottom) B. B. Jones. *49:* Fulvio Roiter, *Réalités. 51:* Edward R. Degginger. *52:* (top) Jack Dermid; (bottom) Robert W. Mitchell. *54:* Andrey Roth. *57:* Grant Haist. *59:* Guy Coheleach. *60:* Ruth Smiley, National Audubon Society. *64, 65:* Ray Atkeson. *67:* Shelly Grossman. *68:* (left) Thase Daniel; (right) M. F. Soper, National Audubon Society. *69:* (top) Thase Daniel; (bottom left) Peter Sanchez; (bottom right) Matthew Vinciguerra. *70:* Kenneth Carmichael. *71:* (top) Helen Cruickshank; (bottom left) Thase Daniel; (bottom right) Christina Loke, Photo Researchers. *73:* Jack Dermid. *75:* Anthony Mercieca, National Audubon Society. *76:* Sandy Sprunt, National Audubon Society. *79:* Juan Antonio Fernández, Estación Biológica de Donaña. *80, 81:* Jack Dermid. *82:* William J. Bolte. *84, 85:* Helen Cruickshank. *87:* Karl Maslowski, Photo Researchers. *88:* (left) Dade Thornton; (right) Stephen Collins. *89:* (left) Harry Engels, National Audubon Society; (right) Edward R. Degginger. *90:* Allan Roberts. *91:* Edward R. Degginger. *93:* Harry Engels. *96:* Guy Coheleach. *98:* Robert W. Mitchell. *100:* Larry Pringle. *101:* Larry West, National Audubon Society. *102:* Matthew Vinciguerra. *103:* Robert W. Mitchell. *104:* Henry Mayer. *105:* (left) William M. Harlow; (right) Hugh Spencer. *107:* (top left) James Alexander; (top right) Larry West, Full Moon Studio; (bottom) Hugh Spencer. *108:* (left) Robert W. Mitchell; (right) James Alexander. *110:* B. B. Jones. *113:* Grant Heilman. *115:* Josef Muench. *116:* William M. Harlow. *118:* David Muench. *123, 124:* Peter David, Photo Researchers. *126, 127:* Douglas P. Wilson. *130, 131:* Ray Atkeson. *133:* Dennis Brokaw. *136:* William H. Amos. *137:* Jack Dermid. *139—45:* Douglas Faulkner. *146, 147:* Jerry Greenberg. *149:* Douglas Faulkner. *150:* James L. Massey. *152:* Peter David, Photo Researchers. *155:* Mick Church. *157:* Douglas Faulkner. *159:* Karl Kenyon, National Audubon Society. *161:* Peter Gimbel. *162:* Jerry Greenberg. *167:* Fred Baldwin,

National Audubon Society. *169:* Arthur A. Twomey, Western Ways Features. *170, 171:* David Linton. *173:* Verne Peckham. *174:* Gerard Bazile. *175:* Michael A. DeCamp. *177–79:* Thase Daniel. *180:* (top) ner. *182:* (top) Fulvio Roiter, *Réalités;* (bottom) Norman R. Light-Thase Daniel; (bottom) Edward S. Ross. *181:* Douglas Faulkfoot. *183:* (top) Roger McKay; (center) T. Hirshfeld, Western Ways Features; (bottom) Robert Halmi, Photo Library. *184:* Crawford Greenewalt, courtesy of The American Museum of Natural History. *185:* Constance Warner. *187:* N. Smythe. *188:* Allan Roberts. *189:* N. Smythe. *190:* (top, left, and bottom) N. Smythe; (top right) Douglas Faulkner. *191–93:* N. Smythe. *195:* Grant Haist. *196, 197:* Jack Dermid. *199:* Kirtley-Perkins, National Audubon Society. *200:* Allan Roberts. *201:* Edward R. Degginger. *203:* Stuart Umin. *204, 205:* David Muench. *207, 208:* Frank and John Craighead. *211:* Wilford L. Miller. *212, 213:* (top) Joern Gerdts; (bottom) Wilford L. Miller. *215:* David Greenspan. *216:* James A. Kern. *217:* (top) Edward R. Degginger; (bottom) N. Smythe. *218:* Emil Schulthess, Black Star. *220, 221:* Jack Zehrt. *224:* Karl Weidmann. *227:* H. K. Wimmer. *229:* R. C. Jennings, Frank Lane. *230:* Harry Engels. *232:* (top) Paul W. Nesbit; (center left) Jack Dermid; (center right) Ray Atkeson; (bottom left) Emil Muench; (bottom right) Josef Muench. *233:* (left) B. B. Jones; (right) Dick Kent. *235:* Leo Ainsworth, courtesy of the National Severe Storms Laboratory. *238:* Howard Koslow. *241:* Sigurdur Thorarinsson. *242:* (left) Sigurdur Thorarinsson; (right) Aevar Jóhannesson. *246:* John Ballantine. *248, 249:* (top) U.S. Department of Commerce, Coast and Geodetic Survey; (bottom) M. Lockman, Black Star. *252:* John Ballantine. *257:* Dick Kent. *259, 260:* NASA. *262:* H. K. Wimmer. *265:* (top) H. K. Wimmer; (bottom) NASA. *266:* NASA. *269:* Chesley Bonestell. *271:* Mount Wilson and Palomar Observatories, © copyright 1959 by California Institute of Technology and Carnegie Institution of Washington. *274:* Douglas Faulkner. *276, 277:* Chesley Bonestell, courtesy of Boston Museum of Science. *281:* (top left) Associated Newspapers, Ltd.; (top right) P. A. Macnab; (bottom right) London Daily Express. *283:* Charles R. Knight, courtesy of The American Museum of Natural History. *284, 285:* George J. Geselschap, courtesy of The American Museum of Natural History. *289:* Durward L. Allen. *291:* John Gerard. *292:* The Metropolitan Museum of Art, gift from the collection of Miss A. S. Colgate. *294:* Robert C. Twist, Camas National Wildlife Refuge. *296:* Thase Daniel. *299:* William Garnett. *301:* Matthew Vinciguerra. *302:* (top) Edward S. Ross; (bottom) Grant Haist. *304:* William H. Amos. *305:* Treat Davidson, National Audubon Society. *306:* William H. Amos. *308:* Leonard Lee Rue III. *309:* Thase Daniel. *310:* James A. Kern. *312:* (top) Edward R. Degginger; (bottom left) Larry West, Full Moon Studio; (bottom right) Leslie Crine. *313:* Leslie Crine. *314, 315:* E. Gockeler, Shostal. *Endpapers:* Bob S. Smith.

PHOTO EDITOR: Robert J. Woodward.

A TOOTH AND A CLAW, by Jean George, cond. from *Audubon Magazine*, © 1965, National Audubon Society. ANIMALS CAN BE ALMOST HUMAN, by Max Eastman, cond. from *The Saturday Review*, © 1957, Saturday Review Associates, Inc. ARE WILD ANIMALS REALLY WILD? by Andy Russell, cond. from *True, the Man's Magazine*, Canadian edition, © 1960, Fawcett Publications, Inc. THAT ASTONISHING ANIMAL: THE BEEHIVE, by Jean George, cond. from *Frontiers, A Magazine of Natural History*, © 1966, The Academy of Natural Sciences of Philadelphia. THE WACKIEST ORCHESTRA ON EARTH, by Jean George, cond. from *National Wildlife*, © 1967, National Wildlife Federation. THE MYSTERY OF THE FIREFLY, by Robert Gannon, cond. from *Frontiers: A Magazine of Natural History*, © 1967, The Academy of Natural Sciences of Philadelphia. NOBODY LOVES A CROCODILE, by Gordon Gaskill, cond. from *U.S. Lady*, © 1964, American Service Pub. Co., Inc. WHAT SNAKES ARE REALLY LIKE, by Alan Devoe, cond. from *Nature Magazine*, © 1955, American Nature Assn. FISH IN LOVE, by Konrad Z. Lorenz, cond. from *King Solomon's Ring*, copyright © 1952, Thomas Y. Crowell Company, New York, publishers. THAT REMARKABLE CREATURE, THE SNAIL, by Oscar Schisgall, cond. from *National Wildlife*, © 1967, National Wildlife Federation. THE MIRACLE OF BIRDS, by Alan Devoe, cond. from *The American Mercury*, © 1953, The American Mercury, Inc. BIRDS LIVE IN NATURE'S INVISIBLE CAGE, by John and Jean George, cond. from *The Christian Science Monitor*, © 1959, The Christian Science Pub. Society. OF SPRING AND AN EGG, by Jean George, cond. from *National Wildlife*, © 1966, National Wildlife Federation. HERE COME THE ROBINS!, by Jean George, cond. from *The Christian Science Monitor*, © 1964, The Christian Science Pub. Society. CONSIDER THE FRAGILE FLAMINGO, by George S. Fichter, cond. from *All Florida Magazine*, © 1959, All Florida Magazine. VULTURE COUNTRY, by John D. Stewart, cond. from *The Atlantic Monthly*, © 1959, The Atlantic Monthly Co. MY WAR WITH THE OSPREYS, by John Steinbeck, cond. from *Holiday*, © 1957, The Curtis Pub. Co. Extract (p. 81) from *Audubon Water Bird Guide*, by Richard H. Pough, copyright 1951, Doubleday & Company, Inc. HIS MAGNIFICENCE, THE MOOSE, by Jack Denton Scott, cond. from *National Wildlife*, © 1965, National Wildlife Federation. PUTTING THE BEAVER BACK TO WORK, by Robert Froman, cond. from *Down East*, © 1957, Down East Enterprise, Inc. THE BEAST WITH THE HIGH I.Q., by Jean George, cond. from *National Wildlife*, © 1964, National Wildlife Federation. THAT CHARMING CHEATER, THE CHIPMUNK, by Jean George, cond. from *National Wildlife*, © 1965, National Wildlife Federation. RHINO! by David Reed, cond. from *National Wildlife*, © 1965, National Wildlife Federation. CAVE OF THE VAMPIRES, by Daniel P. Mannix, cond. from *Collier's*, © 1947, The Crowell-Collier Pub. Co. THE MARVELS OF CROSS-POLLINATION, by Rutherford Platt, cond. from *This Green World*, © 1942 and pub. by Dodd, Mead & Co., Inc. PLANTS THAT EAT INSECTS, by Jean George, cond. from *Au Grand Air*, © 1962, by Jean George, pub. by Rod & Gun Pub. Co. THE WORLD'S MOST EXOTIC NUISANCE, by James Poling, cond. from *Shreveport Magazine*, © 1964, Shreveport Magazine. THE WONDER OF WOOD, by Donald Culross Peattie, cond. from *American Forests*, © 1947, American Forestry Assn. INEXHAUSTIBLE RICHES FROM THE SEA, by George A. W. Boehm, cond. from *Fortune*, © 1963, Time Inc. WIND AND WATER, by Rachel L. Carson, cond. from *The Sea Around Us*, copyright 1951, Rachel L. Carson; pub. by Oxford University Press. THE MYSTERY OF LIFE AT THE SEASHORE, by Rachel L. Carson, cond. from *The Edge of the Sea*, copyright © 1955, Rachel L. Carson; reprinted by permission of Houghton Mifflin Company. THE SQUID: NATURE'S NIGHTMARE, by Ronald N. Rood, cond. from *Down East*, © 1961, Down East Enterprise, Inc. BEWARE THE DEADLY MAN-OF-WAR! by Fred Warshofsky, cond. from *National Wildlife*, © 1966, National Wildlife Federation. THE LOBSTER: ODDBALL OF THE OCEAN, by David MacDonald, cond. from *The Atlantic Advocate*, pub. by University Press of New Brunswick, Ltd. SEALS FOR TEXAS, by N. J. Berrill, cond. from *The Living Tide*, copyright 1951, N. J. Berrill; reprinted by permission of Dodd, Mead & Co., Inc. THE UNPREDICTABLE SHARK, by Jacques-Yves Cousteau with Frédéric Dumas, cond. from *The Silent World*, copyright 1950, Time Inc.; copyright

1953 and pub. by Harper & Row. LAND OF FANTASY AND PHANTOM, by Thomas R. Henry, cond. from *The White Continent*, © 1950, Thomas R. Henry, pub. by William Sloane Associates. AUGUSTO RUSCHI'S JUNGLE PARADISE, by Allen Rankin, cond. from *Frontiers: a Magazine of Natural History*, © 1965, The Academy of Natural Sciences of Philadelphia. THE AWAKENING, by Franklin Russell, cond. from *Watchers at the Pond*, copyright © 1961, Franklin Russell, pub. by Alfred A. Knopf, Inc. FROM SPRING TO SUMMER, by Edwin Way Teale, selections from *Circle of the Seasons*, copyright 1953, Edwin Way Teale, pub. by Dodd, Mead & Co., Inc. AUGUST BOUNTY, by Hal Borland, cond. from *Sundial of the Seasons*, copyright © 1964, Hal Borland and copyright © 1943 through 1963 (inclusive), The New York Times; pub. by J. B. Lippincott Co. AUTUMN FLIES HER FLAGS, by Donald Culross Peattie, cond. from *Holiday*, © 1946, The Curtis Pub. Co. SNOW IS TO LIVE WITH, by Jean George, cond. from *National Wildlife*, © 1962, National Wildlife Federation. TWENTY TIMES HIGHER THAN NIAGARA, by Michael Scully, cond. from *The Kiwanis Magazine*, copyright 1954, Kiwanis International. THE WONDER OF THE WINDS, by J. D. Ratcliff, cond. from *U.S. Lady*, © 1965, American Service Pub. Co., Inc. THE MIRACLE OF LIGHTNING, by Ira Wolfert, cond. from *Popular Science Monthly*, © 1959, Popular Science Pub. Co., Inc. RIDING HERD ON THE TWISTERS, by James H. Winchester, cond. from *Empire*, © 1964, The Denver Post, Inc. HOWL OF THE HURRICANE, by Benedict Thielen, cond. from *Holiday*, © 1959, The Curtis Pub. Co. AN ISLAND IS BORN, by Sigurdur Thorarinsson, based on the book *Surtsey*, copyright 1964 in all countries of the international copyright union; © 1966, Almenna Bokafelagid, pub. by The Viking Press, Inc. WHEN KRAKATOA BLEW UP, by Ernst Behrendt, cond. from *Nature Magazine*, © 1946, American Nature Assn. THE EARTH RANG LIKE A BELL, by Earl Ubell, cond. from *The New York Herald Tribune*, © 1964, New York Herald Tribune, Inc.; with additions by the author. THOSE AWESOME EXPLOSIONS: EARTHQUAKES, by Ira Wolfert, cond. from *The Denver Post*, © 1958, Post Printing & Pub. Co. FOOTPRINTS OF THE GREAT ICE, by Ralph K. Andrist, cond. from *American Heritage*, © 1960, American Heritage Pub. Co., Inc. THE THING THAT HIT US FROM OUTER SPACE, by Wolfgang Langewiesche, based on the following articles in *Scientific American*: "Meteors," by Fletcher G. Watson; "The Great Meteor of 1947," by Otto Struve; "Astroblemes," by Robert S. Dietz; "The Age of the Elements in the Solar System," by John H. Reynolds; "The Origin of Meteorites," by Fred Singer, © 1954 Scientific American, Inc. SPACE FLIGHT AND THE SPIRIT OF MAN, by Arthur C. Clarke, cond. from *Astronautics*, © 1961, the American Rocket Society, Inc. THE VIOLENT SUN, by Herbert Friedman, cond. from *National Geographic*, © 1965, National Geographic Society. SO YOU'RE GOING TO MARS? by Arthur C. Clarke, cond. from *Holiday*, © 1953, The Curtis Pub. Co. OUT OF THIS WORLD, by Wayne Amos, cond. from *The American Magazine*, © 1953, The Crowell-Collier Pub. Co. DOES THE STAR OF BETHLEHEM STILL SHINE? by Arthur C. Clarke, cond. from *Holiday*, © 1954, The Curtis Pub. Co. OUTER SPACE—WHAT IS OUT THERE? by Arthur C. Clarke, cond. from *Horizon*, © 1958, American Horizon, Inc. CLOSING IN ON THE LOCH NESS MONSTER, by David Scott, cond. from *Popular Science Monthly*, © 1966, Popular Science Pub. Co., Inc. THE CASE OF THE VANISHING DINOSAURS, by J. D. Ratcliff, cond. from *The Kiwanis Magazine*, © 1964, Kiwanis International. THE BUFFALO IS BACK! by Bill Surface, cond. from *The Kiwanis Magazine*, © 1967, Kiwanis International. BRINGING BACK THE CHESTNUT TREE, by J. C. Furnas, cond. from *American Forests*, © 1963, The American Forestry Assn. THE TRUMPETER RETURNS FROM OBLIVION, by Robert Murphy, cond. from *National Wildlife*, © 1967, National Wildlife Federation. OUR VANISHING TIDELANDS, by Polly Redford, cond. from *The Atlantic Monthly*, © 1967, The Atlantic Monthly Co. BE A BACKYARD EXPLORER, by Edwin Way Teale, cond. from *The American Magazine*, © 1952, The Crowell-Collier Pub. Co. THE MAGIC OF A MIDSUMMER NIGHT, by Jean George, cond. from *Audubon Magazine*, © 1961, National Audubon Society. WHY BE BLIND TO BEAUTY? by Donald Culross Peattie, cond. from *Guideposts*, © 1951, Guideposts Associates, Inc.

Meadow Lark

Ivory-billed Woodpecker

Mallard Duck

White=crowned Sparrow